Managing ENVIRONMENTAL SYSTEMS

Robert Prosser

Nelson

Thomas Nelson and Sons Ltd
Nelson House Mayfield Road
Walton-on-Thames Surrey
KT12 5PL UK

Nelson Blackie
Wester Cleddens Road
Bishopbriggs
Glasgow
G64 2NZ UK

Thomas Nelson Australia
102 Dodds Street
South Melbourne
Victoria 3205 Australia

Nelson Canada
1120 Birchmount Road
Scarborough Ontario
M1K 5G4 Canada

First published by Thomas Nelson and Sons Ltd 1995.

I(T)P Thomas Nelson is an International Thomson Publishing Company.

I(T)P is used under licence.

ISBN 0-17-448223-X
NPN 9 8 7 6 5 4 3 2

Printed in Hong Kong

CONTENTS

Foreword

For the student: making the best use of this book

Managing Environmental Systems consists of a set of case studies which focus upon management options and issues in different environments. It is not a textbook, which presents you with a broad coverage of geographical knowledge, chapter by chapter, with examples presented as addenda. The approach here is the opposite. It concentrates on specific examples and assumes that you already possess or are in the process of acquiring some knowledge of the broader topic. Each case study becomes a vehicle to explore a topic or issue, to enrich your understanding and to help you think critically.

Management concerns the rational and orderly allocation and use of resources according to a set of objectives and priorities. This basic definition applies to all of the environments covered in this book, natural and human, urban and rural. It is important to remember that the way a particular set of resources has been developed – the form of a city, the economy of a farm, the management of a wilderness area – presents only one management solution. The decision-makers could have made other choices. So, in each case study you should be asking yourself questions such as:
• what decisions have been made?
• who made them?
• why have they made them?
• what has influenced the choice?
• what has been the outcome?
• what other options are possible?

Some of the case studies are 'issues-based'. Alternatives are presented and it is your task to evaluate them.

The case studies vary in length, level of difficulty and character of materials used. You may wish to begin with shorter, straightforward topics, then as you gain experience, challenge yourself to longer, more complex studies. You will find that these study skills give you confidence to tackle articles in geographical journals. Despite their diversity, every case study is built of the same four components.

Background sets the materials into their broader context and identifies the main issues.

There is a list of the *Key Understandings* you should acquire from the case study.

The case study itself is set out. It is important that you give the 'Resources' – tables, graphs, diagrams, photos, maps, extracts – as much attention as the text, for much of the central information lies within them.

Activities are included to allow you to review the materials, to check how much you have learned, and to give you practice in a variety of response types. The tasks suggested by no means exhaust the possibilities, and you may find other activities more appropriate to your syllabus and examination preparation.

CHAPTER 1

Managing water resources

Introduction

Water is the foundation of life on earth; without it there would be no plants, no animals, no living thing. Many of us take it for granted, because it is always there ... ready and waiting our convenience. But in many parts of the world, water is a rare commodity and precious thing, more valuable than gold (Bellamy & Quayle, *Turning the Tide,* Collins 1986).

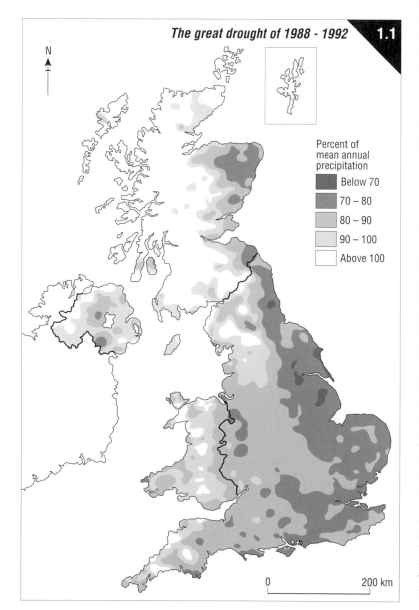

The great drought of 1988 - 1992 1.1

N

Percent of mean annual precipitation

- Below 70
- 70 – 80
- 80 – 90
- 90 – 100
- Above 100

0   200 km

Although water is a **renewable** resource, it is also **finite** and **unevenly distributed** across the earth. This is of particular importance as human populations increase and their demands continue to grow. Water has become a **scarce resource.** Its availability and quality have become major environmental issues. For example, a United Nations forecast predicts that *in North Africa and the Middle East ... meeting the expected demands by the year 2000 could require virtually all of their usable fresh-water supplies* (UN *Global Outlook 2000. Economic, Social, Environmental*, 1990). Not surprisingly, National Geographic claimed that the next war in the Middle East will not be about oil as was the Gulf War of 1991, but about water.

The control and ownership of water carries financial and political weight, not only in arid regions such as the Middle East. The *Great Drought* of 1988–92 has caused a major reconsideration about the way we manage our water resources in the UK. The most important realisation about this 'water crisis' was that it occurred only across central, eastern and southern England; northern and western UK received above average precipitation during this period. The 'crisis' was intensified by the concentration of population and intensive agriculture in the drought regions. The demand was, therefore, greatest where supply was most limited, leading to a 1994 publication of a proposed National Water strategy by the National Rivers Authority (NRA). The proposal is based upon extensive projects for inter-basin water transfers to match the geographical distribution of supply and demand. Since much of the surplus water collects and is stored in Scotland and Wales, while the deficit occurs in southern and central England, there is considerable controversy on who 'owns' this precious resource.

As demand and scarcity increase in all environments, so the need for effective resource management becomes more urgent. Management is responsible for the organised control and allocation of the water resource according to a set of priorities and criteria. Water management policies

River transfers may satisfy water needs

Paul Brown
Environment
correspondent

Drinking water will be delivered by pipeline and river from Wales to London and from Nottinghamshire to Essex under a National Rivers Authority plan published yesterday.

The authority calculates that to move water between river systems by pipeline would be cheaper than reservoirs. Thames Water has already put its plan for a new reservoir in south Oxfordshire on hold.

[*The Guardian*, 30.3.94]

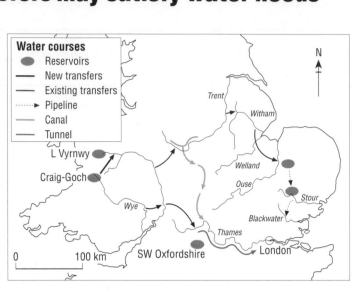

Water courses
- Reservoirs
- New transfers
- Existing transfers
- Pipeline
- Canal
- Tunnel

focus upon that part of the hydrological cycle between the input of precipitation to the earth's surface, and the output from rivers to the oceans. Managers learn to understand the capacity and behaviour of the stores such as lakes and groundwater aquifers, and how water moves between them. They may then add stores such as reservoirs, or control the natural stores by extracting water from or adding water to the groundwater aquifers, for example. They aim to match supply with demand over time and space; to turn an unreliable and unpredictable material into a reliable and predictable resource.

The most common unit of river management is the **river basin**. This is an area bounded by a **watershed**, within which water is collected, stored and moved. The river channel network acts as the main **transfer system.** It is fed by and links the surface and sub-surface stores, eventually conveying the water to the oceans or inland 'sinks'. The essential role of water managers is to control this channel transfer system. However, it is important to remember that river basin management is not about water alone. Resource 1.4 indicates that water management can only be effective if it fits within the broader dimensions of

1.3 A systems diagram

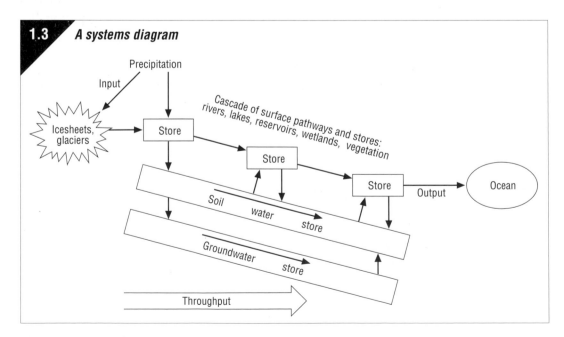

development strategy. Furthermore, the emphases and priorities may vary according to the character of the environment.

Three of the case studies in this chapter are based on the river basin system, and illustrate the social, economic, political and environmental tensions associated with water resource management. Tensions are potentially most explosive where a river basin covers more than one nation state. Case Study 1.1 examines these issues in two huge basins: the Mekong in the humid region of south-east Asia and the Tigris-Euphrates system in the arid Middle East. In the Mekong intensive river management is in its early, but rapidly-growing phase. The Tigris-Euphrates, on the other hand, has one of the longest histories of water management schemes in the world, but massive new schemes and political conflicts are threatening further war.

Case Study 1.2 shifts the focus to impacts of river management at the community level. The understanding that a river basin behaves as a system, and that a change to any one component of that system will inevitably affect other components is illustrated by an examination of the Hadejia-Jama'are valley in Nigeria. The way of life of an agricultural community in the middle section of the basin is affected by development schemes both upstream and downstream.

Case Studies 1.3 and 1.4 cover examples from the USA, the country with the most technologically-advanced projects for water management and the highest per capita consumption in the world. The study of the Ogallala aquifer (Case Study 1.3) is an excellent example of the issues connected with the reliance upon the groundwater store. It illustrates the need to control extractions from aquifers, so that their recharge capacity is not reduced. The emphasis is to take out less than is being put in.

In 1993 the middle Mississippi basin suffered severe flooding. Case Study 1.4 explores the nature and cause of this disaster along a river with some of the most extensive and sophisticated control systems in the world. The floods have generated a fierce debate about the most appropriate management strategies for powerful, major rivers and, in particular, the role of channels and floodplains. The re-evaluation focuses on whether to continue with the 'hard' engineering approach of channel levées, for example, or whether to adopt the 'soft' approach and use the floodplain as a planned surplus store area.

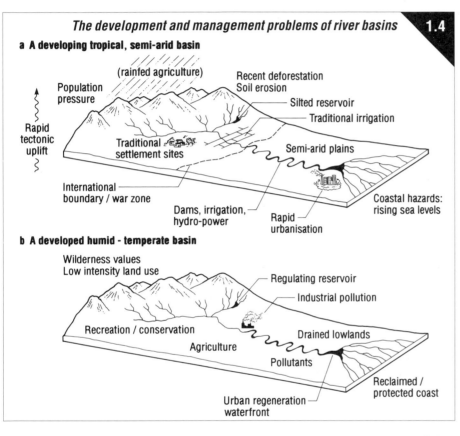

The development and management problems of river basins | **1.4**

a A developing tropical, semi-arid basin

- Population pressure
- (rainfed agriculture)
- Recent deforestation
- Soil erosion
- Silted reservoir
- Traditional irrigation
- Rapid tectonic uplift
- Traditional settlement sites
- Semi-arid plains
- International boundary / war zone
- Dams, irrigation, hydro-power
- Rapid urbanisation
- Coastal hazards: rising sea levels

b A developed humid - temperate basin

- Wilderness values
- Low intensity land use
- Regulating reservoir
- Industrial pollution
- Recreation / conservation
- Agriculture
- Drained lowlands
- Pollutants
- Reclaimed / protected coast
- Urban regeneration waterfront

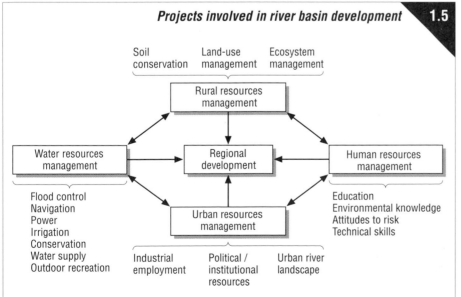

Projects involved in river basin development | **1.5**

Soil conservation — Land-use management — Ecosystem management

Rural resources management

Water resources management — Regional development — Human resources management

Flood control
Navigation
Power
Irrigation
Conservation
Water supply
Outdoor recreation

Urban resources management

Education
Environmental knowledge
Attitudes to risk
Technical skills

Industrial employment — Political / institutional resources — Urban river landscape

CASE STUDY 1.1 *The political geography of water resources*

Background

Wherever water is shared by more than one community, there is the potential for tension and perhaps direct conflict over allocation policies, even when the resource lies within a single nation state. In the UK, for example, some Welsh people protest against the use of 'their' water by English regional water companies. In the USA, despite longstanding formal agreements, there is constant argument among six states over the distribution of the waters of the Colorado River: California demands the largest share although its land contributes no water input to the river. Mexico, too, demands its share as the Colorado delta lies within its boundaries. The disputes do not arise only from the supply and storage of surface water. Groundwater stores frequently extend beyond local or national boundaries. For example, the huge Ogallala aquifer lies under parts of six of the High Plains states of the USA. Allocation disputes between states and between water districts within states are recurrent (see Case Study 1.3). In the United Kingdom, the recharge exposures of important aquifers may not lie within the boundary of the water company which makes the greatest abstractive use of the aquifer.

When a river basin or groundwater system becomes international, then the potential for conflict escalates. The situation is likely to become more tense when any one or more of the following situations exist:

- The climate becomes progressively drier downstream.
- Relationships between neighbouring countries are poor.
- Population and use pressures are high, particularly in countries of the upper basin.
- When at least one country in the basin has few alternative sources of water and, hence, is heavily dependent upon this single source.
- When the natural regime of the main river is one of extremes or highly irregular.

Water quality is as sensitive an issue as water quantity, both internally and internationally. In Australia, for example, farming practices in the Murray-Darling basin of New South Wales and Victoria are blamed by the downstream state of South Australia for increased salinity in the waters of the lower Murray. In Europe in 1986, chemical pollution of the Rhine near Basle in Switzerland moved downstream, affecting France, Germany and the Netherlands.

This case study examines two major river basins from contrasting environments, where there is a long history of political tension and suspicion among the sharing nations. The first is the Mekong basin of south-east Asia, which lies within a humid environment under moderate development pressures. The second, the Tigris–Euphrates basin of the Middle East, has perhaps the longest history of conflict over water use of all major basins. The competition for the resource has been sharpened by the arid climate of all but the headwater sections of the basin.

1.6 River pollution hits water supply

People in the Worcester area whose supply is drawn from the R. Severn have been warned not to use their tap water. Severn - Trent Water have admitted that toxic chemicals are polluting the river. At least 100 000 people are affected, and long queues wait at road tankers and temporary standpipes provided by the water company. The National Rivers Authority believe the source of the pollution is a factory some 80 kilometres upstream near Wem, in Shropshire.
[*Hereford Times*, 21.4.94]

Part A: The Mekong basin, south-east Asia

The River Mekong emerges from a glacier over 4500 m high on the Plateau of Tibet in China. From its ice- and snow-fed headwaters, the river flows through or past six countries for 4200 km before building a huge delta out into the South China Sea. By the time it reaches this delta, the mean discharge is 14 000 cumecs (high flow 52 000 cumecs; low flow 1750 cumecs). It is the twelfth longest river in the world and the seventh longest in Asia, draining a basin of 790 000 km². In both its natural and managed hydrology, the Mekong basin is divided into two parts. An upper basin, wholly in China, covers approximately one-half of the river's length, while a lower basin lies downstream from the point where the river enters Myanmar (Burma).

Unlike so many great rivers, the Mekong has not been subjected to many control measures, especially in the upper basin. It retains much of

---

Key understandings

- The water resources of many river basins are shared by more than one country.
- All forms of management modify river regimes, the changes being dependent upon the nature and purpose of a scheme.
- Because a river basin functions as an integrated system, downstream countries are vulnerable to effects from developments further up the basin.
- Political and social tensions are almost inevitable as pressure for water resource development increases in shared water basins.
- Effective management of shared river basins can only be achieved by long-term trust and co-operation between all the countries involved.
- Countries within a river basin may have conflicting priorities for water resource use.

management

its natural hydrological regime. As a result, international tensions and conflicts over water have not been severe despite political conflicts and recurrent wars between the countries in the lower basin, for example, the Vietnam War. In 1992 a traveller wrote:

The Mekong has remained wild and free, moving to immemorial rhythms: the monsoon, the flood, the giving of its waters to nourish the lands and people along it. For all its length, it has spawned only one metropolis, one dam, few bridges, and no industrial complex (O'Neill, *NGM*, Feb 1993).

This freedom seems about to end as all six countries in the basin accelerate their development programmes. It is perhaps ironic that while political and military conflicts appear to be subsiding in the region, the potential for conflicts over water may be increasing, as more control schemes and irrigation projects are introduced.

Changes in the upper basin

As always in river basin management, the downstream countries are anxious about management methods upstream. In the Mekong basin this means looking towards China. (While Myanmar is steadfastly isolationalist and non-cooperative in its policies, it controls little of the Mekong drainage and is likely to remain a minor player.) Resource 1.8a shows the mean and minimum flows at the Chiang Saen gauging station where the Mekong emerges from the upper basin. It indicates that as late as 1985 the natural regime of the river had not been disturbed.

In 1995 China is to complete the first high dam along the main Mekong channel. The Manwan or Man Wong Dam, set within a steep gorge (see Resource 1.7), will provide 1500 megaWatts of electricity for the expanding mines and industries around Kunming, the capital of Yunnan province. This is a 'run-of-the-river' scheme which generates HEP from the natural river flow. It does not rely upon controlled releases from a large storage reservoir and so the discharge regime will not be greatly affected.

However, China plans to build eight more dams along a 500 km stretch of the upper Mekong north of the China–Laos border. This project is to be completed over the next thirty years as part of the drive to develop this remote region. Fortunately for the areas of the lower basin, the primary purpose of this system will be to generate power rather than flood control or irrigation. The upper basin is long and thin, the river and its tributaries running in deep gorges between steep

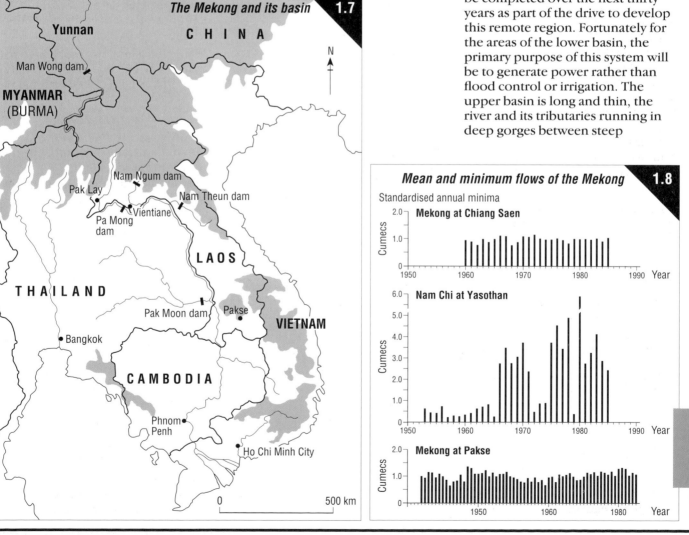

The Mekong and its basin — 1.7

Mean and minimum flows of the Mekong — 1.8
Standardised annual minima
Mekong at Chiang Saen
Nam Chi at Yasothan
Mekong at Pakse

CASE STUDY 1.1 *The political geography of water resources management*

mountain ridges. Half of the river's length occurs in only 20% of the river basin area. Although the activities of the downstream regime are likely to be determined by the release policies of the Chinese water managers, the overall volume entering the lower basin may not be seriously affected. Power generation relies on the maintenance of throughput, whereas flood control is based on storage, and irrigation on abstraction or reduced downstream discharge. Water quality, however, may become a contentious issue, as industry, agriculture and associated population growth generate more effluent.

Natural rhythms in the lower basin

The lower basin covers 607 000 km², almost 80% of the total basin area, spread across four countries. The natural regime of the Mekong in the lower basin is determined by the input from the upper basin, which is reliant on the Himalayan snows, and the seasonal rainfall pattern across the tributary network of the lower basin. The Great Lake is a distinctive surface store which influences the lowest sections and the delta of the Mekong. The lake level is replenished by reversal of water flow upstream from the main Mekong channel during spate-flow periods.

The rainy season lasts from mid-May to mid-September as the south-west monsoon sweeps warm, moist, unstable Tropical Maritime air across the basin. This input and the arrival of the snowmelt from the upper basin combine to give peak flows along the main Mekong channel in late August–September in the north, and in late September–October in the lower reaches. Minimum flows are recorded in March–April. Although the lower basin enjoys an overall humid climate, rainfall totals vary between 1000 mm in north-east Thailand and 3000 mm in north-east Laos. Potential evapotranspiration (PET) is at least 1500 mm. In the dry season, therefore, there is a moisture deficit in some regions, and a number of the upper tributaries in north-east Thailand dry up.

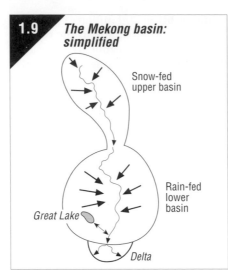

1.9 *The Mekong basin: simplified*

Snow-fed upper basin

Rain-fed lower basin

Great Lake

Delta

The seasonal changes of the natural regime are summarised in Resource 1.10. The flow records are from the Pakse gauging station for the 1923–65 period, before there were any major regulatory works on upstream tributaries. Note that this is a cumulative frequency graph plotted on a logarithmic scale. It tells us that the dry season base flow is between 1000 and 2000 cumecs (A–B on the graph); that the flow exceeds 5000 cumecs for about six months of the year (C); and that the peak flows of August–September exceed 30 000 cumecs (D–E).

Impacts of regulation

Between 1965 and 1991, nine dam and reservoir structures were built along the tributaries of the lower basin. (The major projects are

shown on Resource 1.7.) These structures regulate about 6% of the catchment basin above the delta – about 33 000 km² out of a total of 545 000 km². Most of the water is used on agriculture. At least 13% of the catchment area above the delta is seasonally flooded and used mainly for paddy rice (8.5 million ha.).

The effects of the regulatory projects up to 1991 are shown on Resource 1.11. If we compare the natural and the regulated figures, we can see that average daily flows are reduced; that minimum dry season flows are increased; and that run-off from the upper catchments is reduced through evaporation and percolation from reservoirs. Thus, regulation reduces the amplitude of seasonal flow variations. Notice in particular, that minimum flows on tributaries in eastern Thailand are greatly increased. Under natural conditions these tributaries almost cease to flow in the dry season. The reservoir stores help to sustain this dry-season flow at the expense of wet-season peaks. So far this tributary storage has not significantly affected the water supply in the main Mekong, but as population continues to expand, and the demand for further abstraction increases, conflict emerges. For example, on Resource 1.8c, the increased variations from the mean minimum flows suggest that dangerously low flows may occur during some years.

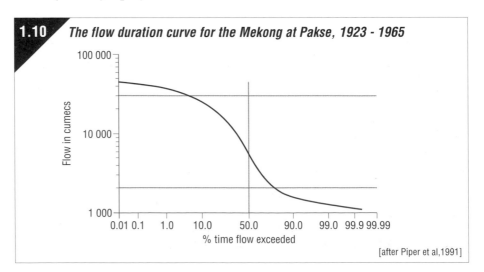

1.10 *The flow duration curve for the Mekong at Pakse, 1923 - 1965*

Flow in cumecs

100 000

10 000

1 000

0.01 0.1   1.0   10.0   50.0   90.0   99.0 99.9 99.99

% time flow exceeded

[after Piper et al,1991]

Changes in the Lower Mekong basin regime 1.11

	Mean daily flow (cumecs)		Change in mean annual min. flow after regulation (%) (1)	Mean annual runoff (mm) (2)	
	natural	regulated		natural	regulated
Mekong at					
Mukdahan	8435	7271	+5	681	587
Pakse	10550	9764	+18	611	565
R.Nam Chi at					
Yasothan	250	179	+500	183	131
R.Nam Mun at					
Ubon	740	660	+430	260	200

(1) The Annual Minimum Flow is the flow in cumecs for the 60 days with the lowest flow records during a year. The average is then calculated from the recording period: (a) Natural flow 1925–65; (b) Regulated flow 1965–85. The % shown is the difference between (a) and (b).
(2) Mean Annual Runoff indicates the supply of water to the river at the gauging station from the catchment basin upstream of that station.
[From: Piper et al,1991]

More serious conflict has emerged from the 1987 plan to change the river into a fully-controlled system by building a set of eight dams with storage reservoirs along the main Mekong channel. The proposed dam at Pa Mong, for example, (see Resource 1.7) would divert large volumes of water to irrigate the dry regions of north-east Thailand. At least 60 000 people would be displaced by this reservoir. Cambodia and Vietnam protest that this would endanger water supplies for agriculture downstream and allow saline water to penetrate the densely-populated delta.

Since 1957 the four riparian countries (those countries which share the river basin waters) have attempted to co-ordinate their water management policies through the Mekong Committee. Their objective has been *to promote, coordinate, supervise and control the planning, investigation and implementation of water resource development projects in the lower Mekong basin*

(Committee statement, 1988). However, the only genuine international project yet completed is the Nam Ngum dam in Laos. Despite the recurring political and economic tensions in the region, the Mekong Committee maintains a data base, carries out planning studies and makes recommendations. It has very little decision-making power.

One particular aspect which makes co-ordination difficult is that the primary needs and objectives vary from country to country. Although Thailand uses most of the present HEP output, its future priority is to increase water availability for irrigation in the drier regions of the north-east. Laos, with its heavier rainfall, is developing HEP capacity and places less emphasis on irrigation. For example, Laos wants to complete the Nam Theun dam in order to sell most of the generated power to Thailand. This would treble its foreign exchange earnings. Vietnam is concerned with gaining a guaranteed flow of fresh water through the delta during the dry season and so prevent salt water from penetrating agricultural land and urban water supplies. It also seeks to increase the size of the area irrigated and its output. Little is known about Cambodia's needs and plans, making co-ordinated planning and forecasting difficult. Each of the four countries seems to prefer a different storage and release policy.

Part B:
The Tigris–Euphrates basin of the Middle East

The headwater catchments of the Euphrates and Tigris rivers lie in eastern Turkey. The headstreams are snow- and rain-fed, but once out of the mountains, the rivers flow through the arid environments of Syria and Iraq. Away from the mountains Turkey is also a semi-arid land. Despite the aridity, the Tigris–Euphrates plain in present-day Iraq was the centre of the civilisation of Mesopotamia ('the land of two rivers') where

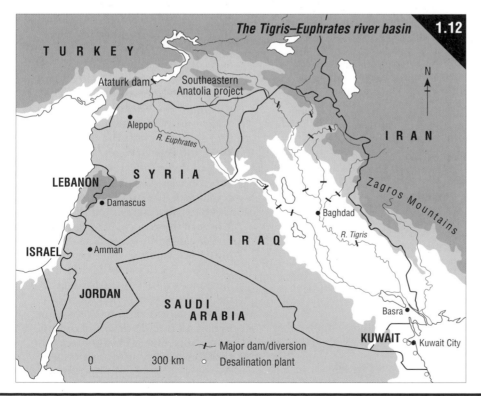

The Tigris–Euphrates river basin 1.12

Major dam/diversion
Desalination plant
0   300 km

CASE STUDY 1.1

agriculture was first practised. The Mesopotamians and those civilisations that followed were entirely dependent upon the river waters from the mountains to the north. This is still the case in modern Syria and Iraq: water is *the* critical resource. Syria has a potential freshwater supply of 2800 cubic metres a year per head of population; Iraq has 5500; Turkey has 4000. Compare this with the USA which has 10 000 cubic metres a year per head of population. The problem is that these waters no longer flow 'freely' downstream.

Turkey is currently developing the South-Eastern Anatolia Project. When completed, in the year 2010, this huge project will create 22 dams on the headwater catchments of the two great rivers. Almost all of them will be dual purpose schemes, combining HEP generation and water storage for irrigation. The power output will be 7500 MW. Three million hectares will be irrigated and 27 new towns built: all at a cost of US$32 billion (1993 prices). This project will transform Anatolia from being one of Turkey's poorest provinces, using agriculture and energy supply as the platforms for infrastructure and industrial

The Ataturk dam: this massive 166 m high and 1.6 km long structure generates 2400 MW of power, directs water through two 8 m diameter tunnels for 60 km to irrigate 500 000 ha of the hot, dry Harran plain.

development. The centrepiece of the project, the Ataturk Dam on the upper Euphrates, is already complete.

A storage and abstraction programme of this scale will transform the regime and discharge of the rivers downstream, and is a serious threat to Syria and Iraq. The tension is intensified by the longstanding suspicions between these three Islamic countries; in 1975, for example, war threatened when Turkey completed two smaller dams.

In river basins shared by more than one nation, an upstream country is not under any legal obligation to provide water downstream. However, a downstream nation can claim historical rights of use and negotiate for fair treatment. In 1987, Syria and Iraq reached an agreement with Turkey that while the enormous reservoir behind the Ataturk Dam was filled up, Turkey would guarantee to sustain a flow of at least 500 cumecs across the Syrian border. Syria and Iraq have also agreed that 58% of the Euphrates water will be exploited by Syria, allowing the remaining 42% to flow into Iraq. Despite these agreements, when the filling of the reservoir began in 1989, Turkey announced that it would hold back the Euphrates for a month. In order to fulfill the agreement, Turkey increased the discharge downstream for two months before the shut-off so that Syria and Iraq could build up their water stores. It is hardly surprising that these two nations protested strongly.

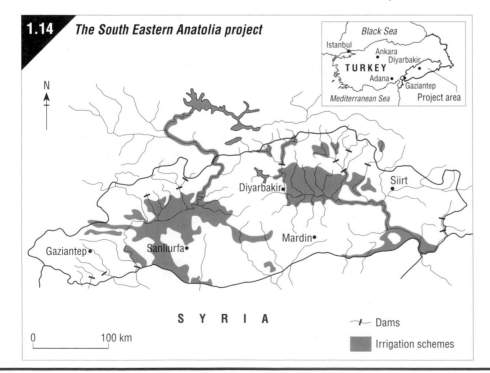

1.14 The South Eastern Anatolia project

A technical committee made up of representatives of the three riparian countries meets regularly but is rarely able to make much progress. In 1987 Turkey proposed that a 'peace pipeline' be constructed to bring water from the Ceyhan and Seyhan rivers in southern Turkey to Syria and other states, but suspicions have been too strong for progress to be made. As some estimates suggest that when the South-Eastern Anatolia Project is complete the Euphrates flow could be reduced by 60%, it seems likely that tensions and conflict will intensify.

Syria already has considerable regulation schemes in operation and with an annual population growth rate of 3.8%, has a steadily increasing demand. In 1990 the population was 12 million – in 2010 it is likely to be 25 million. At present the largest project is the Euphrates Dam at Tabqa, completed in 1975. Waters from its reservoir irrigate 220 000 ha in the semi-arid lands of eastern Syria and the government plans to have a further 450 000 ha under cultivation within the next decade.

As the rain-fed farmland of western Syria is already highly cultivated, much of the additional land is found in the drier eastern regions. Yet by 1992, water levels in the river upstream from the dam were unusually low and presented the

1.16

The Shatt al Arab

water managers with a dilemma. In order to sustain levels in Lake Asad and hence the quantity available for agriculture, less water had to be released from the dam. Discharge through the turbines of the HEP plant was reduced and, in turn, reduced electricity output. During 1992, only two of the eight turbines were in regular operation and electricity supplies to cities were rationed. Equally seriously, water quality is deteriorating in cities and on agricultural land.

The impacts of water regulation schemes upstream of Iraq are difficult to assess because of the protracted period of war, first with Iran and then during the Gulf War. It has been claimed that water quantity is not the problem: *Iraq has a surplus of river water; its shortcomings are in management, investment and control of pollution. During four decades of oil wealth, Iraq gave its rivers and agriculture low priority* (Vesilind, *NGM*, May 1993). Iraq almost engaged in war with Syria in 1975 when the Syrians reduced the Euphrates flow in order to fill Lake Asad. As Resource 1.15 shows, there are four dams and barrages across the Euphrates which irrigate extensive areas, but Iraq's big advantage is that it controls much of the length of the Tigris. The headwater catchments which lie in Turkey are so far relatively undeveloped. However, they do lie within the planned later phases of the South-Eastern Anatolia Project. Discharges may be increasingly affected.

A final example of how the water resource can be used as a political weapon is the Shatt al Arab below the confluence of the Euphrates and Tigris rivers. This extensive area of wetlands is the traditional home of the distinctive cultural group referred to as the Marsh Arabs. They are Shi'ite Muslims, opposed to the Sunni government of Saddam Hussein. Strong evidence suggests that the primary purpose of new drainage channels being cut through these marshes is to reduce the discharges into the wetlands. This would lower the water table, causing the marshes to dry out and so deprive the marsh Arabs of their way of life. There is a danger, too, that lowering the water table in the lowest reaches of the river will allow sea water to penetrate further inland, increasing soil salinity and threatening local populations.

Activities

1 Explain why a downstream nation may be differently affected by whether or not an upstream nation is managing a river basin for (a) HEP generation; (b) flood control; (c) irrigation.

2 In what ways do the two river basins of this case study illustrate the idea that a river basin functions as a system and needs to be managed as a single, coherent unit?

3 What strategies can a downstream nation adopt to minimise its dependency upon an upstream controller of a river basin?

The Tigris - Euphrates river basin **1.15**

TURKEY

Ataturk Dam

Euphrates Dam

SYRIA

Samarra Barrage

IRAN

Ramadi Barrage

Baghdad

IRAQ

R. Tigris

R. Euphrates

Shatt al Arab

KUWAIT

N

Major dams and barrages

International boundaries

Rivers

0   300 km

CASE STUDY 1.2   *Conflicts of interest in water management in Nigeria*

Background

Traditional societies have for centuries based their economic systems upon the natural rhythms of river regimes, especially in regions with a long dry season and a single, erratic, wet season. When river channels reach bankfull flow during the wet season and eventually spill over the floodplains, wetland crops such as rice are planted. Crops such as millet and sorghum are grown and animals are grazed when the flood levels decline and the land dries out. The soil fertility levels are sustained by the annual deposition of silt. A proportion of the floodwaters infiltrates the regolith to refill the groundwater store. This groundwater can then be raised back to the surface by such ancient methods as the shadoof (Resource 1.17). It is then used to extend the size of the irrigated area and season of wetland harvest. The floodplains also supply fish and fuelwood. Pastoral societies such as the Fulani of northern Nigeria move their animals on to the floodplains where forage survives long after the savanna vegetation has become desiccated. The productive wetlands are especially important during drought years.

Unfortunately, the value and role of wetlands in rural economies has often been underestimated or ignored by development planners.

Geographers working in Nigeria claim that *as a result they [the wetlands] are inadequately taken into account in decisions about development* (Kimmage & Adams, 1992). Large-scale water management projects involve dams, reservoirs and canals which alter the rhythms of rivers and modify the character and distribution of groundwater stores. The water stored in the reservoirs is used to bring new land into cultivation and allows cropping to continue throughout the dry season. Production and productivity are increased. This is particularly important where annual population growth may exceed 2%, food intake levels of most of the population may be low, and there is a need for export crops to raise foreign capital. However, there is growing evidence that the damage done to traditional systems offsets potential benefits.

This case study uses examples from northern Nigeria to address the following questions:

- Are large-scale river basin management projects necessarily the best choice?
- Do modern high-technology schemes weaken the sustainability of traditional systems?

Matching old and new in northern Nigeria

The water environment

Nigeria stretches northwards from the permanently-moist west African coast to the semi-arid Sahel zone . The few permanent rivers which cross this northern zone are the foci of a wide range of agricultural and pastoral societies. Resource 1.18 shows the two main river basins – the Sokoto-Rima in the west, flowing into the River Niger, and the Komodugu Yobe flowing eastwards to Lake Chad. Over the past 30 years the regimes of both basins have been fundamentally altered by a series of control schemes.

One important area of traditional and productive agriculture in the Komodugu Yobe basin is the Hadejia-Jama'are floodplain. It stretches from the junction of these two rivers some 150 km upstream, and is seasonally flooded. It is also crossed by a series of low, sandy hills, which are permanently above flood level. The underlying sedimentary rocks provide good groundwater storage. Although the annual rainfall in the headstream catchment around Kano exceeds 1000 mm, the floodplain around the towns of Hadejia and Nguru receives barely 500 mm. The rainfall is unreliable and falls between May and September. During 1972–78 and 1980–87, however, this region suffered a series of drought years. The seasonal floods, which peak in August and September, are vital. Over 80% of the river discharge at the junction of the two rivers occurs between late July and the end of September. The timing, extent and duration of flooding depend upon the rainfall in the catchment and the amount of water in the groundwater store at the start of the wet season. After the drought years of the 1980s, for example, the groundwater store had been depleted and water tables were low. This meant that even when river flows returned to their higher levels, the floods were reduced until the groundwater store had been replenished.

Key understandings

- Traditional societies have developed sophisticated systems of water management.
- Modern river basin management schemes attempt to control the storage and throughput of water to increase usage.
- Modern schemes need to consider the qualities and sustainability of existing systems.

1.17

Raising water: on the left, the shadoof, a traditional device; on the right, a BUMI hand pump system, a modern, low-tech method suitable for small-scale irrigation.

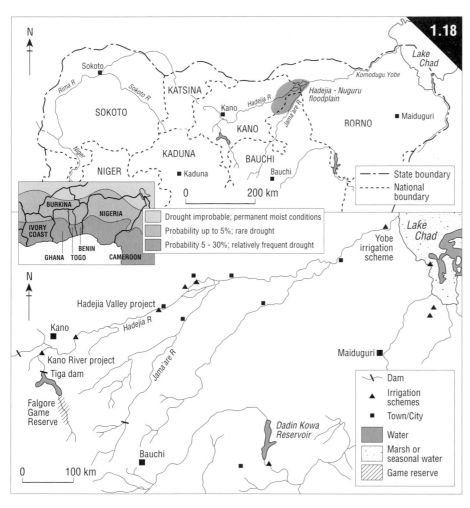

State boundary
National boundary

Drought improbable; permanent moist conditions
Probability up to 5%; rare drought
Probability 5 - 30%; relatively frequent drought

Yobe irrigation scheme

Hadejia Valley project
Kano
Hadejia R
Kano River project
Tiga dam
Falgore Game Reserve
Bauchi

Maiduguri

Dadin Kowa Reservoir

Dam
Irrigation schemes
Town/City
Water
Marsh or seasonal water
Game reserve

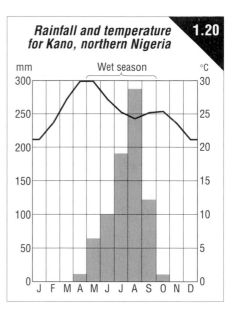

Rainfall and temperature for Kano, northern Nigeria

Wet season

People and production

Approximately one million people live in the Hadejia-Jama'are floodplain. Although increasing numbers are moving to the towns, in 1991 over 40% of the population (around 73 000 households) made their living from agriculture. Approximately half of these farming families have access to some floodable land, using the agricultural system summarised in Resource 1.19. A survey carried out in 1990 estimated that 152 500 ha were being cultivated during the main wet season. Of this total, 27% was flooded wetland (*fadama*) leaving 73% as rain-fed land (*tudu*). During the dry season, 77 500 ha were cultivated. The fadama land yields two crops a year because of the longer season of water availability. This amounts to 50% of the total crops, including vegetables for sale in local markets.

The 1990 survey was carried out in five villages and found that yields varied widely between farms and in different years. This made the estimation of the productivity and production capacity of the floodplain difficult. The researchers then ranked the yields per hectare for each family for the major crops, and using the bottom and upper quartiles of this productivity list, calculated low and high estimates of the

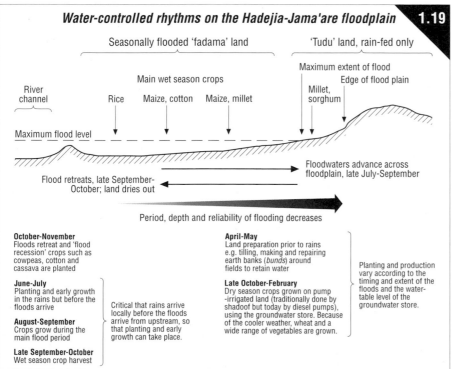

Water-controlled rhythms on the Hadejia-Jama'are floodplain

Seasonally flooded 'fadama' land | 'Tudu' land, rain-fed only

Maximum extent of flood
Edge of flood plain

Main wet season crops

River channel
Rice | Maize, cotton | Maize, millet | Millet, sorghum

Maximum flood level

Floodwaters advance across floodplain, late July–September

Flood retreats, late September–October; land dries out

Period, depth and reliability of flooding decreases

October-November
Floods retreat and 'flood recession' crops such as cowpeas, cotton and cassava are planted

June-July
Planting and early growth in the rains but before the floods arrive

August-September
Crops grow during the main flood period

Late September-October
Wet season crop harvest

Critical that rains arrive locally before the floods arrive from upstream, so that planting and early growth can take place.

April-May
Land preparation prior to rains e.g. tilling, making and repairing earth banks (*bunds*) around fields to retain water

Late October-February
Dry season crops grown on pump-irrigated land (traditionally done by shadoof but today by diesel pumps), using the groundwater store. Because of the cooler weather, wheat and a wide range of vegetables are grown.

Planting and production vary according to the timing and extent of the floods and the water-table level of the groundwater store.

CASE STUDY 1.2 *Conflicts of interest in water management in Nigeria*

1.21 (a) Agricultural production, 1990

Crop	Production (tonnes) Low estimate	High estimate
Rice	9 060	35 610
Wheat	28 900	57 800
Cow-peas	9 860	40 210
Peppers	13 850	50 950
Millet	22 570	78 260
Sorghum	15 420	85 210
Maize	12 780	18 630
Tomatoes	14 490	17 420
Onions	3 030	20 820

NB: These are main crops only, and exclude cotton for which no figures are available.

(b) Value of production, 1990 (million Naira)

Component	Production Low estimate	High estimate
Agriculture	250	850
Fishing	45	45
Wood	8	14
Total	303	909

NB: Livestock figures are excluded.

floodplain production. On Resource 1.21a the 'low estimate' of production is the crop tonnage if all farms produced at the yields of the lowest quartile. The 'high estimate' is based upon the yields of the top quartile of farms. Whichever estimate we accept, this floodplain production has considerable value to the regional economy, particularly when the fish and wood yields are added in Resource 1.21b. Remember too, that the survey did not include the output from animals grazing the floodplain. The conclusion *suggests a gross value of production per hectare of between 1250 and 3700 Naira* [the Nigerian currency] (Kimmage & Adams, 1992).

Threats to the floodplain

Despite the fact that the 40 500 ha irrigated by informal schemes on the Hadejia-Jama'are floodplain is larger than the area irrigated by all of the major formal schemes across northern Nigeria, there is evidence that the needs of the floodplain have not been addressed in water management planning. The river basin has been divided into into three sections, shown in Resource 1.23. The floodplain (Section B) receives its input of water and silt from the upper catchment basin (Section A).

Schemes such as the Kano River Project, based upon water storage behind the Tiga Dam, reduce the discharges passing downstream and alter their timing. According to Resource 1.22, the floods seem to cover smaller areas than in the past, although before the building of the upstream dams, annual floods fluctuated as rainfall varied. Evidence from other projects in northern Nigeria support the view that the upstream storage and release systems are reducing the input to downstream floodplains. For example, the Bakolori Dam and reservoir on the Sokoto River have brought at least 20 000 ha of new land into cultivation, but the traditional fadama lands downstream have suffered severely-reduced seasonal flooding.

Engineering schemes are altering the river regime, even in the Hadejia-Jama'are floodplain itself. The Hadejia barrage at the upper end of the floodplain has created a small lake in the floodplain itself and extracts water for the 12 500 ha of the Hadejia Valley Project. A more serious threat, however, comes from districts *downstream*, i.e. Section C on Resource 1.23. Here, in the lower section of the river basin, the farmers have seen reduced flows resulting from the upstream projects. Their politicians are lobbying for a series of channels to be cut through the Hadejia-Jama'are floodplain (Section B). This would carry water more quickly across the floodplain and further reduce the water available to the Hadejia-Jama'are farmers.

The conclusions are that the Hadejia-Jama'are floodplain should be given

1.22 Area covered by flooding, 1950–89

Year	Area (sq.km.)	Year	Area (sq.km.)
1950	2026	1986	1186
1969	2043	1987	700
1974	2004	1989	950
1978	1825		

greater consideration in water management plans, and that integrated river basin management, i.e. consideration of the *whole* basin, is essential. In 1990, the Hadejia-Nguru Wetland Conservation Project was set up to bring together the interest groups and managers from the various sections of the basin to create a sustainable management system for the flooplain.

[Based on Kimmage K. & Adams W.M. 'Wetland agricultural production and river basin development in the Hadejia-Jama'are valley, Nigeria'. *The Geographical Journal*, 158(1), March 1992, 1–12]

Activities

1 Outline how the traditional agricultural system of the Hadejia-Jama'are floodplain is an indication of a sophisticated understanding of the regional water regime.

2 In what ways are the input, stores, throughput and output of the natural system being modified by water management schemes? What are the benefits and costs of these schemes? Suggest reasons why an integrated basin approach seems the only answer to developing a sustainable water management system for the floodplain.

1.23 Threats to the water regime of the floodplain

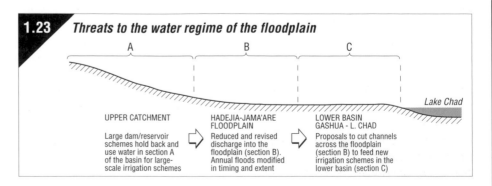

UPPER CATCHMENT
Large dam/reservoir schemes hold back and use water in section A of the basin for large-scale irrigation schemes

HADEJIA-JAMA'ARE FLOODPLAIN
Reduced and revised discharge into the floodplain (section B). Annual floods modified in timing and extent

LOWER BASIN GASHUA - L. CHAD
Proposals to cut channels across the floodplain (section B) to feed new irrigation schemes in the lower basin (section C)

CASE STUDY 1.3 *Facing the finite: conserving the Ogallala aquifer, USA*

Background

Groundwater is the general term used for all water stored in aquifers below the land surface. It accounts for at least 90% of the world's accessible freshwater (excluding that stored as ice), and one-half is found within 800 m of the ground surface. So is is not surprising that, for centuries, people have drawn upon this groundwater store. Yet it is only in the past 50 years that the demands made on the world's aquifers have accelerated alarmingly. In south-east England, groundwater stores accommodate two-thirds of the water demands, and water-tables have fallen significantly.

If a groundwater store is to be used, it is important to know whether it is **live** or **fossil**. A **live** aquifer is one which is being replenished by present-day input of water. The water in a **fossil** aquifer is a store

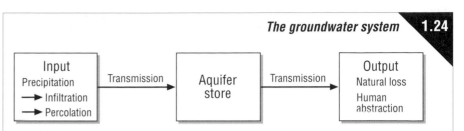

The groundwater system 1.24

Input
Precipitation
→ Infiltration
→ Percolation
— Transmission → Aquifer store — Transmission → Output
Natural loss
Human abstraction

which had accumulated when the regional climates were moister, perhaps as much as 100 000 years ago. Today there is no substantial recharge and any abstraction is not replaced. For example, cropland has been declining in parts of Arizona because it has relied on fossil groundwater stores. Pumping caused the water-tables to fall and wells to dry up. The land has been abandoned unless water from the Colorado river has become available via the canals of the Central Arizona Project.

Groundwater works as an **open system**. As with all systems, a groundwater basin functions in a state of **dynamic equilibrium**, where the store makes medium term adjustments to changing input and output. A live aquifer system, therefore, has a **budget** i.e. a relationship between input and output. One aim of water management is **sustainable yield.** The fundamental understandings are of how much water enters the aquifers in a given time, i.e. the **recharge rate**, and how much the store can hold, i.e. its **capacity**. These properties determine how much water can be taken out in a given time without reducing the size of the store, i.e. its **abstraction capacity**.

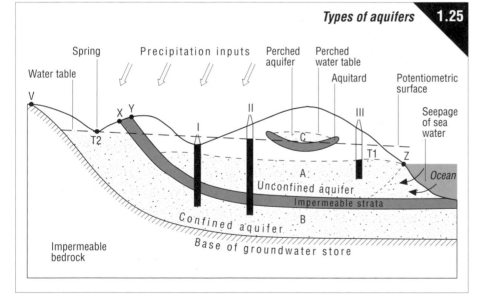

Types of aquifers 1.25

Aquifers may be unconfined, confined or perched, depending upon their positions in relation to aquitards, or less permeable formations which retard the transmission of water. Perched aquifers are often local and limited in capacity. Unconfined and confined aquifers each behave differently. It is, therefore, necessary to know the nature of the aquifer if the groundwater store is to be exploited. For example, water in unconfined aquifers functions under atmospheric pressure, whereas water in confined aquifers is under hydrostatic pressure. Such confined water stores are often known as artesian. This characteristic will influence the water-level in any particular well.

[It will be useful at this stage for you to check your understanding of the following hydrological terms – water table; potentiometric (piezometric) surface; hydrostatic pressure; artesian; permeability; primary and secondary porosity.]

1.26 **The extent of the Ogallala aquifer**

CASE STUDY 1.3   *Facing the finite: conserving the Ogallala aquifer, USA*

Through a study of the Ogallala aquifer, the largest groundwater store in North America, this case study illustrates the nature of groundwater basins and the application of technology to satisfy the explosion of demand. The Ogallala aquifer stretches beneath the High Plains of the USA and the southern half of the temperate grassland biome known as the Prairies. It is the key resource in the human use of the High Plains. As you read through the case study, take particular note of the changing relationship between human needs, perceptions and understandings, the environment and the Ogallala aquifer over time.

Changing attitudes to the Ogallala aquifer

The nature of the aquifer

The Ogallala aquifer lies within the Tertiary strata which form the youngest formations of a huge sedimentary basin. It extends eastwards from the Rocky Mountain front for 800 km and underlies the western half of the Mississippi drainage basin. The strata are a complex succession of gravel, sand and clay beds up to 800 m thick. The sediment sequence and character varies from place to place. The Ogallala consists of a large number of units, each requiring distinctive management strategies, although we think of it as a single aquifer.

The water-holding beds vary in thickness and depth because of how the sediments were originally laid down, later tectonic stresses and more recent erosion and stream incision . The aquifer averages 60 m in thickness but varies from less than one metre to 400 m. In some places the upper surface may be as deep as 80 m below the ground surface. It consists of intercalated sand and gravel beds and is mainly a confined aquifer, i.e. it is overlain by aquitards. Thus, where the potentiometric surface reaches ground level there are bubbling springs sustained by hydrostatic pressure. In Nebraska, for example, an aquifer with an area of 174 000 miles^2 contains enough water to fill Lake Huron, one of the Great Lakes.

Key understandings

- ◆ The Ogallala aquifer is the largest groundwater store in North America and is the key to the patterns of human activity across a large part of the High Plains and Prairies.

- ◆ A groundwater store works as an open system, with a finite budget: input from percolation; storage with a measurable capacity; and output into streams and lakes.

- ◆ An aquifer may be confined, unconfined or perched.

- ◆ All too frequently, the use of aquifers such as the Ogallala has been exploitative rather than sustainable, resulting in serious recession in the water-table and the volume of water stored.

- ◆ Sustainable groundwater management depends upon controlling abstraction (withdrawal of water) within the recharge capacity of the aquifer, i.e. balancing output with input.

- ◆ Human perceptions of and use of aquifers change over time.

1.27   *The physical nature of the Ogallala aquifer*

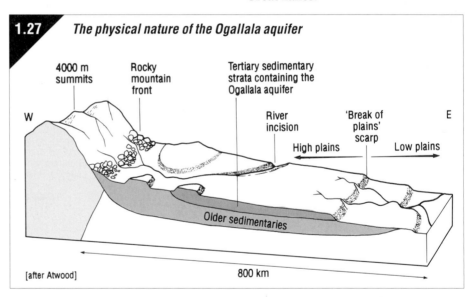

[after Atwood]

1.28   *Cross section through the Ogallala aquifer*

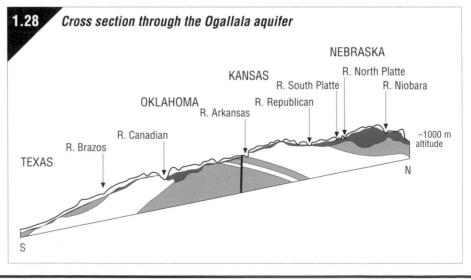

Most importantly, the Ogallala is a live aquifer, with two sources of natural recharge. The major source is direct input from precipitation, which percolates through the overlying strata in the unconfined sections of the aquifer. The second component is recharge by percolation from the channels of the east-flowing rivers, such as the Red and Arkansas, which cross the High Plains. At periods of high flow, significant volumes percolate from the beds and banks of these rivers . Although the direction of water movement is reversed at low flow periods, when groundwater sustains the base flow there is a net annual surplus into the aquifer. As Resource 1.27 shows, the Rocky Mountains are not a direct source of water for the Ogallala. They are, however, an important indirect source, because the headwater catchments of the High Plains rivers lie in the mountains. Much of the water which percolates from the channels into the aquifer is Rocky Mountain water.

Use and management

Even though the relationship between the aquifer and human society is constantly changing, five main phases can be identified:

1 Pre-1850 – the Native American phase
2 1850-1930 – the Pioneer Settlement phase
3 1930-1950 – the Dust Bowl
4 1950-1985 – the Irrigation phase
5 Post-1985 – the Conservation phase

The dates are approximate, the phases overlap and the story varies from region to region. However, they do provide a framework within which to follow the attitudes to, management of and use of the groundwater resource.

Buffalo (North American Bison) on the North American high plains

1 The Native American phase

The diverse Native American cultures varied in the balance between hunting and agriculture and, hence, in their use of water. The best-known group are the 'Plains Indians' who based their economy around the seasonal migrations of the 60 million or more buffalo which grazed the Prairies. During spring and summer when grass and water are most readily available, the herds dispersed across the High Plains, and the Native Americans moved with them. In autumn and winter, as the animals concentrated along the river valleys, so did the people. The surface streams, sustained at times of low flow by recharge from the Ogallala aquifer, were their main source of water. In addition, where the aquifer reached the surface, springs and pools were important focal points on the movements of animals and humans across the plains.

2 The Pioneer Settlement phase

By 1850, the Prairies had already been labelled 'the Great American Desert', despite the fact that these were one of the world's largest and richest grasslands. Almost all the explorers came from the humid forested environments of western Europe or eastern America.

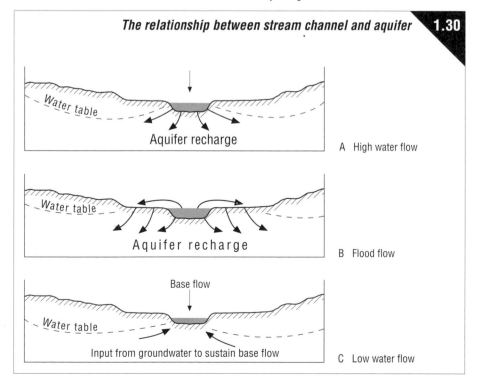

The relationship between stream channel and aquifer 1.30

Water table

Aquifer recharge

A High water flow

Water table

Aquifer recharge

B Flood flow

Base flow

Water table

Input from groundwater to sustain base flow

C Low water flow

CASE STUDY 1.3 *Facing the finite: conserving the Ogallala aquifer, USA*

To them, the treeless expanses were barren lands. An expedition leader to the High Plains wrote in 1820: *It is almost wholly unfit for cultivation, and of course uninhabitable by a people depending upon agriculture for their subsistence*.

What he was referring to, of course, was non-irrigated agriculture, and in those terms, there was considerable truth in his judgment. Unfortunately, the advice was ignored. The US government pursued a vigorous policy of settling the American West, especially after the Civil War ended in 1865. They offered cheap land to settlers. Railway companies lured people with promises of prosperous futures on the rich lands of the West. Banks and agricultural merchants encouraged settlers with ready loans. The immigrant population responded with an enormous surge of energy which saw at least 70% of the Prairie grassland ploughed up by 1920. By 1900, they had reduced the buffalo numbers to less than 2000, by limiting their grazing range and carrying out large-scale slaughter to take away the main food source of

the Native Americans. This, in turn, forced the Native Americans off their traditional lands.

With the exception of the drier grasslands of Texas where cattle-grazing remained important, this arable agriculture was dominated by corn (maize) and wheat. Irrigation was not used, except along some of the river valleys. The Ogallala aquifer was tapped by wells only for domestic and animal use on farms and in towns and cities. Surface water remained the main source of supply.

3 The Dust Bowl
We now know that the arable cropping of the High Plains without irrigation survived as long as it did only because of a series of above-average rainfall years in the early twentieth century. From 1930, however, drier conditions prevailed and within five years the Dust Bowl had been created. In parts of Oklahoma and Kansas, over 50% of farms were abandoned as crops failed, the topsoil blew away and the farmers went bankrupt. John Steinbeck's novel, *The Grapes of*

Wrath, vividly describes this scene. From the mid-1930s until the late 1940s the region fought to survive. Government schemes encouraged the return of land to pasture and cattle-grazing and new techniques of 'dry farming' were introduced, which meant leaving a proportion of the land fallow each year to reduce water demand. Increased surface stores were being created by the construction of dams and associated reservoirs along the headwaters of the rivers flowing from the Rockies, such as the North and South Platte and the Arkansas. The true extent of the Ogallala aquifer and its potential was becoming known.

4 The Irrigation phase
By 1950 increased surface-water supply from the reservoirs and abstraction from the Ogallala aquifer brought about a transformation of the High Plains. Since then, the intensive exploitation of the aquifer *has transformed the very acres that blew away in the Dust Bowl of the 1930s into an agricultural phenomenon. Because of Ogallala*

The Dust Bowl

Cattle in a feedlot

1.34

Crop watering machine, Oklahoma

water, Nebraska can add 700 million more bushels of corn [maize] to its annual crop; Kansas can fatten 3 million more head of beef cattle; Texas can produce 2 million more bales of cotton (Zwingle, *NGM*, 1993). A government survey in 1982 showed that over six million hectares were being irrigated by Ogallala water pumped from 150 000 wells. This represented 30% of the US total of groundwater used for irrigation. Only 10% of the pumped Ogallala water is used by cities and industries. The rest is swallowed by the main crops of cotton, sorghum, wheat, corn (maize), much of which are fed to fatten 40% of the US total of feedlot beef. It is hardly surprising that local people should look on the Ogallala with reverence (Resource 1.33).

The basic technology of this revolution has been the **centre pivot** irrigation system, thousands of which pock-mark the prairies with their brown, green and gold circles (Resource 1.34). They are simple constructions which use huge quantities of water. With a 400 m long arm slowly rotating around the central pivot, the sprinklers can spray 1000 gallons per minute over a 60 hectare circle. If programmed, the system can operate 24 hours a day, throughout the three month growing season. In Nebraska, using centre pivot rigs, it takes about 240 000 gallons (the equivalent of 500 mm of rain) to grow each hectare of corn (maize). As the average annual rainfall totals in this region may be less than 500 mm, and as less than one-half of this precipitation will percolate to the aquifer, there has been an inevitable overdraft of the groundwater store. Between 1950 and 1980, the water table fell by an average of 3 m, attaining 30 m in parts of Texas. By 1982, Kansas had used 38% of the total Ogallala store within the State boundaries. The Ogallala aquifer was being exploited, not managed sustainably.

Several dry years in the 1970s worsened the situation, but humans too had altered the way the Ogallala system works. The creation of dams and reservoirs along the headwater stretches of the rivers which cross the High Plains have reduced the flows and floods along the downstream sections of these rivers. Thus, bank recharge from the rivers

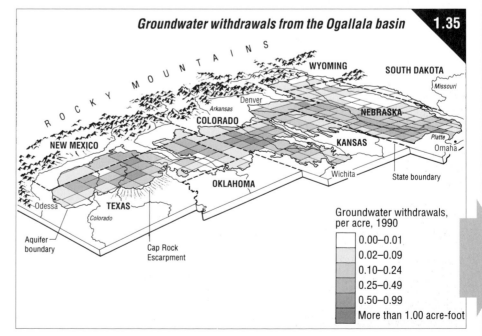

Groundwater withdrawals from the Ogallala basin **1.35**

Groundwater withdrawals, per acre, 1990

- 0.00–0.01
- 0.02–0.09
- 0.10–0.24
- 0.25–0.49
- 0.50–0.99
- More than 1.00 acre-foot

to the groundwater store has declined (Resource 1.30). There is only a finite input of water to the region and its storage distribution has been greatly altered.

Water quality, too, was suffering. There were increasing numbers of incidences of water contamination, since farm, domestic and industrial effluents were allowed to percolate untreated in most rural and small town districts.

5 The Conservation phase

By 1980 it was clear in all states dependent upon the Ogallala aquifer, that extraction seriously exceeded recharge and that the water was being used wastefully. As a result, tougher controls, new technologies and conservation-based approaches, aided by several 'wet' years in the early 1980s, reduced the overall fall in water level to 0.3 m over the decade. However, there were wide variations, with serious falls continuing in parts of Kansas and Texas. When this map of water-level change is compared with that showing rates of water withdrawal, it does seem that those areas with the most intense use were experiencing the most serious falls in water level.

Before we accept this simple relationship, we must remember how irrigation works: in areas where wells are concentrated, cones of depression will develop, and the

water level will fall. In areas where the water is used, a proportion may not be taken up by the crops. This will either evaporate or percolate into the groundwater store and so raise the water table, producing a water mound. Consequently, we cannot assume that the areas on Resource 1.35 showing water level rises are necessarily recovering by natural recharge; they may be benefitting from water pumped elsewhere.

1.36 Using water from the aquifer

Colorado farmer

'How much water you need depends on how effectively your soil uses it. How easily the aquifer can be replenished, or recharged, is determined by the soil texture.'

Soil scientist

'We put water on the soil too often. Wet soils will not take water – dry soils do. But the equipment dealers have been telling farmers to speed up the centre pivot rotation. They end up harvesting in December because the mud kept them from harvesting earlier.'

Strategies for water conservation

The conservation effort follows three main directions:

- Take land away from farming and return to natural grassland for conservation and recreation values.
- Change the land use from arable to grazing, which has much lower water requirements and retains greater surface cover (See Case Study on Grasslands use, p 43).
- Retain arable cropping but adopt either dry farming strategies or irrigation techniques which use water more efficiently.

The main efforts so far have been directed at the introduction of conservation-oriented methods into irrigated farming. The base-line for sustainability, i.e. sustained yield over time, is that the water budget of the Ogallala aquifer must balance: recharge should equal abstraction. So, to control water use, the irrigation district managers set pumping limits, and monitor the abstraction by metering systems. A farmer may have an allocation set for a five-year period and can then decide how best

1.38 Gypsum block diagram

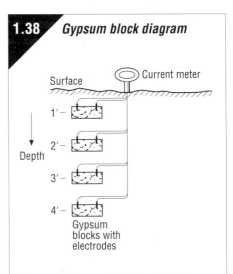

Gypsum blocks, each with two electrodes, are buried at depths of 1 to 4 feet in the soil. As the soil gains or loses moisture, the current between the electrodes changes and can be read on the current meter. This is a simple way to monitor soil moisture, and hence, to assess the need for irrigation rights.

1.37 Diagram of cones and mounds

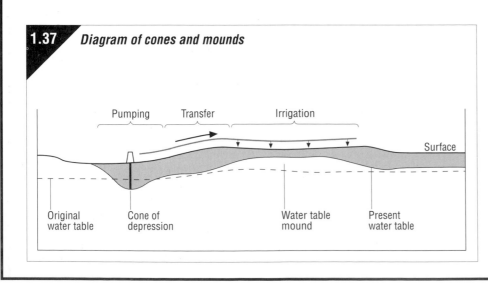

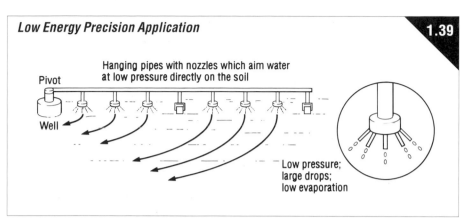

Low Energy Precision Application `1.39`

Pivot

Hanging pipes with nozzles which aim water at low pressure directly on the soil

Well

Low pressure; large drops; low evaporation

to use it. Many districts have introduced such policies.

Pricing mechanisms, too, can form effective controls on water-use. Until the 1980s, cheap water and government crop price supports encouraged farmers to use water liberally. Today, government support is reduced and water prices are increasing.

Applying water at the right time

If soils receive the right amount of moisture at the time the plants need it most, then less water needs to be pumped. In turn, less water will be wasted in run-off and evaporation, since the plants use the water efficiently. This optimises growth and sustains crop yields with less irrigation. Thus, a knowledge of how much water soils contain and hold, is vital. One simple monitoring system is illustrated in Resource 1.38. The effectiveness of the

gypsum block technique is exemplified by the experience of one Colorado farmer: he was using 1000 gallons a minute to water 50 hectares. By monitoring the soil moisture via the gypsum block record, he is now able to irrigate 100 hectares and yet pump only 800 gallons a minute.

Applying only the amount of water plants need

Matching the amount of water a plant needs to the amount applied has been made easier by advances in centre pivot technology. The most widely used is LEPA (Low Energy Precision Application), which directs larger drops at lower pressure than traditional sprinklers do. It thereby reduces evaporation loss by 90% and ensures that a high proportion of the water applied is actually taken up by the plants.

Reducing evaporation loss

Evaporation loss and wind erosion can be reduced by the simple strategy of leaving the grain stubble on the fields. This 'reduced tillage' or 'residue management' technique shields the soil and helps to retain soil moisture. Remember that one metre of soil can hold up to 24 cm of moisture.

Recycling and re-using water

One strategy which is growing rapidly in popularity is the re-use and recycling of water. Resource 1.40 shows how one large enterprise optimises water use. The Reeve Cattle Company, Kansas, fattens 17 000 cattle in feedlots. The alfalfa and corn (maize) feed is provided from 1820 hectares, most of which are irrigated from 30 wells, each with a 1000 gallon a minute capacity. The entire operation employs 35 people. Because of the grain surplus, the owner has built an ethanol plant which produces seven million gallons of saleable fuel a year. (Ethanol is at present used as an additive in petrol). The warm water effluent from this process is then fed into tanks where white tilapia fish are raised. Over 200 000 lbs are sold per year. When cooled, the water is passed on to holding ponds before percolating into the aquifer or distributed to fields directly. The owner says that *the objective is to use the by-products (outputs) of one system for the inputs of another. That's one reason to conserve water: because you're conserving everything else.*

Another conservation strategy is to recycle water according to its quality. Rural water districts provide potable, i.e. fresh drinkable water to urban districts. In return, these districts send back treated waste water for use in irrigation. Such schemes are successfully in operation in Kansas and Nebraska.

The central management issue

Whichever combination of conservation policies and techniques is employed, water managers face a central dilemma. At one level the Ogallala aquifer functions as a single system,

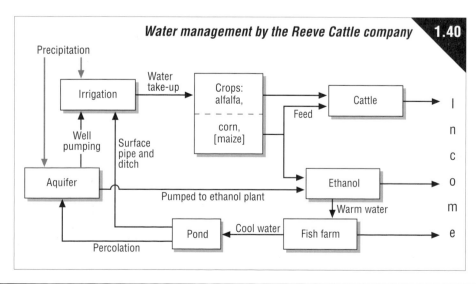

Water management by the Reeve Cattle company `1.40`

Precipitation

Water take-up

Irrigation

Crops: alfalfa, corn, [maize]

Cattle

Feed

Well pumping

Surface pipe and ditch

Aquifer

Pumped to ethanol plant

Ethanol

Warm water

Pond

Cool water

Fish farm

Percolation

Income

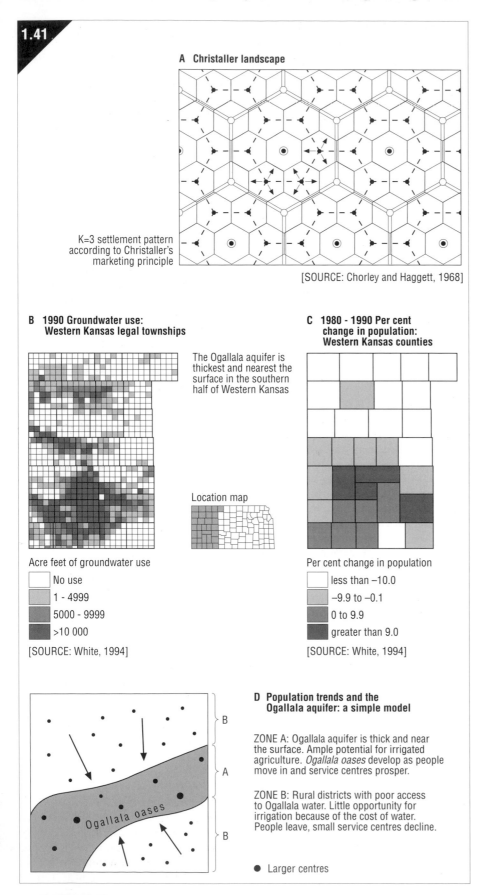

1.41

A Christaller landscape

K=3 settlement pattern according to Christaller's marketing principle

[SOURCE: Chorley and Haggett, 1968]

B 1990 Groundwater use: Western Kansas legal townships

The Ogallala aquifer is thickest and nearest the surface in the southern half of Western Kansas

Location map

Acre feet of groundwater use

- No use
- 1 - 4999
- 5000 - 9999
- >10 000

[SOURCE: White, 1994]

C 1980 - 1990 Per cent change in population: Western Kansas counties

Per cent change in population

- less than −10.0
- −9.9 to −0.1
- 0 to 9.9
- greater than 9.0

[SOURCE: White, 1994]

D Population trends and the Ogallala aquifer: a simple model

ZONE A: Ogallala aquifer is thick and near the surface. Ample potential for irrigated agriculture. *Ogallala oases* develop as people move in and service centres prosper.

ZONE B: Rural districts with poor access to Ogallala water. Little opportunity for irrigation because of the cost of water. People leave, small service centres decline.

Ogallala oases

- Larger centres

requiring unified management. At another level, there are a number of distinct water basins and numerous water districts where managers make decisions appropriate to the local circumstances. At present, there is a mixture of both overall and localised policies. Although the general overdraft is reduced, some districts are much more conservation-oriented than others.

A new conservation direction

An increasingly popular conservation option is to reduce the farmed area and adopt policies which restore the natural grassland ecosystem. More and more Americans appreciate the beauty of the natural Prairies. Subsequently, once-extensive areas of grassland are re-established to encourage the wildlife to move back in. This includes the buffalo which has become a major tourist attraction and is also increasingly popular for its meat. The return of deer and prairie birds increase the potential for hunting and watching wildlife. Conservation values are, therefore, achieved without making further demands upon the Ogallala aquifer, while providing additional income .

[Based on Zwingle E. 'Wellspring of the High Plain', *NGM*, 183(3) March 1993, 80–109]

Activities

1 How does the Ogallala aquifer acquire its water?

2 Use the Ogallala aquifer to illustrate the idea that a groundwater store works as an open system and that any management policy must be based on 'balancing the water budget'.

3 From Resources 1.37 and 1.38, describe what was happening to the Ogallala aquifer during the 1980s.

4 Use Phases 4 and 5 (Irrigation; Conservation) to illustrate the differences between exploitation and sustainable management.

5 Suggest how restoring Prairie grassland ecosystems will be helpful to the water managers of the Ogallala aquifer.

CASE STUDY 1.4

'The Mississippi – coming soon to a town near you'

Background

The title to this case study was taken from graffiti on a wall in St Louis, Missouri, in July 1993.

River valleys, floodplains and deltas have proved attractive places for human activity. They encompass fertile, easily-worked land, easy river crossings, navigation access, a ready water supply, sheltered climate and great recreation potential. These lower lands lining many of the world's great rivers have become intensively occupied. However, people have since realised that such locations can be hazardous. All rivers have identifiable rhythms or regimes, but they occasionally generate exceptional flows well beyond the normal rhythms. During these extreme events, the discharge may exceed the channel bankfull capacity and spill over on to the **floodplain**.

The realisation of this danger has caused communities and governments to take flood preventitive measures. As technology has advanced, so the schemes have become increasingly ambitious and expectations of their capabilities higher. Whether simple or sophisticated, the flood prevention principles have always remained the same four options:

- Store water upstream in dams and reservoirs.
- Divert the water through additional channels.
- Improve the capacity and flow of existing channels by straightening or deepening.
- Protect low-lying areas with levées and embankments.

All modern water control schemes are based on the understanding that a river basin functions as a system, with input, throughput, stores and output. Each scheme is designed to cope with a finite flow and storage of water in a given period of time: it has a **finite design capacity**. The decision on this capacity is based upon the understanding of the river basin discharge characteristics – how the river behaves – and on the availability of money and technology. Thus, a flood control project may be designed with the capacity to absorb a *hundred year flood*, that is, the discharge that is forecast as having a likely return interval of 100 years. Few schemes are designed to prevent all possible discharge scenarios. Cost, environmental impact and imperfect knowledge all play their part in the extent of the control and protection. Yet communities who live along these floodplains and in these deltas, tend to perceive the engineering works as flood **prevention** measures rather than flood **control** measures. When a river does not behave and the flood control system does not respond as the community expects, then a flood, a natural occurrence on a floodplain, becomes a **disaster**. The event could be further classified as a **natural** or a **technological** disaster.

In the summer of 1993, the communities along the floodplain of the middle Mississippi, USA, endured just such a disaster, suffering some of the most serious floods ever recorded on this river. This case study analyses the causes of the flood and why it has opened up a fundamental debate about whether we need to rethink our approach to river management, flood control and floodplain use.

Key understandings

- ◆ River management schemes have a finite design capacity and are more concerned with flood control than total flood prevention.

- ◆ Floodplains are attractive for human settlement but are also zones of hazard.

- ◆ The 1993 floods across the middle Mississippi basin were caused by a combination of unusual weather conditions and human modification of the river system.

- ◆ Management policy for the Mississippi basin has been based upon a very expensive hard engineering strategy, yet the flood protection system still failed in 1993.

- ◆ The 1993 Mississippi floods have caused all those involved in river management to give greater consideration to soft engineering strategies which include the use of the floodplain as a floodwater store, thereby imitating its natural function.

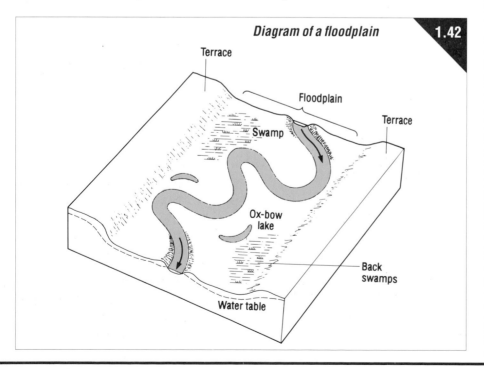

Diagram of a floodplain 1.42

Terrace
Floodplain
Terrace
Swamp
Ox-bow lake
Back swamps
Water table

Effects of the Mississippi flood

Setting

The Mississippi system drains 40% of the USA (excluding Alaska and Hawaii), and at 1.24 million miles² is the world's fifth largest drainage basin. When the two main rivers, the Mississippi (3700 km) and the Missouri (3900 km) are put together, they become the third longest river in the world. Beginning in a small lake in north-west Minnesota, the 'Father of Rivers' finally discharges 100 trillion gallons a year into the Gulf of Mexico. Some 15% of all US internal freight moves along this mighty river.

Individuals and communities have tried for more than 200 years to control the Mississippi. Yet it has been only since 1928, with the passing of the federal government Flood Control Act, that the US Army Corps of Engineers (the organisation responsible for river basin management schemes) and the Mississippi River Commission (representing states within the basin) have put together a comprehensive management plan for the basin. Their strategy has been based firmly upon **prevention** and **hard engineering**, through a complex system of dams, reservoirs and barrages in the upper and middle sections, and levées, floodwalls and channelisation along the middle and lower reaches. By 1992, over 5500 km of channel (main stream and tributaries) were lined by embankments and walls.

Despite all this effort by the wealthiest and most technologically-advanced country in the world, the middle Mississippi basin suffered catastrophic floods in July 1993. More than 70% of the 1600 separate levées and embankments suffered damage or were breached above the Mississippi-Missouri confluence. Land and homes in the floodplain are relatively cheap, and so poor and vulnerable families were most severely affected. At least 50 people died, 72 000 homes were flooded, and over four million hectares were inundated. The expense has been estimated at over $10 billion.

Seeking the causes – natural factors

There is no doubt that even if there had been no human intervention in the natural regime of the Mississippi, the river would have spilled over its floodplain in the summer of 1993. This was a '500 year' flood, that is, a flood which is expected to return after an interval of 500 years. It was not only the scale which was exceptional, but also its timing. The normal spate discharges occur in the spring as the snows melt across the upper and middle basin. Summers in the American Mid-West are generally hot and dry, with irregular thunderstorms. From June onwards, river levels tend to fall. In 1993, however, the June/July rainfall across the middle Mississippi basin was double the average amounts. In many districts at least 600 mm of rain fell

1.43 *The Mississippi basin*

1.44

A freighter and a 'pusher' barge along the lower Mississippi

between the beginning of June and late July. In Cedar Rapids, Iowa, 850 mm fell between April and July, an amount equal to the average annual total. This made 1993 the wettest summer on record. As water tables were already high, quick-flow run-off delivered water rapidly to the river channels, causing unusually steep rising arms to the storm hydrographs along all the tributaries and the main Mississippi channel.

The meteorological cause of these unusually heavy and prolonged rains is shown on Resource 1.47. A wave on the upper troposphere jet stream settled much farther south than usual. This allowed cool, dry continental (Pc) air to move southwards, where it came into contact with warm, moist tropical maritime (Tm) air. The tropical maritime air usually moves northwards from the Gulf of Mexico as part of the clockwise circulation around a high pressure system to the east. As the land mass heated up during June and July, the Tm air became increasingly unstable, and as it rose over the cool Pc air, vigorous convection storms with heavy rainfall were generated. In a 'normal' summer, these thunderstorms would move away eastwards, but in 1993, the Bermuda high pressure cell refused to weaken and thus blocked this movement.

Levées near Baton Rouge: the river is beyond the trees on the left. The levée slopes down to the floodplain on the right, about 10 m below the river level.

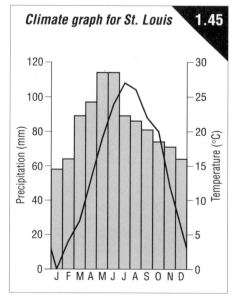

Climate graph for St. Louis **1.45**

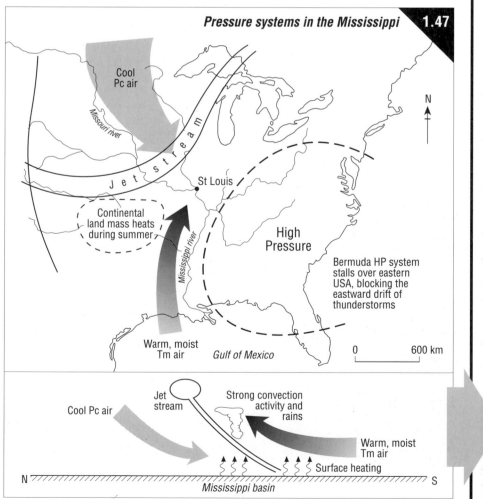

Pressure systems in the Mississippi **1.47**

CASE STUDY 1.4 *'The Mississippi – coming soon to a town near you'*

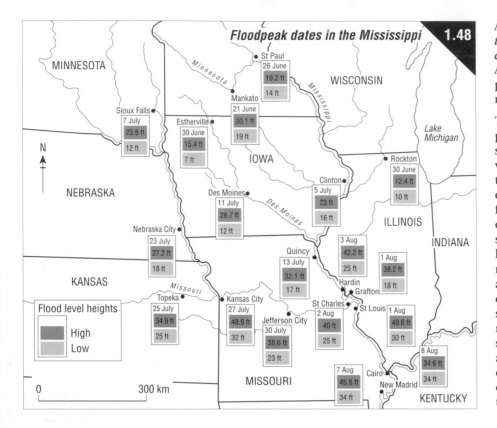

Floodpeak dates in the Mississippi 1.48

Flood level heights

High
Low

0 | 300 km

As a result *the storms stayed put and the rains kept coming ... and coming* (Mairson, *NGM*, Jan 1994). At the same time, the stalled high pressure system was causing a record heatwave over east coast USA.

The effects of this exceptional and prolonged input of water can be seen on Resource 1.48. Notice the vast extent of the affected area and the way the flood peak surge moved downstream. For instance, the floods peaked in Minneapolis-St Paul on 26 June and by late July, were subsiding. Five weeks later, the surge had reached St Louis and did not reach Cairo until 7 August. However, an analysis of the flood as it developed through July records a series of discharge surges. Once the reservoirs, groundwater and other stores were full, any further deluges across different parts of the huge catchment brought another pulse of discharge down one or more tributaries, and on down the main

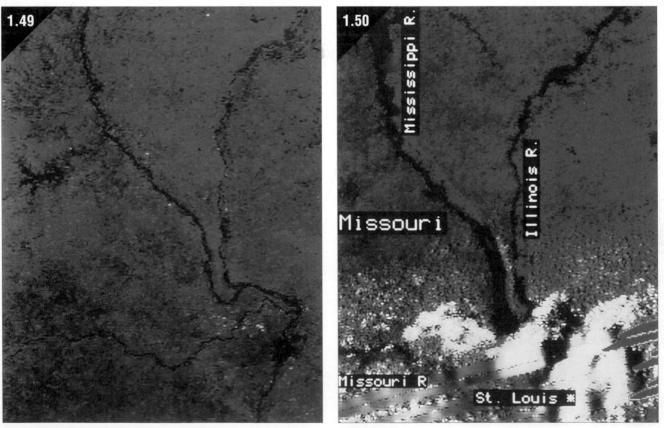

The Mississippi – Missouri junction under normal conditions

The Mississippi – Missouri junction under flood conditions

N

St Charles

St Louis

Missouri River

Mississippi River

Mississippi River

ILLINOIS

MISSOURI

0   10 km

The Missouri River broke through a levée near St Charles on 16 July. Floodwaters surged northward, merging with Mississippi backwaters 20 miles upstream from their normal confluence.

Mississippi and Missouri channels. This continued until they filled up, spilled over their floodplains and backed water up the tributaries, in some cases reversing the flow. For example, when the Mississippi was full, it backed up along the River Illinois tributary *which swelled like a blocked blood vessel* (Mairson, *NGM*, Jan 1994).

The successive surges made forecasting very difficult. For example, a bulletin issued by the US Central Weather Service on 16 July forecast that the flood peak would reach St Louis on 19 July, but as further storms dumped rain on Iowa and Missouri, the arrival date was modified three times. *When television weathermen pointed to a heavy thunderstorm in North Dakota or Iowa, everyone downstream knew that another surge of water would pulse through the system and eventually get to them* (Mairson, *NGM*, Jan 1994).

The pair of remote sensing images of Resources 1.49 and 1.50 illustrate the final outcome around the confluence of the two great rivers. Resource 1.51 focuses on one locality .

By mid-August the discharge peak was moving south of Cairo. The flooding along the Mississippi below this city was less severe, largely because of the broader channel capacity and less continuous levées,

1.52

The main distributary channel of the Mississippi at New Orleans flows between levées to protect the city from flooding.

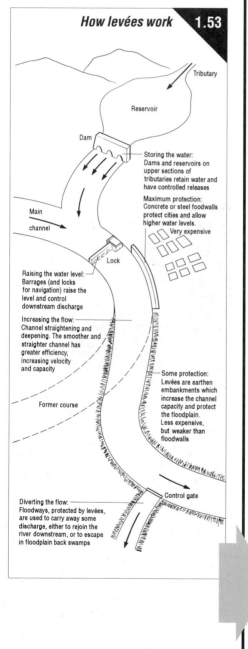

How levées work **1.53**

Tributary

Reservoir

Dam

Storing the water:
Dams and reservoirs on upper sections of tributaries retain water and have controlled releases

Maximum protection:
Concrete or steel foodwalls protect cities and allow higher water levels.
Very expensive

Main channel

Lock

Raising the water level:
Barrages (and locks for navigation) raise the level and control downstream discharge

Increasing the flow:
Channel straightening and deepening. The smoother and straighter channel has greater efficiency, increasing velocity and capacity

Former course

Some protection:
Levées are earthen embankments which increase the channel capacity and protect the floodplain.
Less expensive, but weaker than floodwalls

Diverting the flow:
Floodways, protected by levées, are used to carry away some discharge, either to rejoin the river downstream, or to escape in floodplain back swamps

Control gate

CASE STUDY 1.4 *'The Mississippi – coming soon to a town near you'*

allowing natural overspill into the floodplain. By late August, the surge had arrived in the Mississippi delta, where there is a complex system of anastomosing channels, lakes and take-off channels. For example, the Atchafalaya channel can be used to distribute and store excess water input. This management system had the protection of New Orleans, which lies beside the main distributory channel as its main goal. The delta water engineers direct the waters through the intricate network rather like rail traffic managers running a complex of lines and sidings.

Seeking the causes – human factors

Today, of course, the Mississippi is a managed system, its throughput controlled by the US Army Corps of Engineers. The extract of Resource 1.54 illustrates the complexity of their decision-making and the growing desperation of mid-July 1993 as the floodwaters just kept coming. One important message within this extract is that while the public relations people may support flood **prevention**, the engineers acknowledged that the reality is flood **control**. Yet, the policy of all of the agencies involved in the management of the Mississippi has been based on strategies of **prevention** and **hard engineering**, or the building of hard structures such as dams, floodwalls and levées. The failure of this expensive strategy in 1993 has opened a vigorous debate as to its actual value.

Levées are earthen constructions. They can withstand several days of bankfull conditions, but under extreme conditions as in July 1993, the continued pressure of the water and the gradual soaking of the levée fabric begins to weaken it. Eventually a leak develops, material is washed out, further weakening the structure. Finally, a breach occurs. Even a single breach of less than 50 m can create saturation of the floodplain, extending many kilometres downstream and affecting areas whose own levées

have held. Furthermore, floods may last for weeks, and even when the waters subside, the mud, debris and pollution may take months to remove from settlements and farmland.

Desperately seeking a solution

The alternative to the above solution is the **soft engineering** approach. The management strategy is based upon the natural behaviour of the river and reducing the attempts to restrict and manipulate its rhythms. For instance, while control dams and reservoirs would continue to be the key control devices in the upper catchments, in the middle and lower sections, the floodplain would be used more extensively to accommodate excess water, just as it would in the 'natural' condition.

Such a strategy would, of course, require a fundamental rethink as to how we use floodplains. Land-use zoning policies for floodplains would need to be changed, and while it is difficult to remove existing settlements, it is possible to prevent further development in vulnerable areas. Part of this land-use zoning policy is the identification of areas in the floodplain which could be used as floodwater stores. These storage areas would be natural backswamps and wetlands. Elsewhere, it may be necessary to reduce arable cropping, and ultimately to relocate farming settlements to the floodplain edge. In this way, land could remain productive as grassland while acting as supplementary floodwater stores. Environmentalists favour this approach as it would restore wetland habitats which have become increasingly rare, and, in turn, provide homes for many animal and bird species. Such environmental enhancement would increase recreational opportunities such as birdwatching, hunting and fishing.

Not everyone is against the levée system: *Any look at the river that does not also consider the structures that provide for recreation, water supply, navigation, and the farm economy doesn't meet the mark.*

We've got all those interests to consider, along with flood control. There's no intent on the part of the Corps of Engineers to line the Mississippi with concrete, but do we want to relocate St Louis and New Orleans? (Director of civil works for the Army Corps of Engineers, quoted in *NGM*, Jan 1994).

Finding the money and then allocating it to the appropriate policies is inevitably difficult. One realistic strategy is to apply existing policies to the problem area. Environmentalists and state authorities are putting pressure on the US federal government to allocate more money to the national Wetlands Reserve Programme. This would pay farmers to restore and protect wetlands on their property and is particularly suited to floodplains. The aim of the Wetlands Reserve Programme is to restore 400 000 ha by 1995, and after the 1993 floods, more attention is being paid to the potential in the Mississippi floodplain.

Another option is to make floodplain occupation less attractive. Although many of the poorer people affected by the 1993 floods did not have insurance, the federal government does subsidise insurance for flood hazard zones through its National Flood Insurance Programme. The recommendation is to stop this support or to make the premiums more expensive. Yet any policy change must distinguish clearly between existing occupants and new developments: many families are emotionally attached to their homes and communities, and are very reluctant to leave. The federal government declared extensive 'disaster areas', the population of which qualified for the $5.7 billion government assistance. Critics argue that if people choose to live in hazard zones without insurance, then they should not qualify for government help.

Activities

1 Outline briefly why the Mississippi flooded so seriously in 1993.

2 The following statements were made 140 years apart, but both express doubts about the wisdom of the 'hard' engineering approach to river management. Explain what each statement means in terms of the way a river system works, and why levées may not be effective:

  a *Charles Ellet (Civil Engineer), 1853*
  Water that was formerly allowed to spread over many thousand square miles of low lands is becoming more and more confined to the immediate channel of the river and is, therefore, compelled to rise higher and flow faster.

  b *Jay Lehr (Hydrologist), 1993*
  Every levee is obsolete as soon as it's built, because it's based on the land as it currently exists. But as soon as you build a new town or clear-cut a forest, you change the numbers, you change the amount of water that goes into the river, and therefore you're facing an almost insurmountable engineering task.

  (Both quoted in *NGM*, Jan 1994)

3 a Describe how 'hard' and 'soft' engineering approaches to flood control are intended to work.

  b List their advantages and disadvantages.

4 Suggest reasons why it will be difficult to shift river management policy from a 'hard' to a 'soft' engineering approach along the Mississippi.

1.54

Nature foils best laid plans to tame mighty Mississippi

By James Coates
Tribune Staff Writer

ROCK ISLAND ARSENAL, Ill. – On the third floor of a century-old granite building, a few dozen men and women from the Army Corps of Engineers monitor the marauding Mississippi.

Before the current flood, they said they were able to "play" with the Mississipi. Now they are sitting on an island surrounded by sullen brown floodwaters.

A movie that is shown to visitors boasts about how every inch of the Mississippi under the control of the corps' Rock Island District has been channeled, dredged, fitted with dams or locks and otherwise altered to meet human needs.

The narrator says at the end of the movie, "With optimal operation of our flood control structures, we can play with the bountiful expanse of this great river."

Nobody's playing anymore. They work feverishly, in the Corps of Engineers' Emergency Operation Center.

They are trying to use an extensive interconnected system of locks, dams and levees to mitigate a flood that the corps' experts had said in 1968 wouldn't likely come along for another 500 years.

"This is a disaster worse than anything anybody ever anticipated, and we're juggling a very complex system," said Ron Fournier, chief spokesman for the Rock Island District.

"Everything is interrelated," Fournier said. "We have to know what is going to happen everywhere in the system before we do anything anything anywhere in the system."

That was demonstrated last week in Iowa.

John Bellizzi, the Des Moines Public Works director, called a press conference Wednesday to charge that the corps callously let a wall of water hit the city's downtown and ruin the municipal water system.

The corps could have kept much of the water that contaminated the water treatment plant behind the Saylorville Dam just north of town, Bellizzi charged.

In response, Keith Haas, one of the corps' engineers on the scene in Des Moines, said if he had done as Bellizzi suggested, the water would have backed up at the other end and cut off U.S. Highway 30 north of town and devastated thousands of acres of cropland.

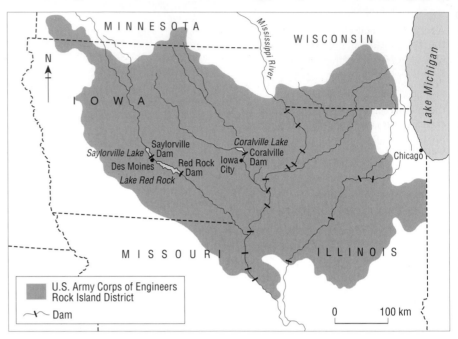

Map legend:
U.S. Army Corps of Engineers Rock Island District
Dam

Map locations: MINNESOTA, WISCONSIN, Mississippi River, Lake Michigan, IOWA, Saylorville Lake, Saylorville Dam, Coralville Lake, Coralville Dam, Des Moines, Red Rock Dam, Iowa City, Chicago, Lake Red Rock, MISSOURI, ILLINOIS, 0 100 km

Furthermore, Haas argued, the dams are under intense pressure because they are holding far more water than anybody ever anticipated.

Spillways must be opened to prevent catastrophic dam bursts, he said.

Even as Des Moines' water treatment plant was inundated, engineers had to decide whether to spare the University of Iowa in Iowa City or an applicance factory complex near the Amana Colonies just east of Iowa City.

The bureau's engineers calculated last Wednesday that if they could release 26,000 cubic feet per second of water from the Coralville Dam near Iowa City, they could keep the Iowa River from rising and flooding the factory of the Amana Refrigeration Co.

But to their dismay, the engineers discovered that if more than 23,000 cubic feet per second were released, the water would contaminate the college's water supply.

So the corps released only 23,000 cubic feet per second instead of the higher amount, which would have spared Amana.

On computer consoles, personnel monitor colossal amounts of data streaming from remote sensing devices, engineers' reports, satellite photographs and other sources along the 314 miles of river from Guttenberg, Iowa, to Saverton, Mo., that is assigned to the Rock Island District.

Hundreds of automatic sensors located in cornfields, along river banks and elsewhere continually read moisture conditions and help the crops predict how high the water will rise and where it will rise next.

The data describe what may be the most completely "engineered" river on the planet.

Since the early 1960s the Mississippi has been operated along the lines of a giant barge highway.

From Minneapolis to New Orleans, the corps cut a channel into the river to ensure a passage at least 9 feet deep, 400 feet wide and 2,552 miles long for the hundreds of barges filled with petroleum, grain, coal and other cargo that ply the waterway.

To provide water calm enough for these immense flat-bottomed barges to float on, a system of dozens of locks and dams keep the flow of what had been a wild and rapids-filled river as steady as a gentle stream.

And to ensure an even flow in times of drought, a system of flood control dams went up on the Des Moines and Iowa Rivers, which feed into the Mississippi.

When the river level drops, the water behind those dams can be released to keep the barges moving.

It is these three dams, Saylorville, Coralville and Red Rock, just south of Des Moines, that the corps now is using to try to prevent the water from the rains that continue over the state from adding to the devastation already rampant downriver in Illinois, Missouri and Iowa.

[*Chicago Tribune*, 18.7.93]

Levees: do they work too well?

As the flood recedes and cities begin the dismal task of cleaning up, sharp questions are being raised about the wisdom of the nation's approach to flood control, and the cost, both financial and environmental, of a program that relies on man-made structures to contain the mighty river. Over the past seven decades, the U.S. Army Corps of Engineers has spent billions of dollars constructing an elaborate flood-control network, including levees, along the Mississippi and the rivers that feed it. The system was intended to protect the communities that sprang up on the river's edge, and most of the time it has. But many environmentalists believe that, over the years, the corps's attempts to control the Mississippi have backfired. Left to its own devices, a flooding river spreads horizontally, filling its natural flood-plain and enriching it with fertile, alluvial soil. Along the Mississippi, however, this pattern of natural flow has been increasingly blocked by a patchwork of levees.

The effect is that an increasingly pent-up river rises higher, moves faster downstream, and is more prone to back up like a clogged drain, increasing the pressure on unfortified areas. "The water has to go somewhere," says aquatic ecologist Richard Sparks of the Illinois Natural History Survey, "and if we don't allow it to spread out, the only direction it can go is up."

Nowhere are these effects more dramatic than in the Mississippi Delta, which used to be replenished every year with rich alluvial deposits. Now the soil, laden with nutrients, is carried by the river, bypasses the Delta and falls into the Gulf of Mexico, where it is contributing to algae blooms and threatening the fisheries. The Delta is sinking, with the result that the levees keeping the river at bay have to be periodically raised.

But it is ordinary human activity – not just the Corps of Engineers – that has robbed the Mississippi basin of its most precious resource: the wetlands and riparian forests that once absorbed excess rainwater like so many giant sponges. In fact, the displacement of this natural flood-control system by an artificial one may, over time, increase the number of record-busting floods.

Even critics of the corps concede that protecting existing cities and towns is appropriate. But absolutely critical to stemming future flood losses, a federal task force concluded last year, is protection of riverine floodplains from further development. In some cases it may even prove cost effective to relocate entire flood-prone communities. "We need to start giving land back to the river," says Larry Larson, head of Wisconsin's flood-plain program. "If we don't, sooner or later the river will take it back."

By J. Madeleine Nash
[*Chicago Times,* 26.7.93]

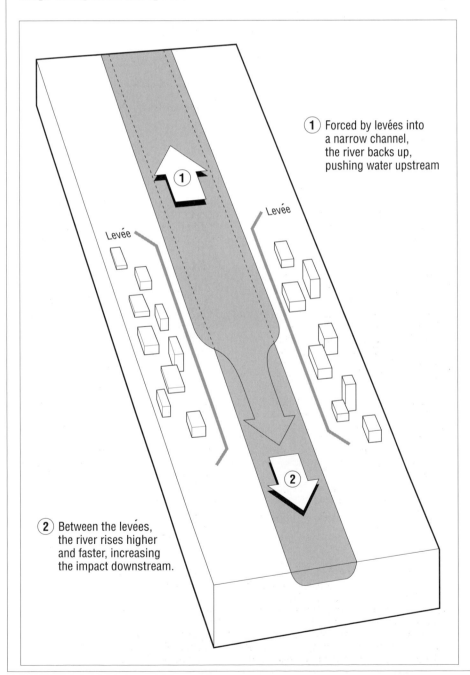

1 Forced by levées into a narrow channel, the river backs up, pushing water upstream

Levée

Levée

2 Between the levées, the river rises higher and faster, increasing the impact downstream.

CHAPTER 2

Managing ecosystems

Introduction

The ecosystem, one of ecology's few unifying concepts, is an essential part of environmental management. An ecosystem may be defined as *the whole complex of living and non-living components in any area, which interact with each other and through which energy and nutrients flow* (Moore, D.M. (ed) *Green Planet*, CUP, 1982). Ecosystems exist at a variety of scales, from the individual tree or pond to whole forests or wetlands. At the largest scale, we classify them as **natural regions** on atlas maps, although these very generalised regions are more correctly called biomes or **life zones.** They are built of a number of related ecosystems. For example, the tropical rainforest biome is distributed across several continents. Each continent exhibits several distinct rainforest ecosystems, each with its own distinctive species.

As each ecosystem is built and functions as a **system**, we can use the same approach to study and understand all of them. Each system has a set of stores and pathways, within and through which matter and energy move. We call these inputs, stores, processes, throughputs and outputs. Although an ecosystem has a boundary, it works as an open system, with inputs arriving from outside and outputs leaving the system. For example, we receive energy from the sun through an open system.

Every part of a system has an important role to play and all the parts work together to achieve a self-adjusting balance. This balanced state is called **dynamic equilibrium**. A significant change in one component is, therefore, likely to have a knock-on effect as the system makes an adjustment. Within certain limits, an ecosystem and individual species within it can adjust to maintain the

2.1

A forest ecosystem: tropical rainforest in Queensland, Australia

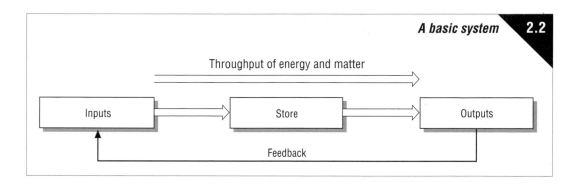

overall balance, within its **range of tolerance.** Ecosystems vary in their tolerance, but all have a limit or **threshold** of disturbance beyond which their structure and functioning begin to break down.

Today, the greatest source of ecosystem disturbance is human activity. We bring about fundamental changes in input, throughput, stores and output of energy via labour and machines. We affect natural systems by our economic processes and technology, for example, deforestation and the application of nitrogen fertiliser. Humans have become the **ecological dominant** in most ecosystems. In general, human intervention results in ecosystems being simplified, either by accident or design. Unwanted species, for example, weeds and predatory animals, are removed and only desired species, such as wheat and sheep, are encouraged. We manage the structure and functioning of ecosystems across a spectrum from minimal impact, as in the removal of wolves in extensive sheep grazing economies, to the imposition of a new ecosystem, such as the monoculture of wheat across the Canadian Prairies. Of course, our introductions or removals may have unexpected consequences, as in the devastating impacts of the introduction of rabbits to Australia.

Modern commercial interests have also exploited ecosystem resources for short term gain and not for sustained yield. Many oceans are over-exploited by the commercial fishing industry, for example. Signs of overuse and mis-use are evident, particularly in subsistence economies. Desertification in Africa's Sahel is as much the result of increased human demands on the savannas, as of prolonged drought.

The case studies of this chapter illustrate how, as evidence of ecosystem damage mounts, so countries are making great efforts to improve their understanding of how their ecosystems work. From this knowledge they can then introduce management methods based on conservation and sustainability rather than exploitation and short-term gain.

Case Study 2.1 uses research results from a small Devon catchment to show what happens to an ecosystem when vegetation is changed from rough pasture to coniferous trees, and when management levels change. Case Study 2.2 presents two opinions on the suitability of cattle grazing on the temperate grassland ecosystems of North America. The next pair of studies, 2.3 and 2.4, focus on different uses of the tropical savannas of Africa: safari tourism and farming. The Sabi Sabi game reserve in South Africa is managed to restore and conserve the natural ecosystem, while the farmers of Zimbabwe are seeking the best way to increase production without increasing soil erosion. Case Study 2.5 examines the role of fire in ecosystem functioning, and how humans, by preventing fires or changing its occurrence, may do more harm than good. Finally, Case Study 2.6 illustrates how computer-based data storage and display resources such as Geographical Information Systems (GIS) are assisting environmental management.

Key questions arise throughout these studies:
- What is the natural ecosystem like?
- Which parts are being affected by human activity, removals and additions?
- Why is the ecosystem being changed?
- How does the management affect the ecosystem especially in relation to conservation and sustainability?

CASE STUDY 2.1

Management levels and ecological impacts of

Background

The UK has a temperate oceanic climate. Up to 80% of its natural vegetation is woodland, much of it deciduous hardwoods such as oak, beach, elm and ash. By 1980, barely 9% of the land area was actually classified as 'wooded', the lowest proportion of any Western European country. We import 90% of our timber needs. This is the outcome of long and intensive settlement and mis-use of our environment.

Yet, the Forestry Commission has been around since 1919 to extend and manage UK forests. It was originally established to build up the timber reserve in case of another war, but today has a wider set of objectives which balance commercial profit with conservation and recreation. By 1993, woodland owned by the Forestry Commission, private commercial companies and landowners, covered approximately 10% of our land area.

The Forestry Commission has done most of the planting. Because the 'harvest' of timber for sale has always been its prime aim, the Commission's planting policy has been dominated by commercially-profitable tree species. These trees must be capable of thriving on agri-culturally marginal land, of maturing quickly, of being easily and cheaply felled and of being in commercial demand. For these reasons, over

80% of Forestry Commission planta-tions have been non-native (exotic) species of coniferous softwoods, for example, Sitka spruce. Large tracts are planted with single species, at one time, to allow cheap felling and easy replanting. The result has been an increase in coniferous forest from 272 000 ha (23% of UK forest area) in 1925 to 1.3 million ha in 1980 (62% of UK forest area). However, it is still estimated that since 1945, one half of the UK 'ancient woodlands' of native species have disappeared. It is this aspect of the planting policy which has become increasingly criti-cised, especially in National Park

landscapes. *This type of planting has been concentrated in upland loca-tions, mainly because the land was economically appropriate rather than being most environmentally suitable for tree growth* (Essex S. & Williams A. *Applied Geography* 12, 1992).

The criticism has not been only made on aesthetic grounds. Research has shown that large-scale coniferous afforestation causes a loss of wildlife habitats, species-poor ecosystems and the podsolisation of soils. However, much of this evi-dence comes from 'intensively managed' forests, those coniferous

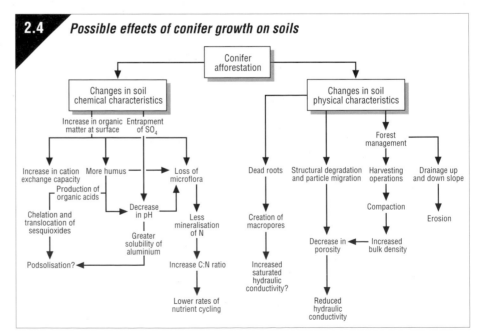

The Silurian Way, Grisedale forest, Lake District National Park. A Forestry Commission initiative to provide recreational opportunities.

Key understandings

◆ Coniferous afforestation does not necessarily result in increased soil and water acidity, podsolisation or impoverished ecosystems.

◆ The ecological impact of afforestation can be influenced by the level and character of forest management.

◆ Low intensity management and longer rotation cycles may minimise ecological changes.

◆ A model of ecological change can be applied to the forest rotation cycle.

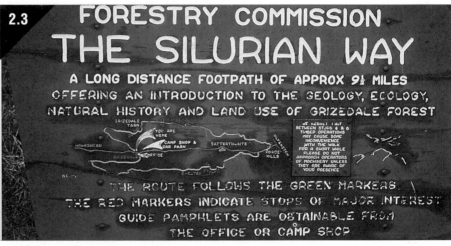

2.4 Possible effects of conifer growth on soils

afforestation

plantations which are densely planted, *brashed* (lower dead and dying branches removed) and regularly thinned (perhaps three times during a harvest cycle). Not all forests are managed so intensively. This case study summarises the results of research carried out on a forest in Devon which has received only spasmodic management. The key question to be addressed is: *Are non-intensive management strategies ecologically preferable to intensive management?*

The ecological effects of afforestation at Burrator, Devon

The development of Burrator Forest

Burrator Forest covers part of the watershed immediately surrounding the Burrator Reservoir, which supplies water to Plymouth and South Devon. It lies about 20 km north of Plymouth, within the Dartmoor National Park. The dams built by Plymouth Corporation were completed in 1898. At that time, and through the first part of the twentieth century, it was common practice for the water companies to buy the surrounding land and for reservoir catchments to be afforested. Several reasons were usually given, including that the trees were a barrier to restrict farming and recreation, that it reduced the silting up of the reservoirs, that it created jobs and that it created extra income for the water company.

By 1916, Plymouth Corporation owned the surrounding catchment, but allowed farmers to use the land until 1925 when afforestation began. When studying the research results, it is important to remember that the land had been farmed, mainly because the soil characteristics had been 'improved'. For example, lime had been applied by farmers to upgrade the base status, and soil horizons had been broken up by ploughing. Resource 2.6 shows the

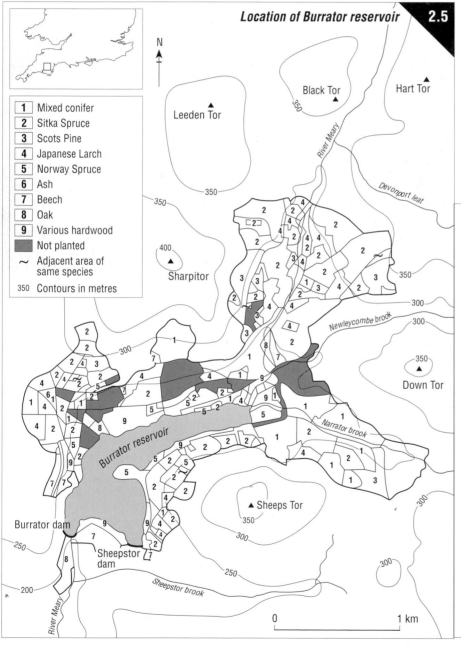

Location of Burrator reservoir `2.5`

Key:
1 Mixed conifer
2 Sitka Spruce
3 Scots Pine
4 Japanese Larch
5 Norway Spruce
6 Ash
7 Beech
8 Oak
9 Various hardwood
Not planted
~ Adjacent area of same species
350 Contours in metres

ALTITUDE *220–335 metres*

ANNUAL RAINFALL *1400–1900 mm, rising with altitude.*

BEDROCK *Granite*

SOILS *Brown podzolics, midway between true brown earths and podsols. Past improvement by farming has increased the base status*

GRASSLANDS *Upland base-poor, i.e. acidic, grassland (Festuca/Agrostis), with extensive bracken invasion. Low species diversity, with only about 20 species. Downslope vegetational gradient as nutrient status increases: upper slopes dominated by nutrient-deficient species such as Festuca and Nardus; lower slopes with higher nutrient status show more Agrostis.*

CONSERVATION VALUE *'Such acid grasslands … represent a plagio-climax which is in equilibrium with the low nutrient turnover (cycling) and low grazing pressure. Although such grasslands contain relatively few individual species, collectively they have great significance for conservation as they are typical of many upland areas'.*

CASE STUDY 2.1 *Management levels and ecological impacts of afforestation*

progression of afforestation, which reached 356 ha by 1990, approximately 16% of the total catchment area. Coniferous species cover 84% of this area, the distribution being determined by soil conditions and the commercial needs for a quick-growing crop. All but four hectares of the native broadleaved stands are the remnants of the woodland left after the flooding of the valley. Small areas of beech and oak have been planted on better soils.

As three-quarters of the present forest had been established before 1940, the forest was mature when the research was conducted (from 1977 to 1990). Management levels, however, had always been low. Since 1951, forestry management has been increasingly influenced by the

policies of the Dartmoor National Park. Their priorities included landscape, nature conservation and recreation. As a result, some areas immediately beside the reservoirs have been left unplanted to accommodate amenity access. The Plymouth Corporation and South West Water only realised the commercial potential in the 1960s, and ten years later, entered the government sponsored Woodland Dedication scheme, now part of the Woodland Grant scheme.

The research

1 Plant cover and species surveys estimated by quadrat sampling on forested and grassland sites.
2 Soil profiles sampled along slope transects.
3 Soil water samples taken from forested and grassland sites, along the slope transects at 90 cm and 180 cm depths.
4 Soil throughflow measured at around a 51 cm depth.
5 Soil chemistry of a network of springs and seepages examined.
6 Stream water samples analysed daily at two gauging sites along the Narrator Brook above and below the forest, over a one-year period. Also, water levels were recorded continuously.

Research results

Ecosystem

The botanical surveys at sampling sites covered species, management and age variations through the forestry rotation and yielded the results set out in Resource 2.7. Notice that the coniferous forest sites vary in age from 15 to 70 years, while the small mixed broadleaf plantation is very young. If we follow the development of ground vegetation over time, it is possible to propose a model of ground flora change through the forest cycle.

Before planting, sites are fenced to keep out sheep. Generally, the seedlings are spaced less than two metres apart. As they grow, insolation reaching the ground is steadily reduced by the leaf cover. After 15 years there is full canopy closure and ground plants are shaded out. After about 30 years the ground vegetation begins to revive, especially following thinning, which opens up the canopy. Bryophytes and grass gradually spread. By 45 years, despite the heavy litter layer of needles which had been shed by the larch, the plant community is well established. After 60 years then, with more light reaching the ground and less litter cover, grasses and herbs

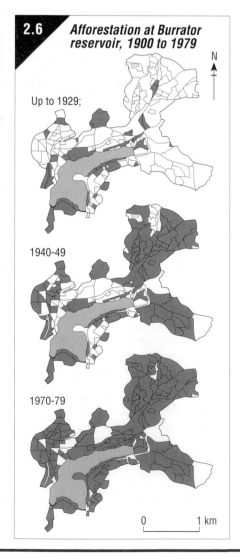

2.6 *Afforestation at Burrator reservoir, 1900 to 1979*

N

Up to 1929;

1940-49

1970-79

0   1 km

2.7 *Botanical survey results for various tree crops through time*

Crop species	Age in years	Management/ spacing in metres	Flora
Larch	15	2	100% litter
Norway spruce	30	2	100% litter
Larch	30	4	85% bryophytes, trace *Agrostis cap*
Sitka spruce	46	5	60% litter, 70% bryophytes
Sitka spruce	55	5	100% litter
Douglas fir	55	10	25% litter, 60% *Agrostis cap.*
Sitka spruce	60	5	25% *Galium sax.*
Sitka spruce	60	5	50% ground cover of 11 species including 60% *Agrostis cap.* No leaf litter visible
Larch	60	10	50% grasses including *Deschampsia flex*
Sitka spruce	70	5	100% ground cover including Pteridium and *Rubus*. 100% ground cover, mainly grasses such as *Agrostis cap*, and *Festuca ovina*.
Mixed broadleaved	2	3	Also *Oxalis, Rubus* and *Vaccinium* present. About 10% bare ground. Grasses, predominantly *Agrostis spp*; *Ranunculus spp.* and *Cirsium* present. *Ulex eruopaeus* invading.

cover an extensive area of ground . The researchers concluded that:

Although the initial impact of afforestation on the existing plant communities was severe, a woodland ecosystem was eventually established beneath the conifers which had greater diversity and a more complicated structure than in the original acid grassland (Essex & Williams, 1992).

Soils

All soils sampled, whether under grassland or forest, were of the **brown podzolic** type. The main differences occurred in the litter layer, pH, roots and biological activity. Under mature forest, about 5 cm of litter was being decomposed; under grassland there was a turf mat. Forest soils were more acidic, with a mean pH of 4.1 compared with a pH of 4.6 under the grassland. Fine and woody roots dominated woodland soils, but finer fibrous roots threaded the grassland soils. The upper horizons of the grassland soils contained more integrated organic matter, reflecting higher rates of biological activity. Forest soils, on the other hand, had higher organic carbon and surplus levels. Importantly, *no evidence was observed to support the contention that increased podsolisation was taking place under conifers* (Essex & Williams, 1992).

Soil water

The soil water chemistry for the sample sites, taken at three depths, is summarised in Resource 2.9. The key findings from this table are:

1 Forest soils are more acidic than grassland soils throughout the profile i.e. forest pH scores are lower.
2 Solutes have higher concentrations under forest vegetation e.g. sodium (Na) and chloride (Cl)

levels are higher, probably due to entrapment of marine aerosols during the winter. On the other hand, the 'biological' ions –potassium (K) and calcium (Ca) – are higher under grassland, especially in the upper horizons. Silica (SiO_2) levels were higher under forest, perhaps indicating more rapid weathering (the bed-rock granites yield silica).

The researchers concluded that *although afforestation led to changes in soil water composition, the main change may be due to entrapment of marine-derived ions* (Essex & Williams, 1992). In other words, the trees entrap more of the marine salts precipitated by rainfall from moisture acquired over the sea.

Springs

The results in Resource 2.10 show clearly that although water acidity (pH) was similar for forest and grassland sites on all solutes, concentrations were higher within the forest. The researchers note, however, that factors other than vegetation type alone may be responsible, for example, the length of time and distance the emerging water has spent as groundwater, the flushing out of salts long held within the soils and weathering.

Streamwater

The information in Resource 2.11 shows that the forest seemed to make little difference to pH, but did increase the solute concentrations. This was particularly noted in sodium and chloride from marine-derived ions entrapped by the trees. The fact that the coniferous forest did not appear to increase soil acidity – a trend commonly found in afforested catchments – is *probably due to the catchment being dominated by brown podzolic soils underlain by 30 m of weathered granite [regolith], which may buffer any changes in the soil water composition* (Essex & Williams, 1992). The greatest differences in pH occur in summer between the streams on the high moorland, where pH falls to 5.0,

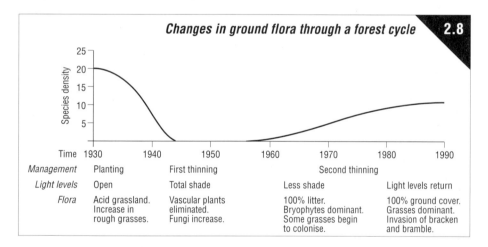

Changes in ground flora through a forest cycle 2.8

Time	1930	1940	1950	1960	1970	1980	1990
Management	Planting	First thinning			Second thinning		
Light levels	Open	Total shade		Less shade			Light levels return
Flora	Acid grassland. Increase in rough grasses.	Vascular plants eliminated. Fungi increase.		100% litter. Bryophytes dominant. Some grasses begin to colonise.			100% ground cover. Grasses dominant. Invasion of bracken and bramble.

Forest and grassland soil water concentrations 1977–78 2.9

[ions except pH, in mg per litre]

	Forest			Grassland		
Depth in cm	53	90	180	51	90	180
pH	4.2	4.7	4.8	4.8	5.6	5.9
Sodium (Na)	5.5	7.1	7.2	6.0	4.9	5.1
Potassium (K)	3.6	0.6	1.3	5.8	0.5	0.6
Calcium (Ca)	1.3	1.4	1.7	2.6	2.7	3.2
Magnesium (Mg)	0.8	1.1	1.2	1.0	0.6	0.7
Silica (SiO_2)	3.0	7.6	9.2	2.1	1.9	2.4
Chloride (Cl)	8.5	11.4	11.6	9.3	9.2	10.3

[Source: Essex & Williams, 1992]

CASE STUDY 2.1 *Management levels and ecological impacts of afforestation*

2.10 Spring water concentrations at forest and grassland sites 1977–78

[ions except pH, in mg per litre]

	Forest	Grassland
pH	4.8	4.9
Sodium (Na)	8.5	6.8
Potassium (K)	1.0	0.8
Calcium (Ca)	2.3	2.2
Magnesium (Mg)	1.3	0.9
Silica (SiO$_2$)	7.8	7.0
Chloride (Cl)	13.7	10.0

[Source: Essex & Williams, 1992]

2.11 Streamwater solute concentrations at gauging stations upstream and downstream of the forest, 1977–78

[ions except pH, in mg per litre]

	Downstream	Upstream
pH	5.4	5.5
Sodium (Na)	6.6	7.1
Potassium (K)	0.9	1.0
Calcium (Ca)	1.1	1.4
Magnesium (Mg)	0.9	1.0
Silica (SiO$_2$)	5.8	6.4
Chloride (Cl)	9.7	10.5

[Source: Essex & Williams, 1992]

and the streams downstream in the Sitka spruce forest where pH may exceed 5.7. Thus, at base flow conditions, the base ion store of the forest is capable of lowering water acidity relative to true moorland streamwater.

Conclusions

1 The combination of piecemeal planting, the long rotation and low intensity management has minimised the long-term influence on vegetation, soils and water chemistry.
2 Towards the end of the rotation period (more than 60 years), a well-developed woodland ecosystem has been established.
3 There is no evidence of increased soil podsolisation as a result of afforestation, because of the high base status of the soil. This has provided a good buffering capacity against the loss of aluminium.
4 The higher solute concentrations in the forest soil waters result from increased ion entrapment by the trees, interception losses and greater evapotranspiration than from grassland and moorland. The effect of a conifer forest on water acidity is greater during the early phases of growth as the system adjusts to the new conditions. Later, equilibrium is restored as the uptake of nutrients balances the release of nutrients,

that is, the dynamic equilibrium mechanisms are at work.

The future: post-privatisation policies

In 1989, South West Water became a commercial private limited company as part of the government's water supply privatisation policy. By 1992, two major shifts in management policy were becoming evident, both likely to lead to intensified management levels:

1 As the company is now responsible for making profits for shareholders, the economic potential of the plantations has been re-assessed. There will be an intensified felling programme. (Remember that much of the forest is mature.) In addition, the income from recreation and tourism is to be increased by the development of an arboretum and addition of paths and facilities. The fact that Burrator lies within the attractive National Park is an added bonus.
2 The new company intends to replant felled areas with native broadleaved species wherever practicable. The forecast is that 50 years hence, the woods will have 90% broadleaves and 10% conifers. There is to be no more planting of commercial conifers. Oak will dominate (60%), with

beech, ash and, at the most fertile sites, alder and walnut. As these species are deciduous, they will be planted at lower densities than conifers, thereby allowing more light to reach the surface. The litter will bear more nutrients and it is anticipated that a more diversified ecosystem will evolve, although the maturation time will be longer than for a coniferous forest. Soils, soil water and streamwater are likely to become less acidic and nutrient cycling will be enhanced.

The future forests of Burrator will give higher priority to conservation and amenity values than to commercial timber values. Nevertheless, it may be that commercial profit will be important in terms of charging visitors to enjoy the forest and the lake. There is no doubt, however, that the local ecology will change once more, and that management levels will be greater.

[Based on Essex S. & Williams A. 'Ecological effects of afforestation: a case study of Burrator, Dartmoor', *Applied Geography* 12, 1992, 361–379]

Activities

1 Explain the forest cycle model of Resource 2.8.
2 Outline the objectives of the research at Burrator and how the data was gathered to achieve these objectives.
3 Most studies of coniferous afforestation schemes suggest that water becomes more acidic, that soils become podsolised and that ecosystems are species-poor. Give reasons for these suggestions and explain why such trends have not been found in the Burrator catchment.

CASE STUDY 2.2
The place of cattle in temperate grasslands

Background

Extensive temperate latitude environments have a natural vegetation of grassland and scrub. One of the most suitable forms of modern agriculture in such an environment, is cattle ranching. It does not involve the breaking up of the surface vegetation cover by ploughing, it is practised at low densities, and cattle merely replace wandering herds of 'wild' animals. Ranching seems well adapted to the rhythms of wet and dry seasons, plant growth and die-back. Nowhere else has this form of land management been more strongly developed than in the western regions of USA. Here, a whole culture and national identity has been built upon the image of 'frontier' and 'the American West': the Marlborough Man adverts; John Wayne; hamburgers; and the cookout.

It is ironic, therefore, that it is in North America that serious questions are being raised about the carrying capacity of these dry grasslands and the impacts of cattle ranching. Many cattle on the western ranges graze on federal (central government) land, and until recently, ranchers have paid very low fees for grazing leases. However, the government has become alarmed at the stocking

Cattle range in western USA

levels and impacts and, in 1993, raised the fees in order to control stock levels.

The materials in this case study are based upon articles published in 1993 by American writers, setting out opposing views. At one extreme there is the argument that even low density cattle ranching is non-sustainable, economically and ecologically. At the other, the claim is made that ranching makes economic sense while sustaining the environment. The issue lies within the broader debate about the human consumption of meat: whether red meat is 'good for you' and whether the world, with its exploding human population and finite capacity for food production, can 'afford' the longer food chains created by eating meat .

Key understandings

◆ There are opposing views about the place of commercial cattle rearing in temperate grassland ecosystems.

◆ Extensive cattle rearing has more environmental impact than was formerly recognised, and so requires careful management.

◆ There are crucial differences between the grazing patterns of native wild herbivores and introduced commercial species.

Part A: The case against

The real cost of a hamburger

No activity uses more native habitat in the American landscape than live-stock production – not even logging, suburban growth or roads. The US government estimates that 44% of the land area (excluding Alaska) is managed for the rearing of cattle and sheep. The impacts are great, especially on the cattle rangelands of the West. The US Department of Agriculture claims that plant cover and productivity are currently only 60% of their natural state. Reduced plant cover means less litter for decomposition, increased evaporation and lower infiltration rates. This could result in faster run-off from rainfall and snowmelt, with the greater likelihood of flooding.

Loss of ground cover also means accelerated erosion. The US Environmental Protection Agency (EPA) has identified livestock grazing as being responsible for 28% of all soil erosion in the West. Sediment which reaches streams from this erosion modifies channel and flow characteristics. Futhermore, the degraded range cannot support the full assemblage of native plant and animal species.

One particularly valuable component of the range ecosystem is the

2.12

riparian zone, the narrow strip of green, water-dependent vegetation that lines the streambanks. Cattle are attracted to this zone, trample the stream banks and channel and strip vegetation, causing accelerated erosion. A 1990 EPA report showed that these riparian zones were in their worst condition this century. Although riparian zones occupy only 1% of the range landscape, at least 75% of all native vertebrate species rely upon this water- and plant-rich habitat. For instance, official estimates are that in Arizona, less than 3% of riparian zones remain in their original condition.

Often, ranchers claim that their cattle have merely replaced the millions of bison (North American buffalo) which used to roam these plains. However, there are critical differences: the native buffalo has, over thousands of years, adapted to the environment. It drinks less water, selects drier forage and wanders more widely than the introduced (exotic) ranch cattle. By following the precipitation and forage growth rhythms of the plains, the extensive migrations of the buffalo allowed grazed areas to rest. In contrast, ranchers use fencing to restrict movement and their cattle are not subjected to the natural population controls of drought, disease, harsh winters and predation. (The predators such as wolves, bears and eagles have been largely eliminated.)

The impact of cattle upon the West's water supply is just as critical. Most cattle depend upon irrigated pasture for a significant proportion of their food, mainly corn (maize) and alfalfa (a grass from which hay is made). Growing this forage requires the expensive damming and draining of rivers in a region which has a serious moisture budget deficit. Potential evapotranspiration exceeds precipitation supply, and fossil aquifers are being heavily depleted. For example, in California, agriculture consumes three-quarters of all water used, with at least one-half of this going to forage crops. The dams disrupt flow patterns and river ecosystems. By

The native buffalo drinks less water, selects drier forage and wanders more widely than the cattle.

altering peak flows, water temperatures and sediment distribution on channel beds, many fish species, such as the Sacramento River salmon, are threatened or eliminated.

At least half of the available forage on the plains today is eaten by cattle. This affects the survival chances of competing native species. Less grass ultimately feeds fewer elk, antelope, bighorn sheep, and the thousands of invertebrate herbivores, such as grasshoppers. Environmentalists want to build up the buffalo population once more, but are concerned about the limited space. In 1790 there were at least 30 million buffalo; in 1890 there were barely 1000, while in 1990, there were

10 000 buffalo. The herds are increasing, but can only really flourish if cattle are removed from buffalo habitat.

Cattle production is competing with humans for space, water and food. Up to one-half of all grain grown in the US is ultimately fed to cattle. If this grain – maize, wheat, barley – was distributed world-wide, it would help to reduce human hunger. *When we consume a hamburger or a steak we are literally eating up the rainforest, destroying Western rivers, crowding out native herbivores, and helping to ensure the extermination or recovery of wolves, ferrets, and grizzlies* (Wuerthner, 1993).

Part B: The case for

Cattle are the green revolution

Cattle are helping to provide an adequate diet for a human population which will double within the next 60 years. Beef is a high-protein food that humans want and, for full health, need. Grasslands need to be grazed if they are not to become wildfire hazards during the dry season. Grazing also keeps more plant species in the ecosystem, preventing the dominance of tall species which would eventually shade out everything else. The buffalo once performed this function across North America, and humans have shifted this role to cattle. Grazing, therefore, remains important for sustaining ecosystems.

There seems little doubt that cattle have contributed to rangeland and watershed degradation, while fencing for stock management has been destructive to many wildlife species. Yet such impacts are largely the result of mismanagement based upon economic greed and poor understanding of the way grassland ecosystems work.

Feedlot cattle being rounded up

Irrigated land near Yuma, USA

CASE STUDY 2.2 *The place of cattle in temperate grasslands*

The image of cattle as environmentally-costly is largely due to the boom in feedlot rearing. Thousands of animals are fed hay, grain, water, and artificial inputs on huge feedlots and never graze the open range. These animals may not be affecting rangelands, but they are very expensive to rear. In the USA it takes 2.25 litres of petroleum fuel, 4.8 kilograms of grain, and 3000 litres of water to produce one kilogram of beef. Much of this energy goes into intensive agricultural practices that cause severe soil damage and erosion, for example, the double and triple cropping on expensively irrigated land.

A case can be made for boycotting feedlot beef. Grass-fed, range beef, however, is another matter. Well-managed cattle ranching can play a role in reversing the damage of the past. To understand this, we need to review the role played by grazing of grasslands. One critical problem faced by humans today is the loss of biodiversity (the mass and variety of plant and animal species and the accompanying genetic diversity). Past practices on rangelands have caused such loss by reducing vegetation, increasing flooding and soil erosion and lowering land productivity. Stock-rearing methods were imported to the drylands of the American West from environments which are humid all year round, and in which the natural ecosystems do not include herds of large, wandering grazing animals. When the land in the eastern USA or western Europe, is farmed for example, taking animals off the land to rest it generally benefits the soil and vegetation. Much of the vegetation stays green and moist through the year and wildfire risk is minimal. Dead plant matter is quickly decomposed and reincorporated into the soil.

This essential recycling is a key to understanding what has gone wrong in environments such as the American Great Plains where the humidity is seasonal. In these environments much of the vegetation is perennial grassland and scrub where plants are not always green and are prone to lightning fires. The vegetation die-back occurs at about the same time as the decomposition organisms also die off. Thus, the decomposition processes are slowed down.

Fortunately, these seasonally dry environments are the natural home of the vast buffalo herds whose numbers were controlled by predation, starvation or accident. Predators forced the animals to roam in bunches for protection. This ensured that dung and urine were concentrated, that the animals would keep moving to avoid feeding on fouled ground, and so allow severely bitten and trampled areas time to recover.

The resting of land as used by ranchers is unnatural in such ecosystems. The concentrated groups of buffalo grazed and trampled the mass of vegetation left at the end of the growing season and so, along with their droppings, assisted the carbon cycle processes. However, cattle, without predators such as wolves, spread out. Because their dung and urine are scattered, animals will remain in an area long enough to overgraze plants and are less likely to trample old, hard vegetation. Where ranchers have adopted the strategy of resting land, the range deteriorates: total rest (no animals for several years) or partial rest (changing the movement behaviour of animals) leads to a build up of forage that chokes on the dead material. Using fire to control this build up merely adds to CO_2 in the atmosphere. The carbon cycle is impeded. This can occur even where cattle stocking densities are as low as one animal per 32 hectares (80 acres).

The answer lies, therefore, in keeping cattle on the range but changing management strategies to imitate the behaviour of the native buffalo. For example, periodically bring a large, concentrated herd of animals into an area, perhaps by using an attraction such as hay or salt. This groups them together much as buffalo used to do and produces the opposite effect from total or partial rest. High biodiversity, ecosystem stability and productivity is encouraged. *On the rangelands, where they naturally belong, cattle can be produced at less expense and without the drugs needs to keep them alive in the unnatural confines of the feedlot. in the process they can be used to restore degraded habitat and biodiversity* (Savory, 1993).

[Based on Wuerthner G. 'The real cost of a hamburger', Avery D. 'Cattle are the green revolution', and Savory A. 'The necessary evil', *Earthwatch* V.XII (5), July/August 1993, 24–29]

Activities

1 What is meant by biodiversity?

2 What role do buffalo play in sustaining biodiversity?

3 How have traditional ranching techniques reduced biodiversity?

4 What land management techniques are suggested for sustaining biodiversity through cattle ranching?

5 Why is the agribusiness policy of feedlot rearing criticised?

6 List the main reasons against the continuation of cattle rearing on rangelands, and a second list supporting ranching.

7 Compare and contrast the movement behaviour of buffalo and cattle and their environmental impacts.

CASE STUDY 2.3   *Conservation, community development and tourism*

Background

Precious ecosystems may stand their last chance of survival if they can be shown to have an economic potential. If a wildlife reserve is set up by a government to protect elephants or gorillas, for example, local people are likely to say 'But what's in it for us?' Unless they can see that the reserve or national park will benefit their lives, they are unlikely to support it and the conservation values it tries to uphold. After all, an elephant may be a menace to an African farmer because it tramples his crops; a leopard may kill his animals. It is understandable, therefore, that local inhabitants may not be in favour of reserves which protect animals and their habitat in order to show them off to wealthy foreign tourists. Although the tourists spend money, this may not benefit the local population significantly. A policy for conservation alone may not be practical.

Equally, policies for economic profit alone will not save the ecosystems and valued species. Governments, resort developers and tour operators are realising what environmentalists have long being claiming: that much

tourist development based on natural attractions has been essentially **exploitative**. The dominance of the profit motive has led to the degradation of the environmental resource base. For example, some Kenya game parks are experiencing the problems of overuse. Management strategies are now turning to one of the buzz words of the 1990s – **sustainability**. This implies that resources will be managed in such a way that their quantity, quality and productivity will not be impaired for future generations. Efforts are being made to balance economic viability for developers and local communities, with conservation of the local resource. Many such strategies give a greater role to local people in the decision-making and management processes. This case study illustrates this trend by examining one reserve in South Africa. It is distinctive in that the tour operator also owns the land and runs it as a private reserve, although in co-operation with the National Park Service. This makes decision-making and policy development easier because the resources and the economic enterprise are under single ownership and control.

Sabi Sabi: An experiment in sustainable development

Setting

The Sabi Sabi game reserve is a privately-owned reserve in the Eastern Transvaal region of South Africa. It has an area of 4453 ha, with a boundary which abuts the Kruger National Park on the east and the rural community of Gazankulu on the west. It is part of the extensive Sabi Sand Game Reserve, designated in 1965, but allowed by the government to be broken up by the sale of what is now the Sabi Sabi Reserve in 1979.

The commercial goal of Sabi Sabi is the provision of a high quality wildlife Safari tourist experience. The tourism product is unashamedly targetted at the wealthy market segment: around £300 per person per day in 1993. The market niche is distinct from the much larger scale offerings of neighbouring Kruger National Park, although both use similar attractive wildlife resources. The Sabi Sabi policy is lucidly stated in a report on the reserve:

Sabi Sabi's philosophy is high value/low density tourism.

Key understandings

◆ What is meant by sustainability in economic, social and environmental terms.

◆ Strategies for balancing environmental conservation with economic and social development.

◆ The use of the pricing mechanism to control tourism carrying capacity while maintaining economic viability.

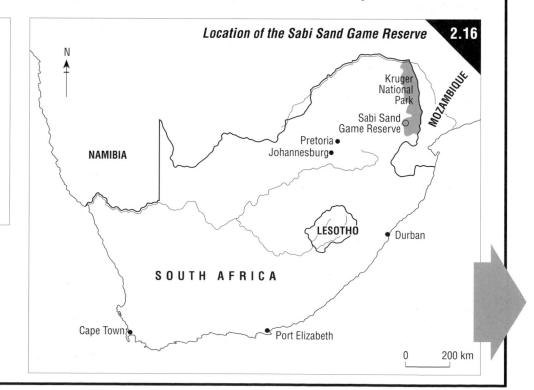

Location of the Sabi Sand Game Reserve   2.16

CASE STUDY 2.3 *Conservation, community development and tourism*

The human impact on the reserve is measured in terms of a Landrover per acre ratio rather than a number of beds per acre ratio. Sabi Sabi has more than enough physical space to build extra rooms. This would reduce tariffs and attract visitors more easily. That in turn would reduce business risk and potentially increase profit. However, Sabi Sabi limits the numbers of Landrovers on the reserve. This assures the minimum possible impact on the environment. Consequently its tariff must be high – both to retain the uniqueness and exclusivity of the bush experience, and at the same time to ensure the on-going commercial viability of the reserve (Rosenberg, H.A, 1993).

Continued commercial success of this type of tourism is seen as being directly dependent upon both the sustaining of a high quality environmental system, and also the ongoing support of local communities. Thus, the Sabi Sabi management policy fully recognises the importance of integrating tourism, conservation and community development. The Sabi Sabi owners see themselves as 'custodians of the environment' and as having 'responsibility' to the local communities.

Environmental background

The natural environment of Sabi Sabi is woodland savanna. This is a diverse ecosystem, comprising 200 mammals, including six species of cats, 20 species of antelope and 350 species of bird. Several species are on the *Endangered Species* list, such as the wild dog. The main attractions are cheetah, rhinoceros and the herds of zebra and wildebeest.

The first vegetation surveys were conducted in the region in the 1940s, when grazing densities of cattle owned by local communities were fairly light. The lightly wooded savanna, with good grass cover was found to be dominant, and was probably close to the local climatic climax vegetation structure. However, over the next 20 years, as population grew, so did cattle numbers and consequent overgrazing. This led to a deterioration of the grass surface coverage, and a spread of 'bush', that is, dense bushes, shrubs and small trees. This closed habitat shaded out the grass ground layer, exposing the surface to desiccation in dry spells and to erosion in the wet season. As the grass area shrank, so the cattle were concentrated on to the remaining areas, leading to further land degradation.

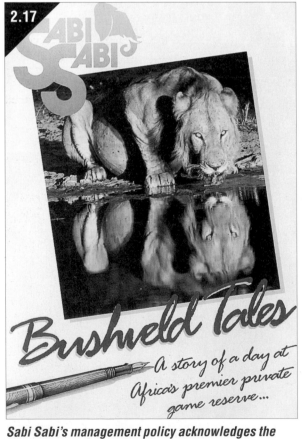

Sabi Sabi's management policy acknowledges the importance of integrating conservation, community development and tourism

Woodland savanna in South Africa

Zebra in the open savanna

Fences were extended to separate cattle from wild species, to prevent predation and to stop the spread of disease by wild game. The continued effect of habitat loss and restrictions on migratory movements led to a depletion in animal species, especially large herbivores such as wildebeest, reedbuck and antelope. This, in turn, affected the predators such as cheetah, which prey on them.

When the Sabi Sand Game Reserve was designated in 1965, cattle grazing was excluded, fences were erected around the boundaries, but little environmental reinstatement took place. 'Bush' continued to spread slowly and soil erosion extended. Thus, when the Sabi Sabi company bought their section in 1979, they took over a degraded landscape.

Environmental management policy

With the realisation that the fragile habitat was its principal resource, the primary goal was to restore the savanna ecosystem as closely to its natural state as possible, in terms of species composition and biodiversity. A management plan is reviewed every five years, and amended bi-annually. The ecosystem management plan has seven main dimensions:

1 Bush clearance

This is an ongoing project to reverse bush encroachment and so restore the grassland savanna. By late 1993, approximately 530 ha had been cleared. This savanna is the preferred habitat of important and attractive species such as wildebeest, zebra, white rhino and cheetah. Added benefits are improved visitor experience, jobs and income for the local communities and a supply of thatching materials and fuelwood for local families.

2 Control of alien (exotic) species

Sabi Sabi is an open system, with seeds and living creatures arriving by land, water (the Sabi river) and air. To prevent the establishment of these exotic species – both wild and

Savanna restored after degradation in the Sabi Sabi Reserve

cultigens from surrounding farmland – the Reserve operates a co-operative programme with the Kruger National Park managers. For instance, non-local reed and grass species are removed from the banks of the River Sabi, thereby benefitting local plant assemblages and the wildlife dependent upon them.

3 Control of soil erosion

Both sheet erosion and gullying were serious problems when the Reserve was established in 1979. Sheet erosion is largely caused by overgrazing of palatable short grass areas – in the past by domestic cattle and more recently by wild herbivores. In order to re-establish the grass sward with its dense and protective root network, brushwood

'mattress packs' are laid across the denuded surfaces. The packing allows new seedbanks to be formed and prevents grazing by herbivores. Once the grasses are established, the brushwood is removed. The grass is mowed to invigorate the grass plants and provide nutrients, and the mown material decomposes. Once more, the zebra and wildebeest can move back in.

Gullies (known as 'dongas') develop on sloping eroded land once the surface is laid bare or the grass cover is weakened. The gully heads are packed with wood and brush cleared from bush-infested areas. Over several years, new plants and their roots stabilise the donga, and the dead woody material decomposes to provide nutrients.

Regenerated grassland with scattered branches to reduce soil erosion

Local population are trained and employed by the Sabi Sabi management

4 Fire management

Fire plays an important role in sustaining the natural savanna cycle by burning off dying and dead vegetation, providing ash nutrients and stimulating new growth. In the past, animals were free to move away from the fires and return later as the young grasses grew. Today, because of perimeter fences, animal movements are restricted, which increases their vulnerability to fire. Burning is, therefore, controlled and follows a 3–4 year cycle. In any given year only designated patches of the Reserve are burned, giving animals ample opportunity to move away.

5 Waterhole management

The number of watering holes for animals must be related to the suitability and availability of grazing, and the desired animal numbers based upon estimates of habitat carrying capacity. Care has to be taken not to place too much stress on the surrounding vegetation caused by the concentration of animals. This stress changes seasonally and from year to year according to rainfall patterns. The Sabi Sabi managers open and close watering holes according to the changing supply and demand balance.

6 Removal of fences

All fences within the Reserve, and the boundary fence with the Kruger National Park are being removed. This will allow animals greater freedom of movement and so reduce stress on particular areas, improve the genetic base by greater breeding choice and increase the species diversity. In turn the quality of experience for tourists will also improve. Only the perimeter fence with the neighbouring Gazankulu community will remain to prevent domestic stock from moving into the Reserve and to stop wild animals becoming a nuisance on farmlands.

7 Game Census

One of the most critical elements of a sustainable ecosystem is the control of animal populations to the carrying capacity of the habitat. An annual aerial census is conducted in the Reserve to monitor numbers, especially of the main herbivore species. The results are used to calculate the following year's culling totals for each species. For rarer species, such as the leopard, cheetah, pangolin and wild dog, there is an on-going monitoring and research programme. Even more intensely monitored is the scheme to re-introduce species which have become locally extinct. For example, the ostrich and the crowned eagle have both recently been re-introduced and their survival is being closely monitored. Wounded or sick animals are assisted, or if the species is plentiful, they become part of the animal cull in order to sustain a healthy population. Much of this work is done in co-operation with conservation organisations, such as South African Nature Foundation; the Endangered Wild Life Trust and World Wildlife Fund.

Community development

Sabi Sabi employs 150 people, 80% of them from the local Gazankulu community. They have a subsistence economy based on crops, cattle and goats, plus income sent back by migrant workers from the cities, mines and large commercial farms and plantations of South Africa.

Local people today occupy all types of jobs, including that of game ranger. The policy is to employ local labour – which is plentiful and in need of the income – rather than buy or hire expensive equipment. Emphasis is placed on 'staff training', to upgrade the skills of the employees and to ensure a high quality experience for the tourists. The training includes not only skills specific to individual jobs, but an understanding of the ecosystems the visitors have come to see and of the conservation principles involved. The Sabi Sabi company also runs educational classes for children and adults to supplement local schools, focusing particularly on English language usage and vocational skills. Money is raised for bursaries to send individuals on specific courses. Artefacts made by local people are sold in the lodge gift shop.

In a broader context, Sabi Sabi supports the *We Care* organisation: *The non-profit body helps to 'build bridges' at grassroots level between the diverse spectrum of young people in South Africa. Sabi Sabi hosts groups of teenagers at its reserve and ranger training camp, with the aim of developing an increased awareness pertaining to conservation* (Rosenberg, 1993).

Activities

1 Define the term *sustainable development* and illustrate how it works using the Sabi Sabi case study.

2 a What is meant by *market segmentation* in tourism and which market segment is being targetted at Sabi Sabi?

   b Is this policy élitist? Does it make conservation and sustainable ecosystem management more realistic than a mass tourism strategy?

3 Outline how Sabi Sabi is trying to balance conservation values, economic values and amenity values in an environmental setting.

4 Use the Sabi Sabi management policy to illustrate the principles of dynamic equilibrium in ecosystems.

CASE STUDY 2.4 *Farming techniques and soil erosion*

Background

A critical management problem for any farmer is how to sustain, and even to increase, output over time without causing soil degradation. A combination of human and natural variables intensifies this problem in less developed economies of tropical and subtropical regions. For example, population growth puts increased pressure on land resources, while the generally intense convection storms of the wet season, followed by a lengthy dry season make soils vulnerable to erosion. As a result, there is serious concern over soil erosion rates across extensive regions of Latin America, Africa and eastern Asia. In 1990 it was estimated that 14% of the total land area in South America was suffering from soil erosion caused by human activities, almost one-half of it being the work of water (UNEP *Environmental Data Report*, 3rd Ed, 1991–92). Resource 2.23 shows the wide variation in erosion rates from cropland in several African environments.

A wide range of land management schemes have been introduced over much of the threatened regions. They may have reduced, but certainly have not halted erosion. Even on gently sloping land, one of the most popular methods of combatting erosion has been the building of low banks across slopes, i.e. contour banks, which breaks the slope into a series of sections. The aim is to control downslope run-off of water and so to reduce gully and sheet erosion. However, there is growing evidence that contour banking on its own is insufficient and that the farming technique practised on the land sections between the contour banks may be equally important in determining erosion rates. This case study follows the first three years of a research project in Zimbabwe which aimed to address the question – does farming technique influence soil erosion rates?

Soil erosion in Zimbabwe

Setting

Much of Zimbabwe's farmland is held and used by village communities rather than owned by individual farmers. This Communal Areas land is known to have serious soil erosion problems caused by a combination of population increase, inadequate livestock management and poor cropping techniques. A 1990 survey classified 27% of the Communal Areas as 'seriously to very seriously eroded', and a further 32% as having 'localised to moderate erosion'. Erosion occurs despite extensive land management schemes using contour banks and storm drainage channels. Such schemes reduce gullying but extensive sheet erosion occurs between the contour banks, and *it has been estimated that farmers in the Communal Areas lose up to 50 tonnes/ha/yr due to sheetwash* (Vogel, 1992).

It is clear, therefore, that the present land management system is not sustainable. It is causing a deterioration of the land resource. However, it may not be the contour bank system which is at fault, but the way farmers till the slopes between the contour banks. In order to determine the type of cultivation methods best suited to the environment, a research project was set up in 1988. Its prime objective has been *to assess the actual magnitude of sheet erosion between contour banks from different tillage methods, with a view to identifying the erosion control measures required for sustainable crop production systems* (Vogel, 1992). Two research sites were established, both on sandy soils developed upon granitic bedrock. One site is at Domboshawa in the sub-humid north of Zimbabwe, and the other, Makoholi, lies in the semi-arid south.

Environmental factors

The **natural vegetation** of the region is savanna with varying densities of woodland, but as the experiment concerns cropland, this is a less significant variable than **soil type**. Much of Zimbabwe, including the research sites, is underlain by granitic bedrock. These rocks weather to coarse-grained sandy soils with low organic content and poor structural stability, that is, they are weakly held together. They are generally infertile, have little cation exchange and poor water-holding capacity. Under the influence of the powerful rainsplash generated by the heavy rainstorms, sheetwash of the finer materials takes place, leaving surface crusts of coarse sand grains. Such soils are easily water-

---

Key understandings

◆ There is a direct relationship between land management strategies and soil erosion levels.

◆ Choice of tillage method will influence soil erosion, but rainfall characteristics also play a significant role in determining erosion rates.

◆ A fundamental principle in tillage is to adopt land management techniques which minimise the period and extent of bare soil surface.

Erosion rates from cropland at selected sites in Africa | 2.23

Locality	Mean annual rainfall(mm)	Slope (%)	Erosion (tonnes/ha/yr)
Ouagadougou(Burkino Faso)	850	0.5	0.6 – 0.8
Sefa (Senegal)	1300	1.2	7.3
Bouake (Ivory Coast)	1200	4.0	1 – 26
Abidjan (Ivory Coast)	2100	7.0	0.1 – 90
Mpwapwa (Tanzania)	570	6.0	78

[Source: Goudie A., *The human impact on the environment*, 2nd ed, 1986]

CASE STUDY 2.4 *Farming techniques and soil erosion*

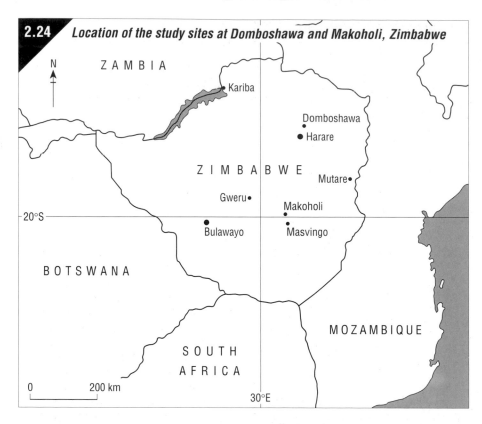

2.24 *Location of the study sites at Domboshawa and Makoholi, Zimbabwe*

study the results for the two experimental sites. It affects the conclusions we draw in this short timescale.

The major human environmental variable to consider is **farming method**. The most common practice on arable land is ox-ploughing with a single furrow mouldboard plough. This turns over a swath of topsoil and surface vegetation, exposing a fresh soil surface. It is done just before or at the beginning of the wet season. Planting takes place in early December and early in the dry season. After harvest, cattle are turned out on to the cropland. Despite the ploughing being done along the contours, up to 50 tonnes of soil are lost by sheetwash from a hectare each year.

The research

The aim of the research was to identify a sustainable cultivation technique which minimises soil erosion. Five tillage methods, including the conventional ox-ploughing were adopted at the two research sites.

Resource 2.28 shows the sheet erosion rates for the Makoholi research site for the first three years of the study. (A sixth category has been included in the data, namely that of 'bare fallow' in order to indicate the outcome of leaving the land bare of crops and vegetative cover for a year.) The relatively low erosion rates for the first year, 1988-89, are explained by the experimental crop plots being cleared from dense grass vegetation. Thus, surface roughness and firm soil structure reduced sheet erosion from all of the plots irrespective of tillage method.

logged, especially where impermeable lateritic bands occur in the soil profile.

The other environmental factor to consider is climate. Zimbabwe has a single wet season concentrated principally from December through March, when the Inter-Tropical Convergence Zone (ITCZ) migrates across the country. The graphs of Resource 2.25 show this wet season

for the two research sites. The convergence of hot, dry Tropical Continental (Tc) and warm, moist Tropical Maritime (Tm) airmasses generates intense convection storms with considerable erosive potential. However, an equally important characteristic is rainfall variability, in total amounts, in timing of arrival and in spatial distribution. This unreliability must be taken into account when we

For the following two years the figures show that the greater the area of bare surface the more active the sheet erosion. Even in the relatively dry year of 1990–91 (Resource 2.25), bare fallow land still lost 34.5 t/ha, with conventional mouldboard tillage ranking second with 5.7 t/ha. It is clear that the two most sustainable techniques appear to be tied ridges and mulch ripping. Tied ridges hold the water in the

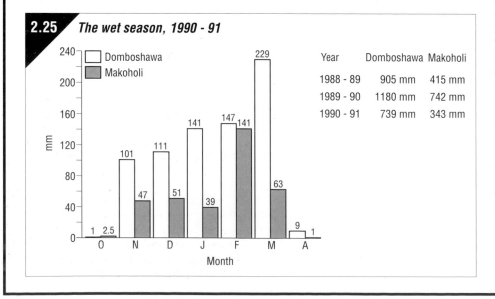

2.25 *The wet season, 1990 - 91*

Year	Domboshawa	Makoholi
1988 - 89	905 mm	415 mm
1989 - 90	1180 mm	742 mm
1990 - 91	739 mm	343 mm

2.26

Domboshawa, one of the research sites

Tillage methods at the research sites

2.27

1 **Conventional tillage** – ox-ploughing with a single-furrow mouldboard plough

2 **Mulch ripping** – using an ox-hook to rip into the soil whose surface is covered with stubble and residue from the previous crop. (An ox-hook is a single rigid, chisel-ended blade which rips into the surface.)

3 **Clean ripping** – using an ox-hook to rip into land left bare after the last crop

4 **Tied ridging** – using an ox-ridger, producing a ridge-and-furrow pattern

5 **Hand hoeing** into bare ground

Sheet erosion rates at Makoholi (tonnes /ha)

2.28

	1988–89	1989–90	1990–91
Tied ridging	0.05	0.1	0.1
Mulch ripping	0.5	1.2	0.8
Clean ripping	0.5	1.3	2.1
Hand hoeing (*)	–	1.1	1.7
Conventional tillage	0.7	1.3	5.7
Bare fallow	3.6	32.2	34.5

(*) Hand hoeing did not begin until 1989

---

cross-slope furrows and there is considerable vegetation cover across the ridges. The mulch ripping also retains much vegetation cover and builds up organic residue over time, thereby retaining firmer soil structure.

The problem with drawing conclusions from the correlation of erosion rates and cultivation method alone, is that it does not take into account the critical variable of rainfall, illustrated clearly by the three wet season totals shown on Resource 2.26. It is not only the variability of the annual total which is significant, but **when** the rain occurs and **how** it arrives, whether in heavy bursts or a steady drizzle. Resource 2.29 shows the relationship between rainfall and erosivity (the liability to be eroded) during the 1990–91 wet season, which produced below average totals. During November and December, approximately three-quarters of the rain arrived in four heavy bursts, with intervening dry spells of two weeks. Because of the lack of early moisture in the soils, crops were planted later than normal. The late planting and continued below-average rain meant that by the end of January the crops were wilting and had achieved poor ground cover. The crop cover on tied ridges averaged only 25% and on mulch-ripped plots, vegetative and residue cover was barely 50%.

Despite the below-average rainfall, sheet erosion had removed 2.3 t/ha from conventional tillage plots, particularly during the sporadic storms of November and December when the surfaces were at their most exposed. The situation changed in February, when 141 mm of rain fell between 7 and 19 February, 60% of this in two 24-hour periods. These intense storms triggered almost all of the sheetwash erosion recorded for the month. This indicates the significance of rainfall intensity, for although plant cover peaks in February, sheetwash also increased. The cumulative graphs of Resource 2.30 show that after the jump in losses from January to February, there was little loss in

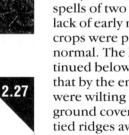

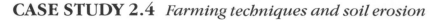

CASE STUDY 2.4 *Farming techniques and soil erosion*

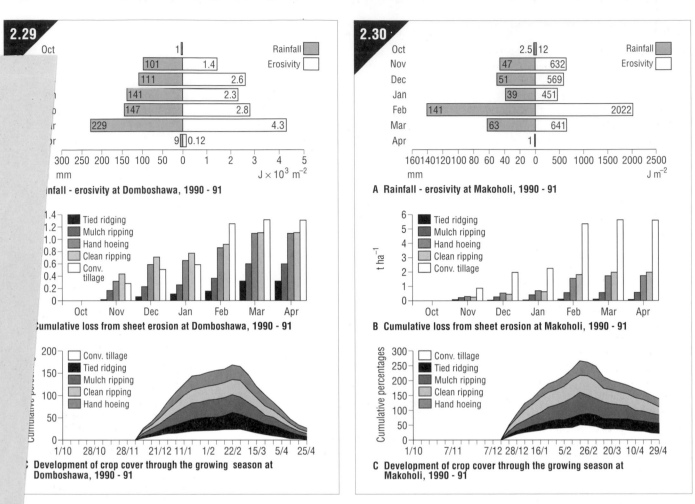

2.29

A Rainfall - erosivity at Domboshawa, 1990 - 91

Cumulative loss from sheet erosion at Domboshawa, 1990 - 91

C Development of crop cover through the growing season at Domboshawa, 1990 - 91

2.30

A Rainfall - erosivity at Makoholi, 1990 - 91

B Cumulative loss from sheet erosion at Makoholi, 1990 - 91

C Development of crop cover through the growing season at Makoholi, 1990 - 91

March and April, despite the fact that crop cover falls as the crops are harvested and die back.

Although all the research plots recorded increased sheetwash erosion as a result of the heavy February storms, the tied ridges and mulch ripping plots suffered significantly less than all other types, especially the plots tilled by the conventional method. The danger of leaving land exposed as bare fallow – with the intention of 'resting' the land – can be seen by the removal of 21.2 t/ha of soil during February.

The researchers concluded for the 1990–91 season at Makoholi: *In the absence of crop cover in November and most of December, and poor cover before the February rain, the differences in sheetwash rates between tillage methods must be attributed to differences in tillage and [crop] residue utilisation*

(Vogel, 1992). Thus, conventional tillage leaves the soil very vulnerable, especially where the ploughing lays much of the surface bare and breaks the surface soil into the finest tilth. Clean ripping opens up only a narrow strip between the previous season's crop rows. Mulch ripping leaves even smaller areas of bare surface. The surface residue layer intercepts raindrops, helping infiltration and slowing down sheetflow. Hand hoeing, although labour-intensive, also minimises surface exposure. Tied ridges are distinctive in that they hold water and soil fines well, reducing run-off and, hence, soil loss. Only the occasional severe storms cause the troughs to fill, overtop the ridges and trigger serious sheetwash erosion.

[From Vogel H. 'Effects of conservation tillage on sheet erosion from sandy soils at two experimental sites

in Zimbabwe', *Applied Geography* 12, 1992, 229–242]

Activities

1 The graphs of Resource 2.29 summarise the 1990–91 season for Domboshawa in the same way the above case study materials have examined Makoholi. Use the graphs for Domboshawa to describe and assess the relationships between

   a rainfall and erosivity.

   b vegetative cover and sheetwash.

   c erosion rates and crop tillage methods.

2 Compare your analysis of the Domboshawa data with that for Makoholi and make recommendations for sustainable land management in these districts of Zimbabwe, giving your reasons.

CASE STUDY 2.5   *The role of fire in ecosystem management*

Background

Fire is an important element in the life of a surprising number of natural ecosystems. For instance, research shows that in the forests of USA, before the waves of modern settlement, fire occurred with a 7–80 year return period, although major fires occurred much less frequently. Most natural fires are caused by lightning, and fall into four main categories (Resource 2.31). Once started, a fire tends to follow a characteristic progress (Resource 2.32).

The role of fire varies. In many grasslands it is the main agent of decomposition and nutrient recycling. Some tree species, including the giant Sequoia Redwoods of California, are resistant to natural fires and rely on fire for seed germination and the survival of the seedlings. Fire speeds up the availability of nutrients by releasing large amounts of potassium, magnesium, calcium and phosphorus through ash. It can get rid of unwanted species; grassland ecosystems such as savannas are thought to be maintained by fire which prevents the further encroachment by trees. In essence, fire plays a significant role in the maintenance of a dynamic equilibrium of many natural ecosystems.

Humans have imposed fire to cause fundamental changes upon a wide range of ecosystems, in many cases where fire is not a part of the natural system, and in other cases to alter the way fire works. Fire as a technique for ecosystem management is used across the world, from 'slash-and-burn' shifting cultivators in south-east Asia to managers of Scottish shooting estates who burn heather to improve grouse habitat. Fires started unintentionally are, today, a growing threat. For example, the disastrous fires of autumn 1993 in the dry chaparral around Los Angeles, California, were ignited intentionally by young people. Conversely, ecosystem functioning can be seriously affected by fire suppression.

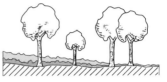

Types of environmental fire   **2.31**

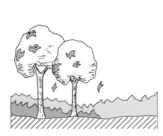

Ground fire
Occurs in sub-surface organic materials such as peat and humus. Spreads slowly, but can kill tree roots.

Surface fire
Runs rapidly across ground-level vegetation such as grasses, low shrubs and surface litter. Recovery usually fairly quick.

Dependent crown fire
Heat and flames from surface ignite tree crowns. Fire in crowns moves at same speed as the surface fire. High temperatures, up to 850°C. Common in savannas. Recovery usually in a few years.

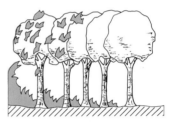

Running crown fire
Independent of and moves faster than surface fire. Moves rapidly, aided by high winds and dry conditions. Very high temperatures (up to 1000°C). A 'fire storm' is an extreme version, where heat causes trees ahead of the main fire, to ignite. Recovery between 10 and 100 years.

Mankind's efforts deliberately to suppress fire may lead to the accumulation of enormous quantities of inflammable materials, which will allow conflagrations of the crown type to develop. Moreover, fire suppression in forests has allowed them to be invaded by species that are intolerant of fire, and to develop a denser vegetation, which means that they burn more readily when fire eventually breaks out (Alexander D. Natural disasters, UCL Press, 1993).

This case study examines the causes of the calamitous fires which swept across almost one-half of the 890 000 ha Yellowstone National Park, USA, from July to September in 1988. *They seemed nature's signa-*

ture written with a grand flourish on an awesome scale (Jeffery D. 'Yellowstone: The great fires of 1988', *NGM*, Feb 1989).

Fire is part of the coniferous forest ecosystem which forms the climatic climax vegetation of this mountain and high plateau environment. However, since Yellowstone became the world's first National Park in 1872, the park managers have altered the fire regime. The case study highlights the dilemma facing managers of ecosystems where conservation values must be balanced with amenity values. *Cannot we have our wilderness wild but keep it safe, keep it NICE?* (Jeffery, *NGM*, 1989).

Key understandings

◆ Fire is an important element in the funcitoning of many natural ecosystems.

◆ Management strategies which aim to control or eliminate fires may disrupt ecosystem functioning.

◆ Altering the fire regime in an ecosystem may increase environmental hazards.

◆ Increasingly, environmental managers are adopting policies which imitate natural ecosystem processes as closely as possible.

The causes of the Yellowstone fires, 1988

Park policies

For the first one hundred years of Yellowstone's history, the management policy was to put out all fires as soon as possible, whether they were natural or started by people in the Park. Then, in 1972, by which time the managers knew much more about the role of fire, the policy changed. Management has since been based upon the *Wildland Fire Management Plan for Yellowstone National Park*, which encourages the Park Ranger Service to let fires burn unless there is a threat to life or property.

This 'let it burn' policy is based upon sound ecological principles. The burn patterns of natural fires stimulate re-growth of diverse vegetation types of different ages, thereby providing a rich habitat for wildlife. Biodiversity is sustained over time. The fires also periodically clear out the dead vegetation from the forest floor, preventing a dangerous build-up of potential fuel for a fire and providing good conditions for rapid re-growth. These natural fires rarely extend over large areas and except for the gaps which act as firebreaks (sites of recent fires), the natural ecosystem is a patchwork within the full forest. Today, fires are monitored but not normally extinguished, in order to fit the management policy as closely as possible to the natural regime of the ecosystem.

The summer of '88

Although the 'let it burn' policy had been in operation for 16 years, by 1988 there were extensive areas

2.32   **The life of a fire**

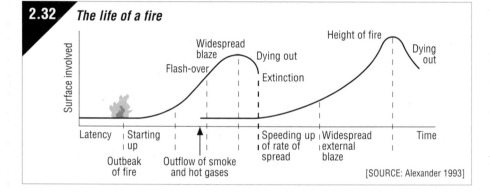

[SOURCE: Alexander 1993]

2.33

It's time to fire Bambi

If you can't stand the heat, get out of the park. Forest fires – at Yellowstone or on the Riviera – are nature's way of renewing forests, writes Paul Simons.

When Yellowstone Park went up in smoke last summer, America was gripped by something approaching hysteria. The survival of their oldest and largest national park became a war of all-America macho fire-fighting versus nature. Yet, despite pouring over a hundred million dollars into tackling the blaze, nature won in a spectacular style with fires burning for three months. Revenge was swift though. The Parks Service was accused of pyromania, for having blessed the fire as a natural phenomenon that gave the park a new lease of life. At stake here is a crucial question: should wilderness be managed for people or nature?

There is no disputing the scale of the Yellowstone fire. At the height of the blaze on August 20, 300-foot-high flames were swept along by 80-miles-an-hour winds. Yet despite the greatest firefighting effort in American history, 6,000 civilians reinforced with four battalions (4,100 soldiers) of the US Army and Marine Corps were overwhelmed. Eventually almost half the park was affected, and a million and a half acres of forest burnt.

Yet only about a tenth of the forest was actually turned into charcoal – most was singed and is recovering well, and the rest wasn't touched at all. So why, might you ask, get so het up about it?

Perhaps the answer lies in the worst fire in American history. In 1942 the cinema-going public watched in horror as screaming animals fled monstrous flames, some of the wildlife crying as their homes burnt. The disaster was from Walt Disney's Bambi and the image stuck, so much so that for years afterwards Bambi and Smokey The Bear were the spearhead of campaigns to prevent forest fires.

What the fire at Yellowstone boils down to now is human emotion versus nature. People don't go on holiday to see burnt tree stumps. They want green trees, furry animals, and lots of other 'nice' things. That creates the political pressure to coax nature into doing unnatural things. But even if the big fires could be extinguished – and that's hardly likely on last years evidence – Yellowstone could be eventually killed by slow atrophy. To put it bluntly, Yellowstone needs fires.

Perhaps the greatest threat to Yellowstone is the spread of cabins and nearby towns, which rely on fire-fighting for their survival. Hence why some £1 million was spent trying to prevent a rubber tomahawk shop from being burnt down. But the loss of three houses, 31 cabins, 13 mobile homes and a few other buildings greatly shocked the American esteem for real estate.

Yet if people had to pay the total costs of protecting their homes in the far flung woodland, says Power, there might be fewer buildings to worry about saving. In the most farcical example of all, a fire deliberately started to clear a break in the forest accidentally destroyed several buildings including a TV transmitting station, surely the most sacrosanct loss of all.

The ecologists under the banner of the Parks Service pronounced the burning of Yellowstone one of the most successful conservation events of 1988. But this does not bode well for the rest of the American wilderness with a public hellbent on making nature do what they supposed it ought to.
[*Guardian*, 8.8.89]

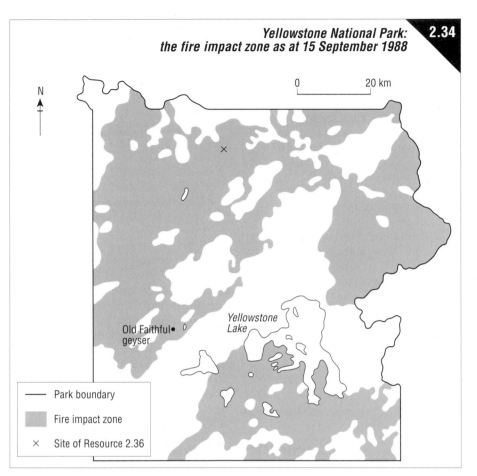

Yellowstone National Park: the fire impact zone as at 15 September 1988 `2.34`

0   20 km

N

Old Faithful geyser • ᴰ

Yellowstone Lake

— Park boundary

▓ Fire impact zone

× Site of Resource 2.36

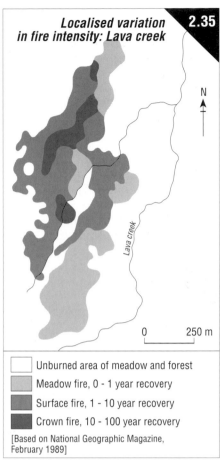

Localised variation in fire intensity: Lava creek `2.35`

N

Lava creek

0   250 m

☐ Unburned area of meadow and forest

▓ Meadow fire, 0 - 1 year recovery

▓ Surface fire, 1 - 10 year recovery

▓ Crown fire, 10 - 100 year recovery

[Based on National Geographic Magazine, February 1989]

which had not burned. In these areas, there remained a large volume of dead, dry wood and other vegetation, the accumulation of the previous century. Despite a wet May, 1988 saw a hot, dry summer, which followed several years with below average rainfall. This forest was literally a 'tinderbox' by the beginning of July.

By mid-July, at least 6500 ha were ablaze in various parts of the park. This was a high level, but not alarming. However, during the next few weeks, a combination of lightning, high winds, continued drought and relative humidities falling below 10% took the fires out of control. They advanced up to 20 km a day in places. By 21 August, fires had extended across almost 400 000 ha, were being fought by over 9000 fire-fighters, and by early September, were threatening to overwhelm the Park visitor headquarters. The map of Resource 2.34 shows the vast

impact zones by 15 September. Resource 2.36 takes a detailed look at a 30 ha area in the north of the Park and indicates how the fire varied in intensity locally. Although the fires reached the intensity of 'fire-storms' which totally destroy the trees and even the organic material of soils in some areas, the burns over large areas were much lighter. Recovery is likely to be relatively rapid. A problem may be the very large areas which have been burned, making seed dispersal difficult.

The inquest

Even as the fires raged, the National Park Service were under criticism for delaying fire control for too long, that is, adhering too closely to the 'let-it-burn' policy. Critics argued that this was no longer a natural forest, but a National Park for people to visit. They postulated that amenity values ought to be given high priority. Park managers, however, ranked conservation values first, believing

that the attractive resource for the visitors could only be sustained by following ecological principles. This controversy is followed in Resource 2.33. You may not agree with the arguments in the article, and indeed, certain statements are open to question. For example, the writer claims that *people don't go on holiday to see burnt tree stumps. They want green trees …* However, looking at Resource 2.40, in 1980 the forests around Mount St Helens, Washington, USA, were destroyed by a violent volcanic eruption. Today, many thousands of visitors are fascinated by experiencing the recovery of the ecosystem, following self-guided trails such as the one shown in the photo.

Finding the balance

Yellowstone National Park is a classic example where conservation values and amenity values meet head-on. It is clear that the Park will continue to be a

CASE STUDY 2.5 *The role of fire in ecosystem management*

managed environment, and a 'commodity' for visitors' consumption. Management policies must give priority to the sustainability of the natural ecosystems which are a central attraction for the visitors. To achieve this, the managers rely on maintaining natural agents and processes wherever possible. Fire is one such agent. To include fire in their management policy, Park managers have to determine what is the most effective *fire regime*. This is made up of three components: *frequency, season, intensity*.

Fire in South Africa

Fynbos is an Afrikaans word meaning 'thin wood'. It is a general name given to a set of ecosystems found in the Cape region of South Africa, and covers about 4.4% of the country's land area. This region is dominated by shrubs and grasses, with varying densities of thin trees. Fire is an important element in the maintenance of its natural biodiversity. However, because of urban growth, the spread of agriculture and increasing recreational use, the fynbos is under stress. In consequence, a research programme has provided the basis for a management plan.

One aspect of the research has been to find out what type of fire regime will be most effective in maintaining biodiversity, reducing or eliminating introduced (alien) species, and preventing hazards to settlements and farmland. The central question in deciding fire *frequency* is how often to burn to ensure the best chance of plant regeneration. The research concluded that as a general rule *prescribed burns [managed fires] should only take place once 50% of the population of the slowest maturing species in a given area has flowered for at least 3 successive years* (Cowling, R. (ed), 1992). The essential requirement is an ample seed supply for germination after a fire. Only mature plants will flower fully, and so yield copious seed loads. The research found that the minimum interval between fires should be four years. At the other extreme, the seed yield of most species declines beyond a certain age and in the fynbos system, the maximum interval between fires is estimated at 45 years. The researchers concluded that the optimum frequency of prescribed burns to provide best seed supply and maintain biodiversity is 10–25 years, dependent upon the local species composition.

The fire *season* in the natural fynbos system is summer, during the hot, dry months of the Mediterranean climate. The most intense flowering activity takes place in late winter and spring (August/October), therefore, the maximum seed loads are available in late summer/early autumn (February/April). Seasonality of fires does have a significant influence on species survival. The research found that maximum seedling recruitment takes place after late summer and early autumn fires.

Two factors influence the *intensity* of fires:

* the fuel load – How much dead and dry biomass is available relates to fire frequency, since fuel load accumulates over time.
* the meteorological conditions –

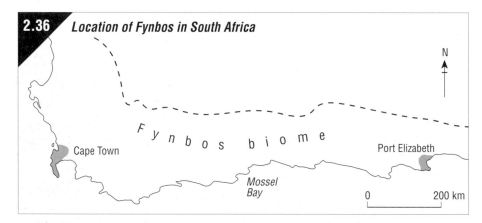

2.36 Location of Fynbos in South Africa

Cape Town

F y n b o s   b i o m e

Port Elizabeth

Mossel Bay

N

0 _____ 200 km

A Protea bush in bloom, an example of Fynbos vegetation

The hot, dry summer months are likely to trigger high-intensity fires. While summer is a good season for prescribed burns in terms of seed availability, it is problematic in terms of intensity. Moderate intensities are required for germination success.

The fire regime adopted is, therefore, tightly constrained by these factors: *Prescribed burning in the summer months (November to February) is seldom attempted ... since the risk of runaway fires is too great. Burning is usually only feasible in March and April; but only about 12 days on weather* (Cowling, 1992).

The coniferous forest ecosystems of Yellowstone function differently from the fynbos systems, with regards to fire resistance of species and seeding patterns, but the park managers are working on the same principles. The USFS has developed fire rating systems and fire prediction models whose purpose is to select those environmental conditions that will lead to the desired type of fire. Tests are being conducted in various locations, but so far, have not proved successful in practice.

Activities

1 What are the objectives of a National Park?

2 What is meant by 'conservation values' and 'amenity values'?

3 What is the role of fire in the Yellowstone forest ecosystem?

4 Why were the 1988 fires exceptionally strong and widespread?

5 Write two brief reports, one supporting the National Park Service (NPS) policies and the other stating the case of the critics of the NPS.

6 Suggest why the requirement to balance conservation values and amenity values presents a dilemma for the Park managers.

7 In what ways might the fynbos research on frequency, seasonality and intensity assist the Yellowstone managers in developing a new management policy?

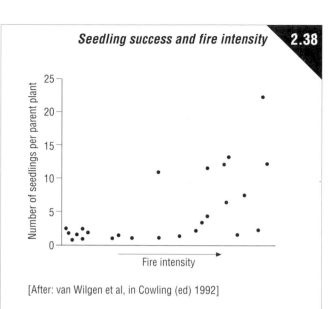

Seedling success and fire intensity 2.38

[After: van Wilgen et al, in Cowling (ed) 1992]

2.39

Visitors to Mount St Helens. The US Forest Service has developed the blast zone as a major tourist attraction. Part of this attraction is the revival of the forest ecosystem. Young trees can be seen along this self-guiding trail.

CASE STUDY 2.6 *Geographical Information Systems*

Background

If we are to make effective decisions about managing the environment, whether on local, national or global scales, we require comprehensive, up-to-date information. In addition we need user-friendly ways of storing this information and having it easily accessible when we need it. The classic environmental **storage** and **display** system used by geographers is the **map**. Like any data store, a map is the outcome of the **information gathering** process: we have to collect the information, which we then transform into map format. The traditional methods of collecting data and producing the series of maps needed for any environmental management scheme are costly and time-consuming.

Today the combination of remote-sensing using satellites and aircraft, and computer capabilities, allow us to

- collect data quickly and up-date it regularly.
- store large volumes of data.
- process data easily.
- select and interrogate data quickly – i.e. ask 'What if … ?' questions.
- display the selected data in a variety of ways.

These computer-based storage-retrieval-manipulation-display

Fieldwork: good data is vital, but is hard work.

systems are known as **geographical information systems**, or as they are usually called, **GIS**. There is little doubt that they are set to become the basic tool of the geographer, the planner and any other professionals concerned with spatial organisation and environmental management. Already in the UK, any planning application for a significant development must be accompanied by an

Environmental Impact Assessment (EIA) statement.

Remote-sensing as a data gathering strategy is the sensing of objects without actually coming into contact with those objects. A photograph collects information by remote-sensing. Environmental remote sensing *is the measurement from a distance, of the spectral features of the Earth's surface and atmosphere* (Mather, P. *Computer processing of remotely-sensed images,* Wiley, 1993).

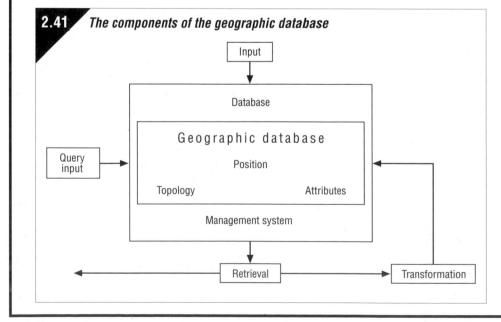

2.41   *The components of the geographic database*

Input

Database

Geographic database

Position

Topology   Attributes

Query input

Management system

Retrieval   Transformation

Key understandings

- ◆ Environmental Impact Assessments (EIA) are an important element in the planning process.
- ◆ Computer-based Geographical Information Systems (GIS), with their data storage, retrieval and display capabilities, are flexible and cost-effective resources for environmental management.
- ◆ Remote-sensing and information technology are powerful tools for decision-making in environmental management.

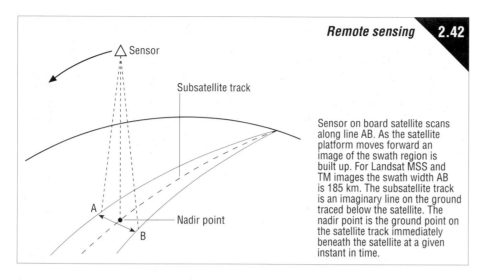

Sensor

Subsatellite track

A

B

Nadir point

Sensor on board satellite scans along line AB. As the satellite platform moves forward an image of the swath region is built up. For Landsat MSS and TM images the swath width AB is 185 km. The subsatellite track is an imaginary line on the ground traced below the satellite. The nadir point is the ground point on the satellite track immediately beneath the satellite at a given instant in time.

Part A: Impact analysis in sensitive rural settings

One important element in evaluating a development proposal is to be able to visualise the site and surrounding area before and after the development; this is impact evaluation. A traditional way of doing this is to produce photograph montages for both stages, with the development and landscape changes superimposed on the second set. This is time-consuming, and once completed is not easily adapted. Another method is to produce a set of maps, shadings and drawings on a set of transparent sheets and overlay them one upon another as required, similar to the overlay technique used with an overhead projector.

We can use a GIS system to do this much more quickly and flexibly. We can call on our digital data base to produce a **digital terrain map** or **DTM**, in either conventional vertical two-dimensional plan view, or as a three-dimensional 'block diagram' view. We can then superimpose or 'drape' (the popular term used in GIS for superimposition) the landscape changes resulting from the development on our DTM in map or model format. We can assess environmental impact by having the system plot the zone of visibility of the development – either the area from which the development can be seen or the extent of view from the development. We should then be able to work out ways of minimising environmental impacts by modifying the location, scale and colour of the development, or by landscape screening. Probability questions can be addressed if we have chosen the appropriate software package and have input the correct data. The following are two examples of this technique in action.

The principal technology used is satellite imagery, that is images communicated in digital form from data collected by sensors carried in satellites. The sensors measure the amount of electro-magnetic energy reflected from or emitted by the Earth's surface. As the satellite moves, so the successive scan lines of the sensors build up an image of a strip of the Earth's surface. Because the satellite returns over the same swath of Earth surface at precise intervals, the data can be accurately updated.

Data gathering by remote-sensing does not replace fieldwork entirely, but reduces it considerably. The satellite information needs 'ground-proofing' or 'ground-truthing', that is, checking by field survey sampling. For example, infra-red records for different vegetation types or energy output (which indicate plant health) are plotted in different colours. Ground-proofing determines what these colours mean on the ground. This remotely sensed information can then be fed into the GIS data bank, to which information on terrain (contours), settlement and various types of secondary data, such as addresses (precise point location), census figures, land use data and population densities can be added. The result is a multi-variate data bank in digital format which can be easily interrogated by the application of appropriate software packages.

This case study illustrates the character and potential of GIS through its ability to assist the decision-making process in planning issues in sensitive rural environments where the development proposed might have significant visual and land use impacts. It can also assess the spatial variation in quality of life in urban areas.

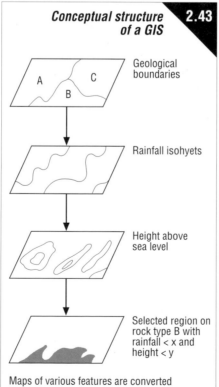

A   C

B

Geological boundaries

Rainfall isohyets

Height above sea level

Selected region on rock type B with rainfall < x and height < y

Maps of various features are converted to a common scale and projection so as to allow the identification of regions that satisfy particular requirements.

Ski developments at Aonach Mor, Scotland

In 1986 a private company applied for planning permission to develop ski facilities at Aonach Mor, in the Nevis Range east of Fort William.

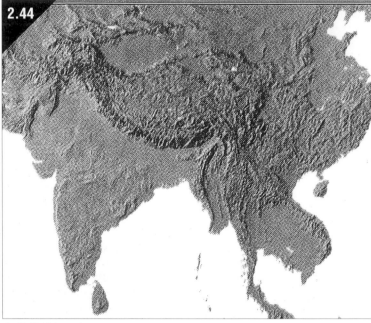

A digital terrain map

The facilities at Aonach Mor consist of a car park and cafe at the foot of the site, a top station, a gondola between the car park and top, a chairlift and six ski tows.

2.46 Key issues in the Aonach Mor project

1 Visual impact of the base station, infrastructure, new road, removal of trees
2 Location of gondola towers
3 Impact on vegetation
4 Impact on streams
5 Effect on public water supply
6 Siting of snow fences
7 Effect on summer recreation
8 Increased risk of forest fires
9 Effect of nearby limestone quarry and blasting

Having been through the planning committee process, permission was granted and the runs opened in December 1989. Resource 2.46 lists the key planning issues.

A GIS system was used to create a detailed DTM for the development area, plus a less-detailed model of the surrounding area to allow analysis of longer distance views into the site. The output from the GIS was of two main types:

- Visibility maps for the following features – alternative locations for the top station; chairlift location alternatives; parts of the development site seen from two popular viewpoints, Ben Nevis summit and the Commando Viewpoint at Spean Bridge; visibility impacts of felling programmes in the surrounding forests.

- A set of DTMs were produced with 'drapes' to illustrate the development plans and the various competing landuses such as forestry, SSSIs and footpaths. For example, the set of overlays could be used to assess the impact on vegetation, using the combined information on soils, vegetation types, and angles of slope to highlight areas of high vulnerability, and so to prevent developments in such areas. Resource 2.47 illustrates the answer to the questions – 'What if the Forestry Commission proceed with their felling programme? What then will be the visibility impact of the ski development?' Equally, if it was suggested to the Forestry Commission that they modify their planned felling to reduce visibility impacts, then a map or three dimensional model could quickly be produced for any management pattern.

Tinto Hills forestry proposal

In 1986 a private company, Fountain Forestry, put in a planning application to afforest 740 ha across the Tinto Hills in Scotland. This area was regarded by planners and environmentalists as being *visually distinctive and ecologically important* (Selman et al, 1991) and much of it lay in an SSSI. The initial application

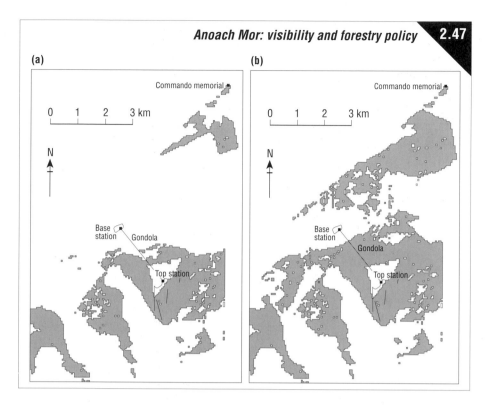

Anoach Mor: visibility and forestry policy 2.47

(a)

Commando memorial

0 1 2 3 km

N

Base station
Gondola
Top station

(b)

Commando memorial

0 1 2 3 km

N

Base station
Gondola
Top station

Part B: Measuring spatial variations in the quality of life

Two indicators commonly used to assess quality of life in urban areas are derelict land as a blight on surrounding areas (negative impact on quality of life), and accessibility to parks and open space (positive impact). A GIS system can be used to store, retrieve, plot and display the precise location of all derelict land sites and open spaces, then by the use of individual addresses, can measure the numbers of people living within certain distances.

A GIS held by Tyne & Wear Metropolitan County has allowed such analysis to be carried out. The potential detail possible from this GIS is indicated by the fact that data are location-coded by grid reference down to one metre. Thus, if we use distance from a derelict site as a

and the accompanying request for government grant aid for the planting and management programme were rejected because of the unacceptable level of environmental impact. In 1988, a modified proposal to plant a much smaller area was accepted, but once again, the Nature Conservancy Council objected strongly and a management agreement was agreed for the SSSI, which avoided commercial afforestation. Resource 2.48 lists the key planning issues.

As part of the evaluation process, DTMs and models were produced for each of the issue areas and various combinations of the variables. The visual impact of the afforestation was one of the most strongly fought issues. Resource 2.49 illustrates the draping technique, i.e. superimposing one forestry scheme over a terrain model.

The two examples above were part of a research project carried out by the University of Stirling to evaluate the usefulness of GIS. They concluded that *its value would seem to lie principally in providing general*

impressions of the sensitivity of application sites and the acceptability of alternative development layouts. DTMs were considered to be the best form of output, with visibility maps ranking second ... A particular advantage was the ability to pinpoint the precise location and boundaries of a development in the landscape ... and the ease of superimposing data on to DTMs and zooming in to critical areas (Selman et al, 1991).

Planning issues in the Tinto Hills 2.48

1 Recreational importance of the area for walking
2 Visual impact
3 Nature conservation
4 Archaeological sites
5 Impact on streams
6 Public access
7 Land ownership
8 SSSI
9 Agriculture

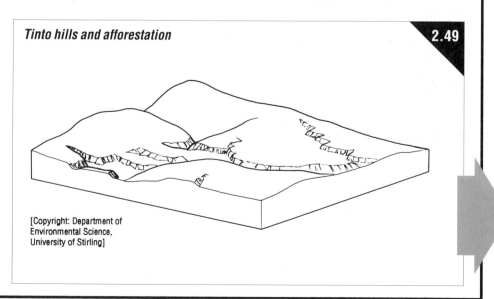

Tinto hills and afforestation 2.49

[Copyright: Department of Environmental Science, University of Stirling]

crucial measure then we can accurately assess the degree of impact for every house. The results are summarised in Resource 2.50.

The figures in Resource 2.50 highlight the significant spatial variations: if you live in Gateshead you have high access to open space, but this is counterbalanced by the high probability of a derelict site nearby. In Sunderland, on the other hand, there is above average access to open space *and* relatively low likelihood of living near a derelict site. Such knowledge is important in making decisions about where to focus land reclamation schemes, or to provide new parks.

The GIS system was also used to identify variations at a much finer scale. Resource 2.51 uses postcode sectors as the areal unit to study variations in accessibility to open space. On the data base the population figures were at Census Enumeration District level (an ED is the smallest unit for which Census data is available). The system aggregated these to postcode sector units for plotting purposes. For each postcode sector a 'score' was calculated from the proximity of the nearest open space, weighted by the size of the population in that postcode sector.

The researchers conclude that planners and managers can *conduct more thorough spatial analyses by varying the criteria used in the measurements. This provides a more solid base for policy discussions, for local comparisons and for monitoring progress against planning objectives* (Wong et al, TPR, 1991).

[Main references: Selman P. et al 'GIS in rural environmental planning' *TPR*, 62(2), 1991, 215–223, and Wong C. 'The environmental quality of residential neighbourhoods' *TPR* 62(2), 1991, 369–373]

2.50 **Quality of life variations in Tyne & Wear Metropolitan County**

District	% district households within 0.5 km of a derelict site	Access score to parks and open space as % county average
Gateshead	90	164
Newcastle	85	98
North Tyneside	60	94
South Tyneside	51	57
Sunderland	38	112
Tyne & Wear	71	100

[Source: Wong et al,1991]

2.51 **Open space access: Tyne and Wear**

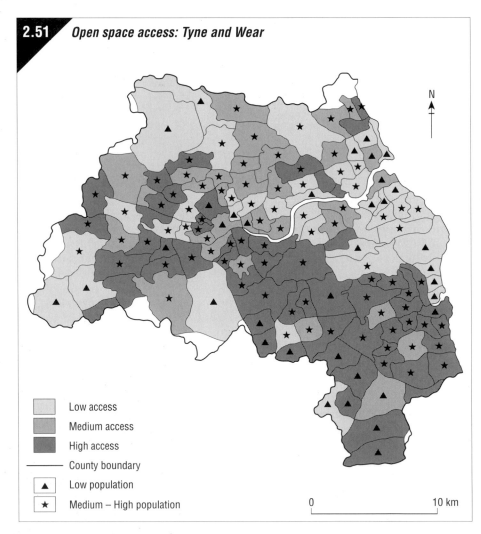

N

Low access
Medium access
High access
County boundary
▲ Low population
★ Medium – High population

0   10 km

Activities

1 Define the terms *remote sensing* and *GIS*.

2 Using examples, support the claim that a GIS assists the flexibility, speed and cost-effectiveness of the environmental decision-making process.

3 Suggest how a GIS might assist in a resolution for an environmental or planning issue in your local area.

CHAPTER 3

Managing change in rural environments

Introduction

Traditionally, rural societies and economies enjoy long periods of relative stability, with low rates of change. This gradual evolution is interspersed with shorter bursts of disturbance and even destabilisation, for example, the Agricultural Revolution from the mid-eighteenth century across Europe, and the collectivisation of agriculture in the USSR after the Russian Revolution of 1919. There are many signs that rural environments throughout the world are undergoing such surges of change. At the heart of this transformation is agriculture, the economic basis of most rural societies. The latest agricultural revolution started in the 1950s. It has been energised by a growth in demand, affected by the global population explosion, rising expectations, and a growth in supply which is aided by science and technology, such as machinery, selective plant and animal breeding, and the development of chemicals. The outcome has been a continuous growth of agricultural production over the past 40 years.

The rise in production and productivity has been achieved by intensifying the environmental impacts and creating entirely new agricultural landscapes. For example, at least 15% of the land in South America has some form of soil degradation resulting from human activities. Around the world, concern is growing for the economic, social and environmental costs of this agricultural transformation. It seems to have helped accentuate rather than reduce contrasts in quality of life in different parts of the world. In many less developed countries (LDCs) the crucial issues are to bring more land into production and to raise productivity in order to feed more people and increase incomes. In contrast, in many developed countries, the size of farmland is shrinking as governments attempt to control overproduction and surpluses, for example, the CAP (Common Agricultural Policy) of the EU (European Union).

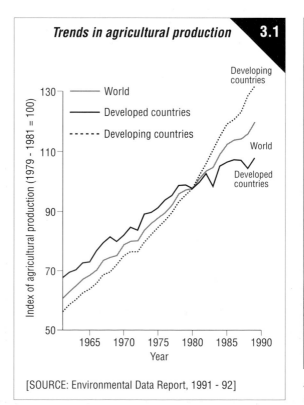

Trends in agricultural production 3.1

- —— World
- —— Developed countries
- ----- Developing countries

Index of agricultural production (1979 - 1981 = 100)

[SOURCE: Environmental Data Report, 1991 - 92]

An agribusiness landscape: irrigated cropland, Imperial Valley, California, USA

As the realisation spreads that land resources must be managed for sustainability not short-term exploitation, this rural revolution is changing direction. Economic sustainability is seen to rely on environmental sustainability. Crop yields can be sustained only if soil fertility is sustained. Rural communities will be sustained only with a sound economic and environmental foundation. Furthermore, the rise of the environmentalist movement means that conservation values are being given higher priority in rural development policy. There is an attempt to maintain diversity in agricultural ecosystems. To hear of 'extensification' in farming, of 'green' or organic approaches which follow natural not artificial processes and rhythms, is not uncommon. There is growing appreciation of the countryside or the wilderness as having potential value far beyond agriculture. It is more often considered for conservation, recreation and living. Policies which focus upon diversification in the way rural resources are allocated and used, are developed. In this way, broadening demand can be satisfied while the supply of opportunities can help sustain rural economies and communities formerly dependent on agriculture.

The case studies in this chapter illustrate the extent of the rural revolution. Case study 3.1 from Java, Indonesia, is an excellent example of population pressures pushing against productivity limits. Notice in particular how the villages absorb population growth, cope with land shortage and adapt to changing markets. Case study 3.2 highlights the shift from exploitation to sustainability in land management. Australia has no land shortage but farmers have realised that their techniques have caused severe land degradation. This study follows a group of farmers in Victoria as they try to restore the landscape and farm on a sustainable basis. Case studies 3.3, 3.4 and 3.5 emphasise the diversification theme. Diversification is popular in western Europe as a way of reducing agricultural surpluses while maintaining rural economies and communities. Case study 3.3 shows the early stages of farm diversification in County Wicklow, Ireland. Case studies 3.4 and 3.5 examine the benefits and problems associated with allocating rural resources to recreation and tourism, in this instance, golf in the UK and winter sports in the French Alps.

3.3 *Leisure is the crop of the future*

What is a farm trail?

A farm trail is a planned tour of a farm designed to show visiting members of the public how modern farming practice can exist in harmony with aspects of wildlife conservation. The tour may be conducted – in which case a modest entrance fee is usually charged – or unaccompanied, when visitors with the aid of a printed guide and directional signs, find their way around the farm.

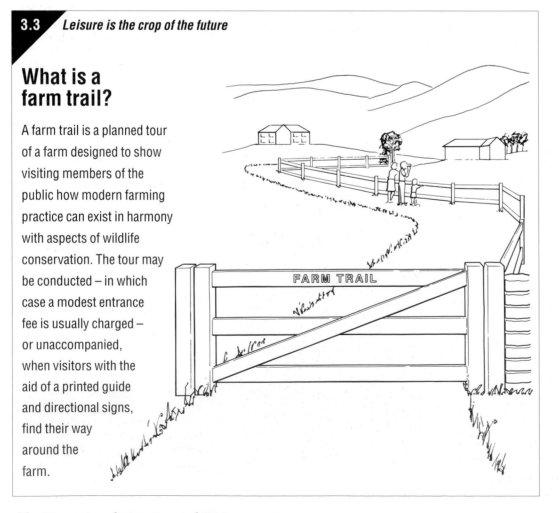

FARM TRAIL

CASE STUDY 3.1 *People, productivity and profits*

Background

Population growth is often identified as the cause of agricultural pressures and accelerating environmental impacts throughout the developing world. Rural societies do, however, adjust both to these internal forces and to external changes in the wider world. Villagers respond resourcefully to the population growth and the changing markets. Their coping strategies include bringing additional land into cultivation in the existing village area or by setting up a new community, introducing new high yielding crops or animals, changing cropping rhythms by introducing or extending irrigation, setting up local industries and migrating to towns. Governments and international agencies assist in this adjustment process. For example, the 'Green Revolution' in south-east Asia was generated by the introduction of high yielding varieties (HYVs) of rice, supported by financial and technical aid from various external sources. (The growing realisation that dependence upon these HYVs may be risky does not detract from the scale of the adjustments made by the villagers.)

The problems created by population growth are serious and widespread. It is particularly noticeable in the semi-arid Sahel region, where environmental carrying capacity is low, and also in in highly productive environments which have intensive, efficient agricultural systems. In such regions there may be fewer increases in productivity should the population continue to grow. Throughout eastern Asia there are examples of such productive but densely populated areas. This case study examines a valley in Java, an island with some of the highest rural population densities in the world. Villages in the intensively farmed valley of the Solo river in central Java were surveyed in 1974 and 1988. During this period, population was growing at above 2.5% a year. The surveys allow us to see how the villagers responded, and what caused change, whether it was government policies, local decisions, shifting food demands or the additional people.

The dynamics of farming systems in the Solo Valley, Java

Setting

The Solo Valley lies in the volcanic mountains of central Java. It is an equatorial environment, with year-round growth, but the altitudinal range produces sufficient climatic zonation to cause a varied management response. The landscape, therefore, exhibits a well-defined agro-ecological zonation. In 1974 a survey of the farming systems of eight villages along this deeply-cut valley was conducted. The traverse route, 86 km long, was chosen to include as wide a range of environments as possible. In 1987–88 the survey was repeated, allowing for a comparative analysis. The factors considered included altitude, soil types, slopes, temperature, rainfall and the full range of village economies. In addition, the second survey considered factors which had influenced changes. The following materials examine the farming systems of two villages at the altitudinal extremes: Tegal Gede in the valley floor (5 on Resource 3.5),

3.4

Intensive paddy rice farming in Indonesia

Key understandings

◆ Javanese agriculture is based upon small holdings, intensive cultivation, high productivity and year-round multiple cropping.

◆ Farmers adjust skilfully to differences in environmental conditions.

◆ Farmers may rapidly modify their cropping systems to changing market conditions.

◆ Change in village economies is the result of internal and external forces which influence decision-making.

◆ Efficient and productive village economies can absorb population growth remarkably well, but a capacity threshold may be reached where further growth endangers the system.

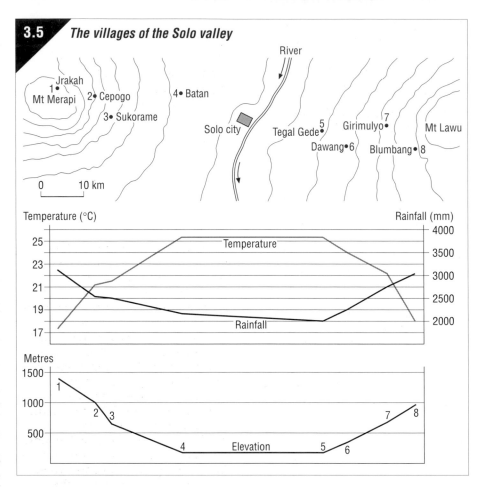

3.5 *The villages of the Solo valley*

River

Jrakah 1•
Mt Merapi
Cepogo 2•
4• Batan
Sukorame 3•
7
Girimulyo•
Solo city
Tegal Gede• 5
Mt Lawu
Dawang•6
Blumbang• 8

0   10 km

Temperature (°C)   Rainfall (mm)

Temperature

Rainfall

Metres

Elevation

The cropping system

The arable land of Tegal Gede is managed as an intensive two-crop system: periods of more or less continuous paddy rice alternate with two-year periods of sugar cane. The sugar cane production is a recent innovation imposed by government policy and has considerable impact upon the way the villagers manage their land. Since the mid-1970s, the Indonesian government has designated several 'programme' crops and assigned quotas to villages. In the Solo Valley the main programmed crop is sugar. A series of sugar factories have been built, each with its own catchment which requires around 2000 ha of sugar cane a year. In Tegal Gede, approximately 39% of the arable land is given over to sugar growing

Sugar cultivation is organised quite differently from the traditional cropping system. The paddy rice is grown in tiny plots which are carefully prepared with earthen banks and channels for the movement of water. These plot channels are fed from a small number of arterial channels which cross the arable land. In contrast, the sugar for the factory is grown in 15 ha blocks. This is not a commercial crop for the farmers to sell. They receive rent and additional payments dependent upon yield and the length of time the land stays under sugar. The farmers and their labourers actually grow the crop under the supervision of the factory managers. If all a farmer's land is taken for sugar then his family must

and Blumbang, high on the mountain slopes (8).

Tegal Gede village – a valley floor economy

The village
Tegal Gede village lies just above the main floodplain of the Solo river. The population of 4450 had risen to over 6500 by 1988, at an average annual growth rate of 3%, within fourteen years. Almost half of the population is younger than 20 years. This exerts great pressure on the land, which is already intensively and continuously cultivated. There is, therefore, little potential for farming to absorb these extra people, who must increasingly find work outside agriculture. Fortunately, the large towns of Karanganyar and Solo City are nearby and as bus services improve, more young people seek employment there. Some people do migrate to these and more distant towns.

As a result, by 1988, only 415 out of the total population were farmers, with a further 600 people working as farm labourers. Bear in mind that these figures are for individuals not households, so the actual numbers involved in agricultural families is much higher. At least 800 people of working age worked outside agriculture or were unemployed.

The land
The fertile soils are a mixture of volcanics and laterites. The land is mostly flat and suitable for the application of irrigation water. The farmed land totals 353 ha, of which 248 ha are in fields and 105 ha are house-garden plots. The domestic plots are used primarily for a variety of trees which yield fruits and nuts, and average 900 m² in size. The average farm size on which the family subsists, is less than one hectare. Thus the overall population density is 18 persons per hectare.

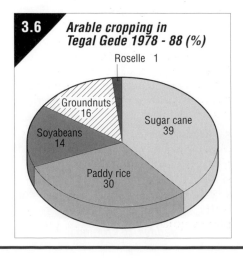

3.6 *Arable cropping in Tegal Gede 1978 - 88 (%)*

Roselle 1
Groundnuts 16
Soyabeans 14
Sugar cane 39
Paddy rice 30

Labour demands of a sugar crop at Tegal Gede	3.7
Task	**Work days (per ha)**
Clear paddy fields	2
Prepare the land	169
Plant	75
Cultivate, e.g. hoe, crop, care and weed	206
Apply fertiliser, e.g. manure, green compost, artificial	21
Irrigate	61
Maintain ditches	166
Harvest and load on to trucks	167
Total	967

[From: Prabowo & McConnell,1993]

buy other supplies for food. There are usually six 15 ha blocks in Tegal Gede, each under sugar for 24–28 months, during which time two crops are produced. Resource 3.7 shows that sugar is a labour-intensive crop. One benefit to the community is that the sugar harvesting, transport and processing do provide jobs.

Under the traditional system, rice is grown more or less continuously, with two crops a year. One crop is planted in November, early in the wet season and harvested in March, leaving enough water available for the second crop to be sown and harvested in September–October. During the 24–28 months land is taken for sugar, the farmer could have grown four rice crops instead. As rice is the main food crop and a commercial crop (75% is sold) many farmers are not happy with the arrangement, despite the rents and the wages from factory work. Furthermore, once the land is returned to the individual farmers, it has to be prepared once more for paddy rice.

Some farmers are aware of the need to maximise the output from their tiny plots. When sugar land is returned to them too late in the season to plant rice, not enough water remains on the fields, so they plant a quick-growing 'catch' crop.

This accounts for the soybean and groundnut production shown on Resource 3.6, which brings in cash income. The final element entering the cropping system in recent years is rosellc, whose fibre is used as a substitute for jute. Roselle is another programmed crop and the village is required to plant several hectares each year.

The shortage of land and the hot, humid climate mean that animals are not important in the farming economy except for work. Between 1974 and 1988, horses for pulling carts were replaced by trucks. Oxen have replaced buffalo for pulling ploughs, since they are easier to keep and have a wider range of uses. Even so, oxen declined from over 400 in 1974 to around 300 in 1988. As land becomes scarcer due to the sugar industry, feed for animals has been reduced. This accounts for the decline in goats from 900 to 300, as their main feed is crop residue.

1974–88: changes in Blumbang village – a mountain slope economy

The village

Blumbang is set across the upper slopes of Mount Lawu, at an altitude of 1600–1700 m. In 1974 the population was 2570, and by 1988 this had reached 3400, an average rise of just under 2%. The predominance of young people in the village means that the population is likely to continue to rise as they have yet to have their own families. Of the 1300 households in 1988, 700 were farming families, and a further 265 were families of landless farm labourers. This number of landless families had risen from 170 in 1974, a sign of land pressure. Blumbang is less accessible than Tegal Gede to larger towns. Fewer people travel to work each day, except to the nearby small resort town of Tawanggmanu. Yet, the extra population has been almost entirely absorbed by the village. There are few signs of permanent out-migration, although some young people do move to towns temporarily.

Land use in Blumbang (ha)		3.8
Type	**1974**	**1988**
Rain-fed crops	121	119
House-gardens	38	39
Government forest	925	925
Estate crops	–	18
Rice	25	–
Total	1109	1101

[From: Prabowo & McConnell, 1993]

The land

The fertile soils are derived from volcanic materials, but slopes, combined with relatively cool temperatures and high rainfall totals strongly influence agricultural practices. In the 1974 and 1988 surveys the village had approximately 120 ha of cropland, with a further 39 ha of house-gardens. The arable land is divided into tiny, intensively-cultivated farms, with the average plot size being only 0.18 ha. Despite the population growth, the cultivated area has not increased, mainly because the village is surrounded on three sides by government-owned montane rainforest, and on the fourth, by Tawanggmanu town. As with Tegal Gede, there is little potential for expansion.

The cropping system

The agricultural economy is based on an intensive, year-round, non-irrigated production of temperate climate vegetables. In the other seven villages of the survey, the house-gardens are used for fruit and nut-bearing trees, not cropping. Parts of the domestic plots are cultivated as extensions of the farmland proper only in Blumbang. This is due to pressure on the land and the attempts by farmers to maximise commercial crop areas. Resource 3.8 shows three significant changes between 1974 and 1988:

- the government had taken over 17.5 ha for estate crops, food crops which play no part in the village economy.
- the disappearance of upland rice plantations reflects a loss to

CASE STUDY 3.1 *People, productivity and profits*

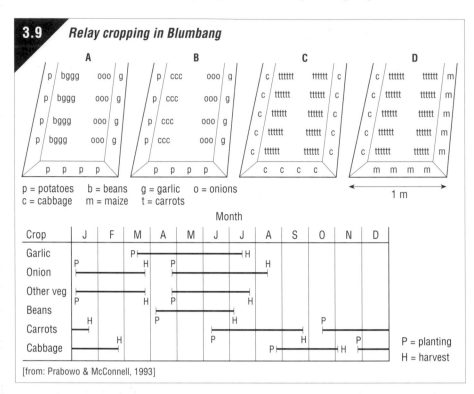

3.9 **Relay cropping in Blumbang**

| p = potatoes | b = beans | g = garlic | o = onions |
| c = cabbage | m = maize | t = carrots | |

← 1 m →

Crop	J	F	M	A	M	J	J	A	S	O	N	D
Garlic			P				H					
Onion	P		H	P			H					
Other veg	P		H	P			H					
Beans	H		P			H		P				
Carrots				P		H		P				
Cabbage		H		P			H	P	H	P		

P = planting
H = harvest

[from: Prabowo & McConnell, 1993]

3.10 **Cropping patterns in Blumbang**

Crop	1974	1988
Maize	37	–
Cabbage	134	30
Garlic	79	120
Onions	21	40
Sweet potato	16	–
Green beans	4	40
Carrots	–	70
Other vegetables	–	40
Total ha grown in relays on 120 ha	291	340
Trees in house gardens (number)		
Citrus	1050	3075
Coffee	–	940

[Source: Prabowo & McConnell, 1993]

estate crops and the shift from subsistence rice to commercial vegetables.

* although the forests are legally out-of-bounds, villagers unofficially collect forest litter and humus to spread as organic manure on their plots.

Vegetables are grown in tiny beds, raised to improve drainage and aeration. Intercropping of several types and relay planting to ensure continuous cropping, supported by heavy applications of manure, maximises the output. Resource 3.10 shows how cropping has changed. Note, that although the actual land remained at 120 ha, farmers managed the land more intensively. By improving their relay planting and changing the crop balance, they raised the use of 120 ha from 291 to 340 ha. An individual hectare would produce 3.4 crops during a 12 month period, instead of 2.91 crops. The surveys showed that the biggest problem the farmers face in further increasing the production is the small size of the farm holdings.

The changes in cropping balance are the result of internal and external forces. As standards of living have

3.11

A roadside market in Indonesia

risen in the towns of the region, eating habits have changed, although rice remains the staple food for all Javanese. For example, traditional staples such as sweet potato, maize and cabbage are less popular as more people can afford onions, garlic, carrot and citrus fruits. The Blumbang farmers have responded to market forces by modifying their cropping system. Furthermore, as their incomes have improved, the farmers themselves have raised their expectations and buy rice and other subsistence foods they once grew. The village has decided upon its own citrus expansion plan, with a target of 140 new trees planted each year for at least five years. Both citrus fruit and coffee raised good prices during the late 1980s. During this time, Girimulyo, the village downslope from Blumbang, was successful with planting and began to crop clove trees for market demand. The Blumbang farmers also tried this tree crop, but the temperatures at that altitude are too low.

The commercial vegetables are marketed in three ways.

- A buyer purchases the standing crop, harvests and transports it.
- The farmer harvests the crop and takes it, roughly bundled, to a roadside. There the crop is sold to a dealer and loaded on to a truck. Other than transporting the crop to the roadside, the farmer has no marketing costs.
- Members of the farmer's family may take small amounts of the produce to local markets and sell them directly, usually to a stallholder.

In all cases, the key decisions are in the control of the farmer, although dealers may influence the price obtained. Overall, farmers' incomes increased by 50% in real terms during the 1974–88 period, but the landless labourers only had an increase of up to 25%. Remember that the numbers of labourers' households increased.

Change in Tegal Gede (A) and Blumbang (B), 1974–88 — 3.12

Village	A Rice	A Sugar	B Sweet potato	B Cabbage	B Garlic/Onion	B Other veg	B Maize	A Soyabean/Groundnut	B Citrus fruit	B Beef cattle
Govt programme										
Import substitution	+	+	+		+					
Price support	+									
Programmed crop		+								
Consumer demand										
Population growth	+	+	+	+	+	+	+	+		+
Changing taste			–	–	+	+	–		+	+
Urbanisation					+	+				+
Better incomes			–	–	+				+	+
Better prices					+					+
Technology	+				+		+	+		+

1974–88: changes in the Solo Valley

The surveys showed that quality of life in all the eight villages had improved partly as a result of government investment and partly from village initiatives: more schools, more roads, more health care, improved transport and many families with more material goods in their homes. In 1974 the upland villages such as Blumbang had been much poorer than those such as Tegal Gede along the valley floor. By 1988, although the lower villages were still richer overall, the upland villages had narrowed the gap. This was due to the improved commercial agriculture. The commercial vegetables of Blumbang and the imposition of programmed sugar cultivation on the valley villages all helped. Resource 3.12 sums up the causes and effects of changes in the cropping systems of Tegal Gede (A) and Blumbang (B).

Researchers who conducted the surveys concluded that the twin threats to future improvements remain continued population growth and lack of potential for increased agricultural production.

They suggest a solution of population controls and the introduction of small industries to provide jobs and income from outside agriculture. Again, such changes can be successful by a combination of internal action by the villagers and external initiatives by the government.

[Source: Prabowa D. & McConnell D.J. 'Changes and development on Solo Valley farming systems, Indonesia', *FAO*, Rome, 1993]

Activities

1 How do the farmers of the Solo Valley ensure continuous year-round production from their land?

2 Compare the farming economies of Tegal Gede and Blumbang in 1988, and suggest reasons for the similarities and differences.

3 Outline the main changes which took place in the two villages. Distinguish between changes resulting from internal decision-making by the farmers and decisions made externally by government and people in towns.

4 To what extent can it be said that population growth has been the main cause of change in the rural economy of the Solo Valley?

CASE STUDY 3.2 *Making farming sustainable*

Introduction

An article published in 1992 stated that *agriculture in Australia is immature … With generally low soil fertility and poor soil structure, the country's agricultural lands suffer from extreme climatic events including prolonged drought and, at times, intense rainfall* (Epps & Crittenden, 1992). It has been acknowledged for some time that the land and stock management adopted by most Australian farmers have been based upon techniques learned in the moister and milder environments of Europe. These have proved inappropriate in the harsher and distinctive Australian environment, and has led to the claim that land degradation is now recognised as Australia's most serious environmental problem (Campbell, 1991). The issue has only recently begun to be taken seriously, probably because there always seemed more land to move on to in this vast country. There is now no more 'frontier', and economic conditions have been getting harsher. World prices for agricultural products have been falling and competition has been intensifying.

Although agricultural products accounted for a quarter of the total export value in 1992, compared with 80% in 1950, it is clear that agriculture will remain crucial to the country's balance of payments. This means that the government cannot afford to simply reduce the land under farming in order to let it rest and revive. Thus, agriculture must be made economically sustainable, that is profitable over time. This can only be achieved if the land is managed sustainably. *A sustainable farming system is one which is profitable and maintains the productive capacity of the land while minimising energy and resource use and optimising recycling of matter and nutrients* (Campbell, 1991). Farmers must perceive their land as a capital asset to be nurtured and not simply as an input to their crop and animal production.

All resource management strategies need to be based upon an evaluation of the current situation. Changes over time can be monitored and measured in relation to this base-line data. Such resource evaluation is a daunting and expensive task in a vast country such as Australia. However, modern technology using satellite imagery, computer storage of data and *ground proofing* (checking the image information by direct field-work at selected sample points), can add to a Geographical Information System (GIS) relatively quickly. Landholders can then be made aware of the nutrient status of their vegetation, and the fertility and salinity of their soils. As fresh data is fed from new satellite data into the GIS, the statistics can be updated and the effectiveness of management methods evaluated.

There are proposals for large scale GIS programmes but the current programmes are on a smaller scale, with low cost schemes in operation. This case study describes one such project in the State of Victoria 1984–90.

Assisted by government and private funding, it was planned and carried out by a group of farmers who saw their livelihoods threatened by the reduced productivity of their land. It is one small piece of a nationwide movement which has been co-ordinated by the Australian government. Called Landcare, this scheme began in 1989 and by 1993, involved over 1400 local groups. The government provides funding and technical support but the farmers make the decisions.

A sustainable farming project in Victoria, Australia

Context

Our perceptions of the Australian environment tend to be moulded by the images of advertisements and films – vast, flat expanses of red, dusty desert with a lone, bare tree or rock ridge on the horizon. Yet a large part of eastern and south-eastern Australia is moist enough to support woodland ecosystems, dominated by varieties of eucalyptus, except in Northern Queensland. Settlers pressing inland from Melbourne from the 1840s found such woodland as far north as the Murray River, across the majority of what has become the state of Victoria. Today, these woodlands have just about disappeared and we see rolling expanses of grassland devoted to the grazing of sheep and cattle. Only relict clumps and scattered trees survive, and while this clearance represents an enormous achievement in terms of effort and commitment, it also lies at the heart of many of the problems the farmers now face.

Key understandings

◆ The meaning of *sustainability* in farming terms, has to be understood.

◆ Traditional farming methods adopted in recently developed regions may not be environmentally sustainable

◆ Environmental degradation has become a serious problem across extensive areas of Australia's animal grazing country because excessive clearance of the natural woodland has led to salinisation and soil erosion.

◆ One method of achieving sustainable farm management in such environments is whole farm planning based upon natural land units and land classes, revegetation and the lowering of the water table.

3.13

The ridge in the background retains the eucalyptus woodland which once covered this part of Victoria

3.14

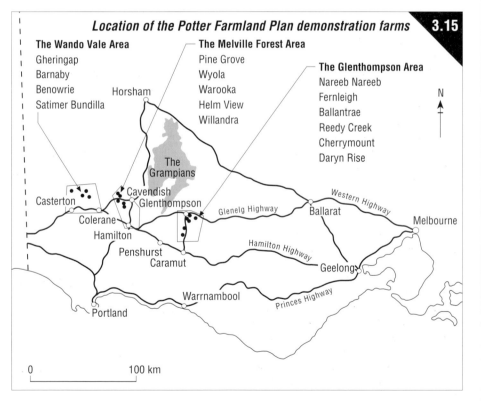

3.15

Location of the Potter Farmland Plan demonstration farms

The Wando Vale Area
Gheringap
Barnaby
Benowrie
Satimer Bundilla

The Melville Forest Area
Pine Grove
Wyola
Warooka
Helm View
Willandra

The Glenthompson Area
Nareeb Nareeb
Fernleigh
Ballantrae
Reedy Creek
Cherrymount
Daryn Rise

N

Horsham

The Grampians

Casterton
Cavendish
Glenthompson
Colerane
Hamilton
Penshurst
Caramut

Glenelg Highway
Western Highway
Ballarat
Melbourne
Hamilton Highway
Geelong

Warrnambool
Princes Highway
Portland

0   100 km

Deforested sheep-grazing farmland showing remnant woodland, Victoria

By the mid-1970s farmers and the Victoria government accepted that land degradation had become a serious problem. Three key indicators were identified:

• *reduced productivity of the pastures, i.e. fewer sheep per hectare could be fed;*
• *increasing signs of soil erosion – sheet erosion, wind blow and gullying;*
• *a decline in water quality, especially an increase in salinity in soil water and stream water, leading to a build-up of salts in the upper soil horizons.*

The symptoms have been identified, but the causes lie in the removal of too much woodland and the practice of land management methods inappropriate to Victoria's environment.

In 1977 the Victoria government set up the Garden State Committee, comprising officials and farmers. Its purpose was to encourage revegetation programmes and improve farm management expertise. By the mid-1980s, a number of *farm-tree groups* had been established across the state, and the committee adopted their idea of *demonstration farms*. Improved land management plans and revegetation schemes had been introduced on these farms, and then used as an example to other farmers.

The Potter Farms project was established in 1984 and involved 15 farms in west central Victoria. (The name 'Potter' is derived from the Potter Foundation, a philanthropic organisation which provided funding support for the project.) All the farmers volunteered to join the scheme and were the prime planners, assisted only by a small project team of experts and some outside funding. This was not a scheme imposed from above,

CASE STUDY 3.2 *Making farming sustainable*

but adopted voluntarily by the farming community.

This case study focuses upon four farms in the Wando Vale district. They lie on the dissected edge of the Dundas Tablelands at 300–400 m altitude and cover a mixture of flat tablelands, extensive slopes and valley floors with permanent streams. The soils are generally sandy loams overlying yellow clays across the slopes, with black clays common on the valley floors. The slopes, once cleared of trees, are prone to gully erosion. The natural vegetation is eucalyptus woodland with shrub understorey, and herb and grass ground cover. As Resource 3.16 shows, the farms range in size from 650 ha to 1880 ha. Their main enterprise is animal rearing, particularly sheep, with very little arable cropping.

Traditional farming methods

The four Wando valley farms had sound but traditional management practices, were typical of the region, showed distinct signs of land degradation and were high on their respective catchments. They were minimally affected by farms upstream from them.

The farms are also low technology enterprises. The climate is mild enough for the animals to remain outside all-year-round and to graze on the pastures. There is little need to grow and store supplementary fodder such as hay or silage, and the only buildings apart from the farmhouse may be the shearing shed and a shelter for vehicles. Farm machinery too, is limited. Paddocks are large and tend to have evolved as the land was originally cleared.

3.16	**The Wando Valley Farms**				
Name	Size (ha)	Rainfall (mm)	Labour units	Crops as % of total area	Economy
Barnaby	650	750	1.1	0	Sheep/cattle
Benowrie	972	710	1.75	1	Sheep/cattle
Gheringap	560	725	1.0	0	Sheep
Satimer	1880	800	4.0	3	Sheep

Wherever possible, each paddock has access to a stream or pond for animals to drink. Fencing and gates control the movement and grazing management of the animals. While the remaining trees are known to give animals some shelter, their survival has generally been haphazard. They grow on poor or difficult ground, and are especially large and difficult to remove. This simple, extensive form of farming has low labour demands despite the large size of the sheep 'mobs' on the four farms. They range from 1000 to 4000.

Identifying the problems

When the project team first visited the farms in 1984 and conducted an initial survey with the farmers, four key problems were quickly identified.

- The paddocks seemed to be poorly laid out in relation to the landscape and to stock movement and management requirements.
- Too few trees remained to provide effective shelter or ground protection, and these survivors showed signs of stress, with no evidence of any natural regeneration.
- There were increasing signs of erosion, especially along stream banks, by gullies extending headwards across lower slopes, and on overgrazed areas on the ridge tops and tablelands. This increased the sediment load in the streams.
- Soils, soil water and stream water were showing considerable increases in salinity as water tables rose. In a number of places, saline springs or 'sinks' appeared. The process of land degradation is summarised in Resource 3.20.

3.17

The Dundas Tablelands. These rolling uplands retain little of their Eucalyptus cover. The bare slopes are vulnerable to erosion, and high water tables are widespread across the lower slopes and valleys.

Barnaby farm. The left-hand section of the slope retains much of the original Eucalyptus woodland, and has been only lightly grazed. On the right-hand section, woodland has almost disappeared and the land has been heavily grazed. Gully erosion and saline 'sinks' can be seen in the centre.

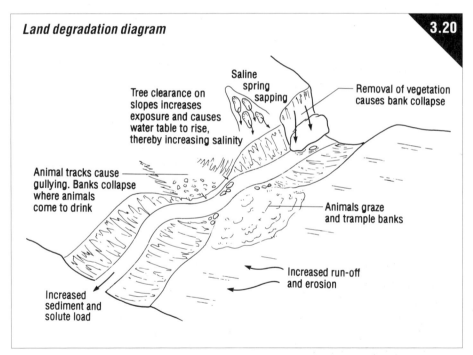

Land degradation diagram 3.20

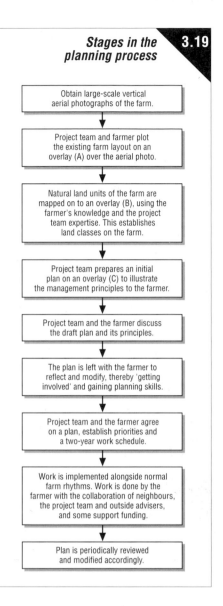

Stages in the planning process 3.19

Obtain large-scale vertical aerial photographs of the farm.

↓

Project team and farmer plot the existing farm layout on an overlay (A) over the aerial photo.

↓

Natural land units of the farm are mapped on to an overlay (B), using the farmer's knowledge and the project team expertise. This establishes land classes on the farm.

↓

Project team prepares an initial plan on an overlay (C) to illustrate the management principles to the farmer.

↓

Project team and the farmer discuss the draft plan and its principles.

↓

The plan is left with the farmer to reflect and modify, thereby 'getting involved' and gaining planning skills.

↓

Project team and the farmer agree on a plan, establish priorities and a two-year work schedule.

↓

Work is implemented alongside normal farm rhythms. Work is done by the farmer with the collaboration of neighbours, the project team and outside advisers, and some support funding.

↓

Plan is periodically reviewed and modified accordingly.

Attacking the problems: the planning process (Resource 3.19)

The fundamental principle throughout the project was *whole farm planning*, the consideration of the farm environment and the economic enterprise as an integrated whole. This process emphasised:

- the farmer's feeling that he owned and developed the plan as it emerged.

- low-tech, affordable-cost techniques, or appropriate technology.
- the farmer's existing knowledge.
- flexibility and adaptability.
- the need for sustainability.

The principal phases in this process are summarised in Resource 3.21.

The first crucial stage is the mapping of the natural land units of the farm. This establishment of *land classes* is

the foundation of the whole farm technique of farm planning and management. A land class is determined according to factors such as slope, aspect, soil type and water conditions. It is important when locating and drawing boundaries around these land classes, that the existing layout of the farm is ignored, since this exercise is about the *natural* components of the farm. The farmer's knowledge is the main basis of the map, rather than detailed and expensive survey techniques.

One of the most important realisations by both the project team and the farmer was that when overlay A (existing layout) was placed on

CASE STUDY 3.2 *Making farming sustainable*

overlay B (natural land units), there was a significant mismatch. It is not always easy to convince a farmer that his farm layout is inefficient. However, as the farmer had been involved in making the land class map, it became easier for him to adjust his paddock boundaries to fit the natural units. Once the farmer realises the logic of using natural units as the basis of his planning, it is possible to establish what is a sustainable pattern of use for this land unit should be.

A new farm layout can then be suggested (overlay C). The layout of the paddock boundaries in the new plan is determined by obtaining a balance between natural land units, size appropriate for the enterprise, and the management style of the farmer. The results of this appraisal can be seen on Resource 3.21. An important feature of using land class units as the basis for paddock size and boundaries, is that it produces a larger number of smaller paddocks. The project team believed that *in order to reduce land degradation and achieve sustainable production in extensively grazed areas, it is essential to move away from the traditional grazing methods towards flexible grazing systems based on smaller management units which reflect land types and which eliminate grazing pressure from those portions of the landscape where grazing is inappropriate* (Campbell, 1991). On the Willandra farm (Resource 3.21) the effects are evident in the increased number of paddocks.

Once an individual paddock falls mainly within one land class, determined by soil type, slope and drainage, it is easier to manage its grazing level. For example, where an old, large paddock included different land classes, the animals would concentrate in the parts with the best vegetation or, in the hot weather, beneath trees or on ridgetops where there is more breeze. This preferential use created patches of overgrazing and increased the likelihood of erosion.

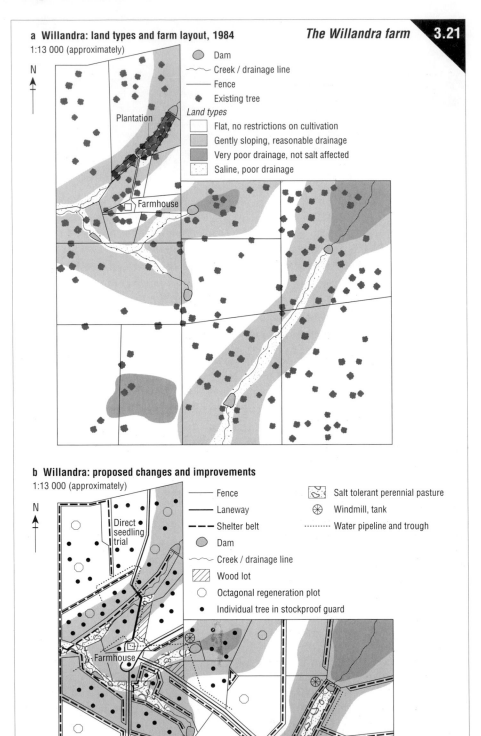

a Willandra: land types and farm layout, 1984
1:13 000 (approximately)

The Willandra farm   **3.21**

- ⬤ Dam
- ∿ Creek / drainage line
- — Fence
- ◆ Existing tree

Land types
- ▢ Flat, no restrictions on cultivation
- ▨ Gently sloping, reasonable drainage
- ▨ Very poor drainage, not salt affected
- ▨ Saline, poor drainage

Plantation

Farmhouse

b Willandra: proposed changes and improvements
1:13 000 (approximately)

- — Fence
- — Laneway
- – – Shelter belt
- ⬤ Dam
- ∿ Creek / drainage line
- ▨ Wood lot
- ○ Octagonal regeneration plot
- ● Individual tree in stockproof guard
- ⬡ Salt tolerant perennial pasture
- ✳ Windmill, tank
- ⋯ Water pipeline and trough

Direct seedling trial

Farmhouse

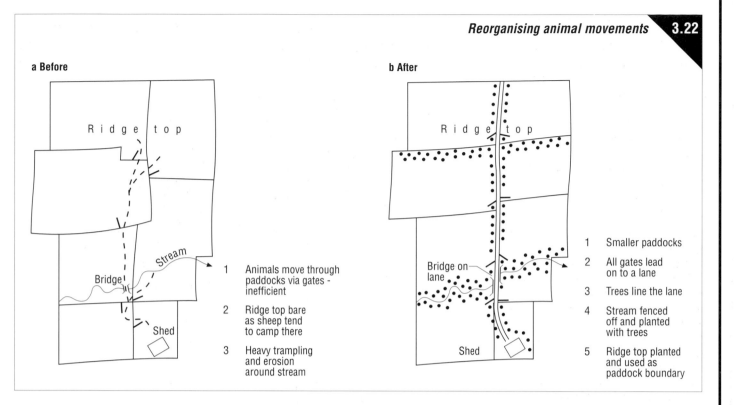

a Before

R i d g e t o p

Stream

Bridge

Shed

1 Animals move through paddocks via gates - inefficient

2 Ridge top bare as sheep tend to camp there

3 Heavy trampling and erosion around stream

b After

R i d g e t o p

Bridge on lane

Shed

1 Smaller paddocks

2 All gates lead on to a lane

3 Trees line the lane

4 Stream fenced off and planted with trees

5 Ridge top planted and used as paddock boundary

Equally important is the movement of animals around the farm: from paddock to paddock and to and from the shearing shed. This creates erosion damage at paddock gates and stream crossings as well as confusion when a group from one paddock has to move through another paddock containing stock. The answer of the project has been to create a system of lanes. The advantages of this system are illustrated on Resource 3.22.

Another major feature of the project plans has been *salinity control*. As this is closely connected with the programme of revegetation, we need to clarify the role of trees in the working of the natural ecosystem. Trees, with their deep rooting systems and considerable thirst for moisture, take up infiltrating water before it reaches the groundwater store. This keeps the water table below the root and soil level. When an area is stripped of its trees, a higher proportion of the rainfall percolates to the groundwater store, and the water table rises. As it rises it brings with it dissolved salts from marine sedimentary rocks underlying the regolith, and the salts

present in the rainwater, into the soil profile and within reach of the plant roots. Once within two metres of the surface, capillary action draws the saline water to the surface, where evaporation leaves a 'skin' of salts. As soil and soil water salinity build up, only salt-tolerant plant species which are of less use as animal fodder, can thrive. Soil structure deteriorates,

clay bands develop and waterlogging becomes a problem. Any remaining trees suffer stress and may die. This process of degradation is summarised in Resource 3.23.

The primary aim of the revegetation strategy is to lower the water table by increasing plant water use. Wherever possible, indigenous species are planted and local seeds are used.

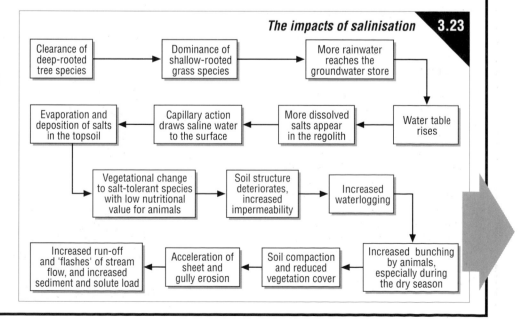

Clearance of deep-rooted tree species → Dominance of shallow-rooted grass species → More rainwater reaches the groundwater store

Evaporation and deposition of salts in the topsoil ← Capillary action draws saline water to the surface ← More dissolved salts appear in the regolith ← Water table rises

Vegetational change to salt-tolerant species with low nutritional value for animals → Soil structure deteriorates, increased impermeability → Increased waterlogging

Increased run-off and 'flashes' of stream flow, and increased sediment and solute load ← Acceleration of sheet and gully erosion ← Soil compaction and reduced vegetation cover ← Increased bunching by animals, especially during the dry season

CASE STUDY 3.2 *Making farming sustainable*

A report on the project states clearly:

Dry-land [i.e. non-irrigated] salinity control ... must attempt to maximise plant water use over the entire landscape, using every drop of rain where it falls, or ensuring that it runs off the farm safely, rather than soaking into the water table (Campbell, 1991).

To achieve this, a farm plan should:

- develop vigorous perennial (permanent) pastures.
- ensure an even distribution of water to those pastures.
- encourage safe run-off of any water not used by plants and animals.
- provide appropriately located areas of deeper rooted trees and shrubs.

The tree planting programme of the Willandra farm has been of most value to the farm in terms of water table and salinity control, shade and shelter, wildlife habitat, fire protection, erosion control, landscape improvement and timber production. An examination of the Willandra plan and of the other three Wando Vale farms, indicates six types of location and purpose for the trees. (Fire control is a factor in all locations and is not mentioned separately.)

Management inputs on Barnaby farm. The rectangular area on the right has suffered gully erosion and surface salinity. It has now been fenced off to allow woody vegetation to grow. This will check the erosion and reduce the salinity by lowering the water table. On the left, a newly-planted strip of trees runs upslope. As they mature, these trees will lower the water table and provide animal shelter.

1 Ridgetops – to absorb as much rainwater as soon as it arrives, i.e. to remove water in the recharge area of a catchment; to reduce overgrazing and soil erosion; to provide shelter; to improve animal management.

2 Along paddock and lane boundaries – to provide shelter; accessible locations for felling of wood for use or sale; to protect fencing; to control water levels; to provide wildlife corridors.

3 Around saline springs and gullies, to control water levels and erosion; to protect from animal trampling.

4 Along and above stream banks, to control erosion and bank collapse; to lower the water table; to filter out some of the salts in the soil water, so improving the stream water quality; to prevent animals from trampling the lower slopes and banks, thereby causing erosion damage; for wildlife habitat.

5 In clumps of various shapes within paddocks, to provide shelter (shape and location determined by wind and storm direction); landscape improvement; timber production.

6 Around the farmhouse, for shelter; for landscape improvement; for fuelwood production.

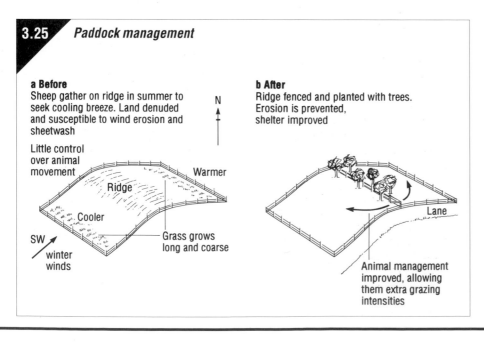

3.25 *Paddock management*

a Before
Sheep gather on ridge in summer to seek cooling breeze. Land denuded and susceptible to wind erosion and sheetwash

Little control over animal movement

Ridge
Warmer
Cooler
Grass grows long and coarse
SW winter winds
N

b After
Ridge fenced and planted with trees. Erosion is prevented, shelter improved

Lane
Animal management improved, allowing them extra grazing intensities

Changing awareness of the problem: farmers' responses `3.26`

1980

Global degradation is widespread, but my farm is not too bad.

The Western District Red Gum belt is beautiful.

The Australian farmer is the most efficient in the world.

I will need to squeeze as much as possible from my farm to survive the tough times ahead.

Destruction of the Brazilian rainforest must stop.

I wonder if all the effort required to produce wool and beef each year is worthwhile.
I won't have anything lasting to leave my kids.

The woodchip industry is damaging our forests.

I know where I can plant some trees if I can get some time after drenching, shearing, ploughing …

With some government grants, I could fence out a couple of gullies and plant some trees.

Massive government assistance for on-ground works to halt land degradation is essential.

Planting trees on my farm is a big job. Fencing is time-consuming and costly. Planting with a spade is hard work, then I have to water them in. Often, survival rates are disappointing.

'Greenies' are radical irritants and a threat to good farmers.

1989

Global degradation is widespread and life threatening. My farm is seriously degraded as part of the global problem.

Yes, but it has been radically changed by agriculture and is seriously ill as a result:

- an aged monoculture with no chance of natural regeneration.
- increasingly saline and waterlogged soils.
- devastation of native wildlife due to removal of habitat.
- soils increasingly acidic, compacted and eroded by water, wind and stock movement.

There is a huge margin between the average Australian farmers. Most farmers have plenty of room to improve production and viability.

I must return my farm to good health, so that it can sustain production into the future and allow us both to survive.

Yes, but with our assistance, as the western world owes the Brazilians a land debt and an alternative lifestyle.

Implementing my farm plan is the most important and rewarding project I will ever be involved with. My kids and future generations will receive lasting benefits from my efforts.

The clearing of open woodlands for farming has been far more ecologically devastating than the forest harvest.

I have prepared a whole farm plan. I know when and how to implement the plan which receives *top priority*.

I don't need any outside help to implement my farm plan over time.

No! Most government assistance should be directed towards education and awareness campaigns on land degradation problems and how to cure them. Minimal assistance and incentive schemes for on-ground works would be helpful in targeted areas of real need.

Planting trees on my farm is a breeze now. Electric fencing is effective, fast and cheap. The Hamilton Tree Planter makes planting faster, easier. Deep ripping and good weed control has eliminated watering. Direct seeding has great potential.

I am a greenie.

Conclusion

Although stocking levels may change over time, this has not been the prime concern of the Potter Farms Project. Improved stock management via more efficient layout has been important, but this arises from the environmental benefits of using natural land units and single land classes as the basis of paddock design. The second focus has been to reverse environmental degradation, especially salinisation and erosion, by lowering water tables to their natural levels through planned and managed revegetation with indigenous tree species. Equally significant in the achievement of long-term sustainability, has been the enhanced awareness and shift of attitudes by the farmers. The questionnaire response examples set out in Resource 3.26 illustrate some of these shifts.

[Based on Epps W.R. & Crittenden R. 'Appraisal of land degradation in Australia', *Land Use Policy*, 9(3), July 1992, 199–208, and Campbell A. *Planning for sustainable farming: the Potter Farmland Plan Story*, Lothian Press, 1991]

Activities

1 Define what is meant by *sustainability* in farming terms and give examples of how and why it was not being achieved on the Wando Vale farms.

2 List the signs of environmental degradation and suggest reasons for their occurrence.

3 What is meant by a *natural land unit* and what factors are taken into account in identifying it in the field?

4 What is meant by *whole farm planning*?

5 Using Resource 3.22 a and b describe and explain the process of whole farm planning and its aims.

6 What has been the primary cause of salinisation of the soils and soil water in this region of Victoria, and what methods are suggested for its reduction?

CASE STUDY 3.3 *Changes down on the farm*

Background

Since the mid-1980s, the combination of overproduction, environmental concerns, changes in EU agricultural support policies and the squeeze on profit margins have put increasing pressures on European farmers. It has become harder for them to make a reasonable living. After 40 years, when intensification and production levels were the driving forces, we are now entering what has been called *a post-productionist era* (Kelly et al, 1992).

If farmers are to stay in business in these changed conditions, they need to cut costs, improve efficiency and find alternative sources of income. Alternative sources of income includes *farm diversification*, and farms vary in their potential for such adjustments. Farm diversification may be defined as *a diversion of resources (land, labour and capital) previously committed to conventional farming activities into non-traditional enterprises on the farm* (Kelly et al, 1992, after Ilbery, 1988a). Diversification takes two forms:

- *Agricultural* diversification, where the farmer introduces new methods and products, e.g. organic farming, deer rearing, aquaculture and woodland.
- *Structural* diversification where the farmer introduces activities beyond crop and animal production, e.g. farm-based tourism, processing and/or direct marketing of food, leasing of land and buildings for non-agricultural uses.

This case study looks at how and why farmers of one area of Ireland, County Wicklow, are adjusting to the changed economic and environmental situation. Adjustment has not been easy, as Irish farmers have enjoyed high levels of subsidy and support, and many are conservative by nature. As you study the materials, note the balance between agricultural and structural diversification. Note too, the way in which geographical character and location influence the potential for diversification.

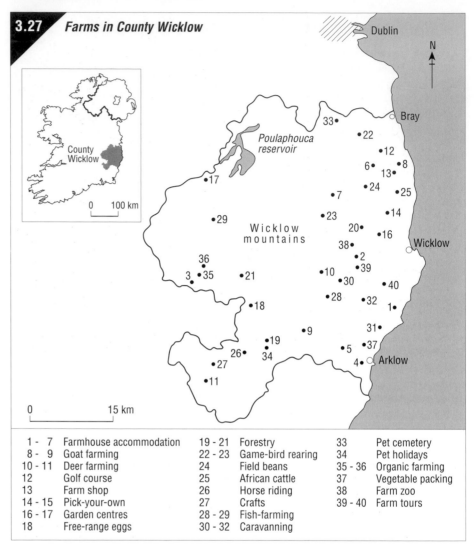

3.27 *Farms in County Wicklow*

1 - 7	Farmhouse accommodation	19 - 21	Forestry	33	Pet cemetery
8 - 9	Goat farming	22 - 23	Game-bird rearing	34	Pet holidays
10 - 11	Deer farming	24	Field beans	35 - 36	Organic farming
12	Golf course	25	African cattle	37	Vegetable packing
13	Farm shop	26	Horse riding	38	Farm zoo
14 - 15	Pick-your-own	27	Crafts	39 - 40	Farm tours
16 - 17	Garden centres	28 - 29	Fish-farming		
18	Free-range eggs	30 - 32	Caravanning		

Key understandings

◆ Diversification means the addition of enterprises to a farm economy and may take two forms – agricultural and structural.

◆ Farmers diversify their enterprises for a variety of reasons.

◆ Some farms have greater opportunity for diversification than others.

◆ Government policy is encouraging diversification to sustain incomes and jobs.

Farm diversification in County Wicklow, Ireland

Setting

County Wicklow is situated along the east coast of Ireland, immediately south of the capital city, Dublin. It is rolling country, with varied landscape and medium to large farms. The beauty of the landscape, the coastal situation and the proximity to Dublin (large population and main entry point for tourists) give the county a considerable potential for diversification.

Types of diversification

In the summer of 1990 it was estimated that there were 67 bona-fide farmers in County Wicklow who had introduced a type of diversification

3.28

Typical farm diversification in Donegal

provision, to *working on the farm*, where visitors experience farm life by helping out with the animals and the crops.

Apart from accommodation, a variety of activities have been introduced: caravan parks, horseriding, farm tours, a small zoo and a craft centre. The investment in and return from tourism is a supplementary rather than a primary element in a farm economy, generally providing less than 25% of income.

Seven farms had introduced direct marketing and processing, thereby adding value to conventional farm products. This category is dominated by PYO schemes, farm shops and garden centres. Although classified as structural diversification, this is an extension of the main farm business.

Agricultural diversification meant mainly the introduction of unconventional animals, or methods. Deer, goats, African cattle and fish were introduced and were increasingly popular. Organic farming too, was gaining in popularity, reflecting a trend of the late 1980s to healthier diets. The marketability of organically grown foods has, subsequently, increased.

The 1990 survey showed that over one-half of all the diversification

enterprise. Of these, 40 were interviewed, and the results are summarised in Resource 3.29.

The two key findings are that a wide range of activities had been introduced, and that there is a predominance of structural rather than agricultural diversification. The location of the sample farms and the type of diversification are summarised on

Resource 3.27. Most of them lie within 15 km of the coast and are accessible to the main north-south route through the county.

Half of the farms had become involved in tourism, a reflection of the rapidly growing popularity of farm-based tourism. This can range from bed-and-breakfast accommodation, through caravan and camping

Character of diversification (Number of farms) — 3.29

a Structural diversification

1 Farm-based tourism		20
– accommodation	10	
– recreation	10	
2 Adding value		7
– direct marketing	6	
– processing	1	

b Agricultural diversification

1 Unconventional enterprises		10
– animal products	7	
– crop products	3	
2 Farm woodland		3
Total farms		40

Symbols
The symbols used are a positive indication of the facilities provided by each farmhouse. If you require any additional information please ask when you make your booking.

- Central Heating
- Babysitting by arrangement
- Cot available
- Childrens play area
- Tennis on premises
- Horse-riding nearby
- Pony trekking nearby
- Angling nearby
- Boats for hire
- Golfing nearby
- Working farm
- Wine licence
- Facilities for disabled
- TV in bedrooms

One of the farms involved in tourism **3.30**

An olde worlde residence in spacious gardens on a family run dairy farm just 3m from Arklow and 60 minutes from Rosslare or Dun Laoghaire. Home cooking, log fires - you may bring your own wine! 6 bedrooms with h/c (4 en-suite, 1 family).

Open 1 March to 1 November.

CASE STUDY 3.3 *Changes down on the farm*

3.31 *Aspects of diversification*

a Tourism

'Located to the south of the county, near the sea, this quite large dairy farm has been offering tourist accommodation for ten years. The enterprise is run mostly by the farm wife for between six and nine months of the year, but only a small proportion of total income (less than 10%) is derived from it. Income benefits and the availability of resources (e.g. large farmhouse) were the main reasons for initiating the venture; high levels of satisfaction were expressed and expansion is being considered.'

b Marketing

'Established a farm shop just over five years ago [1985], in order to avoid expensive middle-men, to raise income and to retail horticultural products grown on the farm. Although a large potential market for fresh fruit and vegetables exists in Wicklow, the farmer feels he is being undercut by intensive competition from foreign producers. Consequently he expects the enterprise to decline in the future.'

c Agricultural innovation – goat farming

'Established ten years ago [1980] … the enterprise is now commercially successful and expansion is planned. The farmer is involved with the production of goat's milk for up to nine months of the year and sells it to selected shops. The farmer received information about the enterprise from the Irish Goat Producers Association.'

d Agricultural change – organic farming

'Introduced organic farming in response to diminishing prospects in traditional agriculture and the possibility of exploiting untapped markets. Income benefits were, however, not a major reason for establishing the enterprise … The initial aims have been achieved and the farmer is very satisifed with the enterprise.'

[Source: Kelly et al, 1992]

3.32

Grazing cattle, green fields and wheat fields in Ireland

projects had occurred since 1985 and that fewer than one in three of the sample farms gained more than half of their income from such innovations. The majority were 'mixed' or livestock (not dairy) farms and tended to be either above average in size (over 28 ha) or small (less than four hectares). The small farms were part-time occupations and the diversification merely meant an addition to an already varied livelihood.

On the 40 farms, some 90 people were employed in the diversification activities: 23 full-time and 67 part-time. All but 15 people were family members and only three full-time jobs had been created for non-family employees. On most farms, all the family members were involved in some way. For example, the mother would run the tourist accommodation while children assisted during the holidays.

Some farm diversification surveys have found that many 'diversifiers' are people who are new to farming. In County Wicklow, however, 28 out of 40 people in the sample had significant farming backgrounds. In contrast, only one-quarter had business experience outside farming, and this lack of expertise was identified as a significant problem. As might be expected however, the diversifiers were relatively young, with 60% under the age of 40 years. Such groups tend to have higher education attainments and are usually less conservative in attitude.

The respondents were asked their reasons for diversifiying. The ranking list of their replies is given in Resource 3.33. As expected, potential income benefit is the most significant, despite the fact that for the majority, the diversification activity was not intended as the primary source of income. The survey concludes *that the introduction of alternative enterprises will not solve most farmers' income problems; however, they can help to supplement farm income and thus sustain the viability of the farm business.* (Kelly et al, 1992). Notice too, that *personal interest* is ranked second.

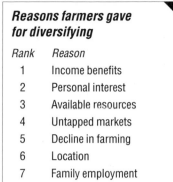

Reasons farmers gave for diversifying

3.33

Rank	Reason
1	Income benefits
2	Personal interest
3	Available resources
4	Untapped markets
5	Decline in farming
6	Location
7	Family employment

The survey further concludes that *rarely, therefore, is financial motivation sufficient in itself; unless real interest is involved, maximum commitment and effort are unlikely to be applied to the venture.* (Kelly et al, 1992). Personal interest ranked particularly highly for specific and specialised activities such as crafts, goats and organic farming, while women expressed considerable interest in farmhouse tourism. In contrast, employment opportunities are not an important factor, nor is the location of the farm. A number of farmers commented that they were not really aware of what resources they had until they seriously considered diversification, often through seeking advice.

When asked what had been the main problems associated with diversification, the top-ranking three were:

1 access to reliable information.
2 availability of resources, especially capital.
3 the difficulty of assessing market trends.

The perceived need and willingness to seek information and advice is an important understanding for the providing agencies such as the Tourist Board, and the agricultural and forestry advisory services. In particular, farmers felt that they needed to go from one agency to another and often received conflicting information. The survey comments: *The lack of a co-ordinated and centralised framework for the provision of advice to farmers thinking of diversifying is, therefore, a real problem* (Kelly et al, 1992).

Although employment opportunities did not rank highly in terms of reasons for diversifying, the deployment of labour did appear as a problem. The key dilemma was how to accommodate the labour demands of the new activity within the regime of the primary farm activities. In tourism, for example, the main demands are during the summer, a time of maximum demands on the farm. Raising the additional capital was, unsurprisingly, perceived as a problem: about one-half of the sample felt that banks and other institutions were less than enthusiastic about the proposed initiative. Getting loans was difficult. Nonetheless, over one-half of the sample felt 'very satisfied' with their alternative enterprise.

[Source: Kelly C.E., Ibery B.W. & Gillmor D.A., 'Farm diversification in Ireland: evidence from County Wicklow', *Irish Geography* 25(1), 1992, 23–32]

Activity

1 Define what is meant by *diversification* in terms of its two main categories.

2 Using materials in the case study, illustrate the ways in which diversification is working on farms.

3 Explain why farmers should be considering diversification and which reasons are important in their decision-making.

4 What are the significant problems and potential solutions regarding farm diversification?

5 Suggest reasons why the women in farming families expressed particular interest in farmhouse tourism?

CASE STUDY 3.4 — *Alternatives for UK farmland: is golf the answer?*

Background

The UK countryside is currently undergoing a fundamental change, perhaps a change as great as that created by the Agricultural Revolution of 200 years ago. Between 1990 and the year 2000, at least 20% of agricultural land may be taken out of production. Some will lie temporarily unused. Through the government and EU Set-Aside scheme, farmers with more than 40 acres of arable land are required to take 15% out of production in any given year, and are given compensation (£85 per acre in 1993). More areas will be assigned to non-agricultural use. One such alternative use will be for conservation values, in many cases combined with amenity uses, for example, the National and Community Forests programmes and the conservation and reinstatement of wetlands. It seems probable, however, that the largest shift will be to a broad diversity of recreational and sporting uses, often associated with secondary conservation objectives. These include holiday villages, fishing lakes, theme parks, private riding and shooting parks, and perhaps most extensively, golf courses.

Golf has become a 'boom' sport across Europe during the last decade, with the UK enjoying a relatively high level of participation. The game has an affluent, fashionable image, and courses are an attractive component of up-market resorts and executive residential developments. For some countries, including the UK, this is the second golf boom, as Resource 3.35 shows. The first boom occurred between 1900 and 1930, by which year a significant proportion of UK courses had been built. For the

3.34 — Golf provision, 1991

Country	Courses (no.)	Pop(mill)	Holes (/100 000)	Courses planned or being built
England	974	47.5	44	200
Wales	118	2.8	63	6
Scotland	425	5.0	133	72
Ireland	261	4.5	80	33
% of European total	56			
France	360	50.0	12	188
Spain	94	36.9	4	13
Sweden	207	8.5	38	220

[From: *Chartered Surveyor*, 23.5.91]

3.35 — When golf clubs were founded (%)

	Pre-1930	1930–49	1950–69	1970–79	1980–89
England	55	10	7	18	10
Wales	78	6	4	9	5
Scotland	83	5	6	4	2
Ireland	64	14	7	10	5
France	26	6	22	16	30
Spain	12	5	29	39	15
Sweden	7	17	44	23	10

[Source: *Chartered Surveyor*, 23.5.91]

3.36 — *Boundary decision for New National Forest*

Plans for a New National Forest in the Midlands took a step nearer to reality when the Commission announced the forest's boundary.

The decision ended months of speculation, following the appointment of a development team whose task has been to whittle down a 450 square mile area of search to 194 square miles now put forward.

The chosen area – 44 square miles larger than originally envisaged – is within the counties of Leicestershire, Derbyshire and Staffordshire. It includes the sites of the ancient Needwood and Charnwood forests and the towns of Burton upon Trent, Swadlincote, Ashby-de-la-Zouch and Coalville.

... Sir John Johnson, Chairman of the Commission, said:

'We shall be creating the forest from the core of two ancient woodlands, an idea which has now gained widespread public support. Within an area of predominantly rural land, approximately 50 per cent of the forest will be planted with trees – most of them broadleaved species. The rest will be a mosaic of farms, towns and villages.

'We are on the threshold of creating a magnificent national asset, a new landscape reshaped by farming and forestry and enhanced by trees for work, recreation and wildlife.'

[*Countryside* January/February 1992]

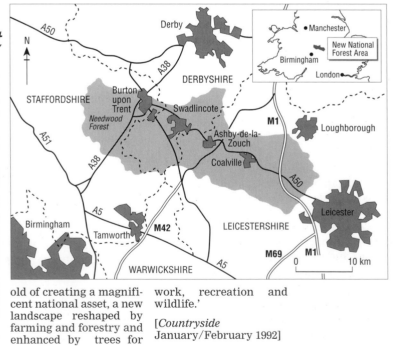

UK, note particularly the very low growth rates 1950–70. This was the result of the restrictive planning policies which gave agriculture high priority in the countryside. Land-owners and potential developers showed little interest as they knew that it was unlikely that they would be given change-of-use permission for golf courses.

This case study outlines what has happened since the mid-1980s and raises key economic, social and envi-ronmental issues about the explo-sion of golf provision. Economic issues focus around whether the huge investments involved will all yield satisfactory returns. Social issues concern inequality of opportunity due to an over-emphasis upon high price, members-only developments, and the effects upon local communi-ties. Environmental issues arise from the voracious space consumption of golf. A full golf facility takes up at least 50 hectares (the area of a medium-sized farm). The course has a strong environmental impact upon the countryside and needs to con-sider the ethical issue of its exclusiv-ity – excluding other uses and users from precious countryside resources.

The golf boom and its implications for countryside management

Energising the boom

A combination of factors in the mid-1980s allowed and encouraged the golf boom to accelerate. As govern-ment and EU support of agriculture declined, so planning restrictions were relaxed to allow farmers to diversify beyond agriculture. This coincided with surveys which showed a shortage of courses. A 1986 report claimed that if all coun-ties in the UK were to achieve an average of one course per 25 000 population, then 341 new courses would be needed (cf. Scotland, 1:12 000; Australia, 1:10 000; eastern USA, 1:20 000). In 1989 another report, this time by golf's ruling body, showed that almost all clubs had long waiting lists, sometimes up to 10 years, and that to match supply with demand, 700 additional courses should be built by the year 2000. At this time, too, golf was achieving a higher profile through increasing television coverage. Landowners and developers could see the clear potential for profitable investments, especially with the increased likeli-hood of obtaining planning permis-sion and with the readiness of the

banks to lend money. All the ingredi-ents for a boom were in place.

Between 1987 and 1990 there was an explosion of planning proposals for 18-hole courses to be run as members-only clubs, especially in prosperous regions. For example, during 1989 alone, 25 courses were approved in Essex and Surrey. The capital investment and the land take-up required for these high-quality facilities are considerable. A full 18-hole course and facilities uses 50 to 80 hectares, and buying the land could cost £500 000. At 1991 prices, to design and build the course will cost between £700 000 and £1 350 000 (£40–75 000 per hole). It is not surprising, therefore, that a golf course with incorporated hotel costs around £13 million.

To obtain sufficient profits from such huge investments a developer or landowner must charge high fees and locate where the course will be fully used. The basis for such a calcu-lation is the *physical* or *design capacity* of the course: an 18-hole course can accommodate about 150 rounds a day, or 50 000 rounds a year. As research has shown that golfers prefer not to have a journey time longer than 30 minutes each way, the supply must be available within 15 km of the demand.

Key understandings

◆ The UK countryside is undergoing an accelerating phase of change.

◆ The demand for golf greatly exceeds the supply of opportunities and facilities.

◆ Golf is a space-consuming and expensive but economically rewarding alternative for countryside resource management.

◆ Golf course developments by the private commercial sector have boomed since the late 1980s.

◆ There is a trend away from high cost, members-only facilities towards more modest, pay-as-you-play courses.

◆ There is increasing concern over the environmental impacts of golf developments.

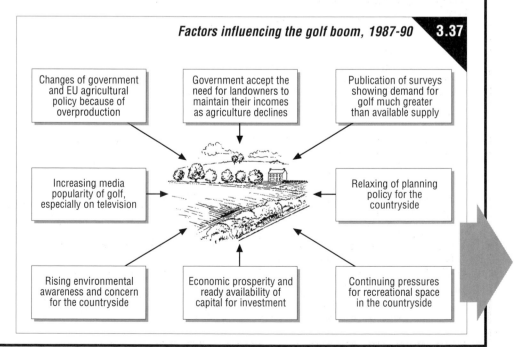

Factors influencing the golf boom, 1987-90 · 3.37

- Changes of government and EU agricultural policy because of overproduction
- Government accept the need for landowners to maintain their incomes as agriculture declines
- Publication of surveys showing demand for golf much greater than available supply
- Increasing media popularity of golf, especially on television
- Relaxing of planning policy for the countryside
- Rising environmental awareness and concern for the countryside
- Economic prosperity and ready availability of capital for investment
- Continuing pressures for recreational space in the countryside

Location accessible to large urban populations is crucial to commercial success. Such sites tend to lie within Green Belts or other land under heavy development pressures for housing, roads, industry and open space. Where planning permission is likely, this land will fetch high prices. For example, between 1972 and 1992, 38 new golf courses were built or planned within 15 km of the M25.

Since 1991 – time for a rethink

The golf course boom took those concerned with the countryside by surprise. Rural communities were increasingly alarmed by the environmental impacts, although local businesses frequently benefitted. At first, planning authorities had little experience and inadequate guidelines from central government. As a result, some poor schemes were given permission. By 1991, a number of county and district councils were developing their own management criteria by which they could make planning decisions. Concern focused too, upon conservation issues, particularly the take-over of fine country houses and parklands, the loss of farm and woodland, and the 'over-manicured', unnatural landscaping of many courses. Conservationists could see that golf courses had the potential to enhance rather than degrade the landscape and put pressure upon planners to insist on designs which provide for semi-natural vegetation, ponds and wildlife habitats. In 1992, the Countryside Commission, responsible for management of the countryside, issued its *Fairway Code* of good practice.

Although there were still 48 planning applications in Surrey and 35 in Kent by 1991, far fewer developments were going ahead. Developers were finding that money was less easy to obtain and not all new clubs were achieving their membership targets, despite continuing waiting lists at older clubs. As planners began to firm up their policies, so planning requirements were becoming stricter. Many councils were insisting upon an environmental

3.38

Golf courses get cool welcome in the country

From the back of his Victorian cottage on the common, Michael Turner surveys hedgerows planted in the time of George III.

The delights of Ellen Mede, the 120-acre cattle-breeding farm ... are unlikely to survive Mr Turner, however. Two 18-hole golf courses, which have a field separating them, are expected to toll the knell of the ancient pastures Mr Turner overlooks as golf becomes the profitable crop of the late twentieth century. Within a four-mile radius of his home at Totteridge, where London and Hertfordshire meet, there are already eight courses.

Mr Turner, aged 66, said: 'I am not against golf. But why do we need yet two more courses in a conservation area? The green belt is not intended just for the use of members of a private golf club. I feel very strongly that the natural beauty of this unspoiled countryside should be preserved and not turned into manmade parkland. There are a lot of keen walkers who love the footpaths.'

Mr Turner's concern about the proliferation of courses is reflected across Britain in the wake of the report two years ago by the Royal and Ancient golf club at St Andrews, the sport's ruling body, calling for 700 new courses by the year 2000. The demands of 1.2 million golfers for more facilities have led so far to planning applications by business consortia for more than twice that number. They would cover an area roughly the size of of the Isle of Wight.

In the south-east, where ten-year waiting lists for club membership are common, 380 applications have been made since 1989.

... The Council for the Protection of Rural England (CPRE) ... believes the granting of planning permission for a change of use from agricultural to leisure purposes can bring about the insinuation of ancillary development as conference centres, hotels and expensive housing.

Neil Sinden, CPRE national planning officer, said: 'Government guidelines are inadequate and this means the environment is being destroyed. On the fringes of urban areas landscapes can be improved by golf courses. But in sensitive areas landscape can be suburbanised.

'It is easy to get permission for change of use from agriculture to golf because that doesn't entail irreversible loss of land. But what happens is that the new golf course doesn't enjoy the same degree of protection. In this way the protection of agricultural land is watered down.' The CPRE says the planning system has been further subverted by the set-aside policy which encourages farmers to make land available for leisure and other uses.

... The Sports Council said: 'We want to see the demand for golf met though not through clubs. It costs an arm and a leg to join. But we are also interested in safeguarding other forms of recreation, including walking, in the countryside. There are conflicting issues.'

[*The Times* 10.6.91]

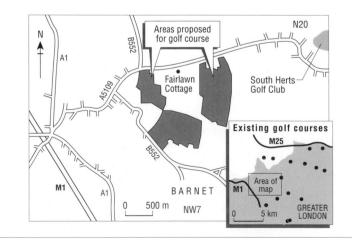

3.39 Golf development guidelines matrix, N.Herts

- The development of golf courses will not normally be permitted if:
  - **a** There would be a significant loss of high quality agricultural land.
  - **b** There would be an adverse impact on the existing landscape or sites and features of nature conservation or archaeological interest.
  - **c** There would be significant traffic problems.
- Golf courses should be developed on suitably sized areas of land, free from constraints, in the proximity of the urban areas they are to serve … Development may be beneficial on derelict land requiring restoration or on land having poor visual quality, on the basis that a properly designed and constructed golf course could result in a significant improvement to the visual quality and habitat interest of that landscape.
- Golf course construction will not normally be permitted where the landscape character and scale of the proposal would result in an unacceptable intrusion in the landscape.
- Golf course construction should not be permitted where (a) access necessitates the widening of country lanes to the detriment of their rural character, and (b) unacceptable levels of traffic are routed through small settlements.
- In the Areas of Outstanding Natural Beauty any change to landscape should represent an enhancement of the landscape quality.

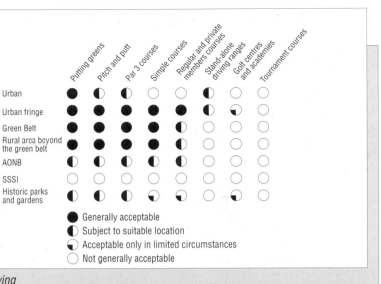

Legend:
- ● Generally acceptable
- ◐ Subject to suitable location
- ◔ Acceptable only in limited circumstances
- ○ Not generally acceptable

- Large scale development not essentially related to the primary use of the land as a golf course, such as hotels, conference centres, sports centres, will normally be resisted in the open countryside. However, District Plans may zone areas for tourism development, or proposals may come forward as extensions to existing hotels. In all proposals of this type great care will be needed to avoid the scale of the proposal having an unacceptable level of environmental impact. Any golf course proposal in the open countryside that is based on residential development being necessary to fund the course will not normally be permitted.

[Guidelines for the location and design of golf courses in Stroud District, *Draft document, 1992*]

3.40 The fairway code

The Countryside Commission wants any plans for golf courses in areas designated for their scenic beauty to be bunkered. In a position statement, shortly to be set out as an advisory booklet for planning authorities and golf course developers, the Commission recommends a general presumption against new courses in: national parks, including the Broads, areas of outstanding natural beauty, heritage coasts, historic parklands, and the New Forest.

In other areas the go-ahead should be given only where such a development would contribute to and enhance the character of the landscape. And it should proceed only after a thorough environmental assessment of the likely impact, says the Commission.

Manicured greens, contouring, planting of often alien species, sandy bunkers and the removal of hedgerows and stone walls can give an 'imposed' look which would conflict with beautiful landscapes – especially as, on average, an 18 hole golf course spreads over 50 hectares of land.

There are fears, too, that such a facility could be the thin end of the wedge, with clubhouses, hotel accommodation, roads, and other development following.

But the Commission is not against the idea of golf facilities in less sensitive areas of the countryside.

Preference should be given, it says, to locating them where they can make a positive contribution to the area – for example, within degraded landscapes, such as those affected by mineral workings or where intensive agriculture has already left its mark.

The 12 new community forests being planted in different areas of England, or the New National Forest being created in the Midlands, could make suitable locations for new golf courses, it suggests.

But, says the Commission, in all circumstances where golf courses are allowed, consideration must be given to their effect on the conservation of wildlife and historic features, as well as on local communities. Furthermore, appropriate management of new or retained landscape elements should be a condition of any planning permission, together with arrangements for the provision of public access to the countryside.

The Commission, with the help of consultants, is later this year to publish an advisory booklet on the subject, giving guidance to local authorities and golf course developers on the way in which the principles should be applied. It will cover matters such as environmental and landscape factors to be taken into account when considering a new course, design guidance for landscape treatment and enhancement, and opportunities for creative conservation, together with guidelines for future management and after-care.

[*Countryside* Feb/March 1992]

impact assessment (EIA) along with the planning application. Such procedures cost time and money. Furthermore, planning committees were becoming more experienced in spotting proposals where the real profits were to be made from associated facilities, such as hotels, timeshare accommodation, theme parks and even executive homes. The developer realised that permission would not be granted for such developments, but hoped to slip them through in the guise of the golf course proposal. Once planning committees rejected such proposals, the project often became less financially attractive.

A further environmental dimension which is under closer scrutiny is the water demand of a facility. Irrigating greens and fairways can consume thousands of gallons a day, particularly during the summer. This has become a crucial resource demand especially in south-east England where groundwater supplies have been depleted by several dry summers and rising overall demand. As a result, all golf course projects are required to obtain a water extraction license before planning permission is granted.

Meanwhile, many golfers or would-be golfers were still finding it difficult to get a game. Many of the new developments required membership or were too expensive. Landowners and farmers realised this frustrated demand from up to two million casual players who simply want to enjoy regular rounds with their friends, and are prepared to pay about £10 a round to do so. The outcome has been that since 1991 there has been an increasing trend to build simple, often 9-hole courses, and run them on a pay-as-you-play (PAYP) basis. Many farmers have been able to carry out their own development by modest modifications to their farmland. Golf, thus, becomes one form of farm diversification. This type of development makes golf more accessible to more people, requires less capital investment, can be integrated with farming, and has less environmental impact .

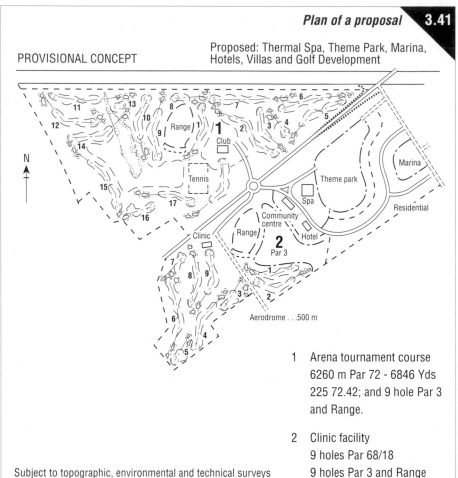

Plan of a proposal 3.41

PROVISIONAL CONCEPT

Proposed: Thermal Spa, Theme Park, Marina, Hotels, Villas and Golf Development

Subject to topographic, environmental and technical surveys

1 Arena tournament course
6260 m Par 72 - 6846 Yds
225 72.42; and 9 hole Par 3
and Range.

2 Clinic facility
9 holes Par 68/18
9 holes Par 3 and Range

3.42 **Value of golf development sites**

Value of golf development sites has been halved by lack of available funding

Funding was now so difficult to obtain for the purchase of golf development sites that prices had halved to twice agricultural value or less.

… Even prime areas around the M25 motorway were down to £5000–£7000/acre – little more than pony paddock prices.

Alan Plumb, head of Savills rural leisure division, said there were now too many golf planning consents, often in poor locations and with 'grandiose' over-expensive plans.

Most schemes now proceeding were a joint venture between landowner and developer, he said, involving lower gearing and less exposure to interest rate and capital value fluctuations. Mr Plumb stressed the supply of golf courses on to the market was still very low. The heady days of 1989/90 when £10m or more was being paid for Home Counties 18-hole golf courses had nevertheless given way to figures of £3m to £5m, or less for provincial courses.

[*Farmers Weekly*, 21.2.92]

A major realisation since 1991 has been that the golf market and product consists of a series of segments, each with its own resource and facility demands. There is a spectrum of facilities from driving ranges, through pitch-and-putt leisure courses, practice and coaching facilities, 9-hole courses, 18-hole courses, to championship courses with hotels, conference facilities, and many more. Each aspect has its own environmental, economic and social impacts and needs independent consideration. The comments of Resource 3.45 reflect the situation in 1993.

Farmer's plan is well on course

Less than 12 months after starting to convert part of his farm into a nine-hole golf course, Bedfordshire farmer David Simkins will be opening the course to the paying public.

With £8000 already in the bank from 120 advance membership fees, and with the project likely to cost slightly less than the budgeted £191,000. Mr Simkins, Mount Pleasant Farm, Lower Stondon, is well pleased with progress so far.

The course has been laid out on 22ha (51 acres) of both arable and grassland on the 88ha (217-acre) farm. Due to the topography of the farm, major earth movement has not been necessary. The main costs have been in the construction of greens and tees and most recently in an extensive tree planting scheme over the area – a planning requirement for the new Mount Pleasant golf course.

The financial viability of Mr Simkins's proposed golf course was mainly established through a commissioned ADAS feasibility study.

It reviewed the UK market for golf, regional demand, local supply and demand for gold courses, local competition, golf course development strategy and specifications for a course at Mount Pleasant Farm. The study also examined pricing policy, project timing, capital requirements, income and expenditure and, most important, the effect of the development of the existing farm business.

Summarising the feasibility study Mr McGann makes the following main points:
• There is an estimated need for an additional 11 golf courses within the catchment area of Mount Pleasant Farm and this may be an underestimate.
• Competition from other proposed courses in the area which have already obtained planning permission does not affect the viability of the nine-hole course planned for the farm.
• The best market opportunity is for pay-and-play courses.
• The total capital requirement for construction, ancillary works, machinery and accumulated bank interest charges is estimated at circa £305,000.
• Budgeted income and expenditure for the first three years indicate that after interest charges, in 1992 the venture will make a loss of £41,968, in 1993 a profit of £52,231 and in 1994 a profit of £109.211.
• The 1994 profit assumes that 37,500 nine-hole rounds are played on the course.

[*Farmers Weekly*, 29.5.92]

Table 1: Projected trading income and expenditure (£)

	1992	1993	1994
Income			
Green tees			
14 000 @ £6.50	91 000		
32 500 @ £6.50		208 000	
37 500 @ £6.50			243 750
Membership fees @ £40/member	6 000	10 000	14 000
Catering (net)	900	2 000	2 500
Pro shop % of sales	–	–	3 000
Gaming machines	–	1 000	2 000
Club hire, booking fees, etc	1 000	3 000	3 750
	98 900	**224 000**	**269 000**
Less VAT @ 17.5%	14 736	33 362	40 063
Total income	**84 164**	**190 638**	**228 937**
Expenditure			
Wages and National Insurance			
Head greenkeeper	16 500	16 500	16 500
Other green staff/casual labour	9 000	9 000	9 000
Professional retainer	4 000	7 000	–
Clubhouse – steward	–	–	–
– bar/catering	–	–	–
Admin/secretarial	–	–	–
Course maintenance	8 000	10 000	12 000
Clubhouse maintenance	–	–	–
Heat, light, power	1 500	2 500	3 000
Rates and water	3 750	5 500	5 500
Insurances	3 500	5 500	5 500
Portakabin hire (x2)	6 000	10 000	10 000
Phone/stationery/office	2 500	2 500	2 500
Marketing	10 000	7 500	2 500
Legal/accounting, etc	6 000	6 000	6 000
Sundries	2 000	2 500	2 500
Total expenditure	**72 750**	**84 500**	**75 000**
Surplus (deficit) (before finance and depreciation)	11 414	106 138	153 937
Less			
Depreciation – machinery	10 000	10 000	10 000
– property	–	2 000	2 000
Interest charged @ 16%	43 382	41 907	32 726
Profit (loss)	**(41 968)**	**52 231**	**109 211**

Table 2: Construction costs

Fairways	earth moving	£5 000
	reseeding 35 acres	8 750
Bunkers/greens/tees	construction/drainage/seeding/ irrigation ring main and supply to greens	148 000
Drainage to approaches		3 000
Water supply and storage	Borehole	3 000
	Above ground holding tank	2 000
	Feeder pipe, services, etc	2 500
Irrigation piping to tees		n/a
Tree planting/landscaping/ pathways/bridges (net of grants)		7 500
Professional fees	course design ⎫ project management ⎬ feasibility study (net of grant) ⎭	1 200
	Total	**191 750**

CASE STUDY 3.4 *Alternatives for UK farmland: is golf the answer?*

Activities

1 What factors have influenced the golf development boom of the late 1980s?

2 Who became increasingly concerned about the developments and what were their reasons?

3 What changes in policy by developers, planners and other interested organisations have taken place since 1991. Why?

4 Construct a matrix similar to the one below, and use it as a basis for an evaluation of golf as a diversification option for the countryside. (Remember to include *who* feel they are gaining or losing.)

	benefits	costs
economic		
social		
environmental		

3.44

A low cost Pay-As-You-Play golf course

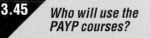

3.45 **Who will use the PAYP courses?**

Chris Lilwall (Golf consultant): 'There are three sources of demand. First the traditional, older and established player from an affluent, suburban community who is largely catered for by existing members clubs. Second, the mobile, younger executive with a growing family who plays at a public course. Then there are those from less affluent parts of the community, where there is a growing interest in the sport. So, most future development opportunities may well exist at the budget end of the market, but this is only because there are currently too few public courses.'

Matthew Page (Land agent): 'There is a gap in the market for a well-branded national network of PAYP golfing academies with a uniform range and standard of facilities.'

Terrance Kaye (Leisure consultant): 'There are going to be two extremes: at one end there will be the very exclusive and expensive facilities, while at the other end there will be the budget, PAYP courses.'

David Greeley (Land agent): 'Golf club fees are a luxury that the middle classes can no longer afford.'

3.46 **Planning Appeal Outcome**

Change of use from agricultural land to golf course at Barlaston, on fringe of the Potteries conurbation – Proposed use appropriate in green belt – Agricultural considerations no longer overriding – Appeal allowed and partial award of costs made against Stafford Borough Council.

Appeal site Station Road, Barlaston
Local planning authority Stafford Borough Council
DOE reference T/APP/Y3425/A/90/151766/P2
Date of inspector's decision December 18 1990
Inspector C F Trewick ARICS
Appelant A J Swift
Appelant's planning advisers Quest Bloomer Tweedale and Countryside Planning & Management

Stafford Borough Council refused change of use from agricultural land to golf course in Station Road, Barlaston. This was an urban fringe site about a mile from the southern edge of the Potteries conurbation. The ensuing appeal turned on the green belt and agricultural implications.

Golf courses, said the inspector, did not conflict with the main objective of green belt policy, which was to protect the openness of such areas. The appeal site was not part of an AONB or other protected landscape and was not prominent in views from the road. The proposal would bring changes, but grass and trees would remain the dominant features. Details of the access and siting of a clubhouse could be safeguarded by conditions. There was no compelling reason why the site's present appearance had to be preserved unchanged.

Agricultural considerations were no longer overriding but, as explained in Circular 16/87, simply had to be weighed alongside other aspects of a proposal. 85% of the appeal site was in MAFF Grade 3 which meant that it was not the best or most versatile land. Use as a golf course did not, in any case, represent an irrevocable loss to farming. Profitability of the present holding could be affected, but it would remain a viable unit for the tenant farmer.

Turning to other issues raised, the inspector did not feel that the possibility of stray golf balls entering the ground of adjoining properties amounted to a serious planning objection and there was no substance in the suggestion that users of footpaths through and adjoining the site would be endangered or inconvenienced.

British Rail had no objection subject to precautions such as the erection of a fence along the boundary with the railway and no objection had been raised by the highway authority subject to satisfactory access arrangements. Some local residents had questioned the need for a golf course, but this, said the inspector, was a matter of commercial judgment.

The appeal was accordingly allowed. A partial award of costs was made against Stafford Borough Council for failing to produce evidence to substantiate three of their four reasons for refusal – a decision which had been taken against the officers' advice.

CASE STUDY 3.5 *Change in an Alpine valley*

Background

Countries vary widely in the emphasis they place on regional planning to manage social and economic change. Since 1945, France has used a strong regional planning policy whose main aims have been:

- to reduce the concentration of economic activity and population growth in the Paris Basin.
- to revitalise declining industrial districts.
- to stem the depopulation from more remote rural areas.

Once problem regions had been identified, the next task was to select a growth industry which would be appropriate for each environment. The French Alps were identified as a depopulating rural region where traditional farming and forestry were becoming increasingly marginal.

The French government selected tourism as one of the growth industries on which they would base their regional development policies. For example, along the Mediterranean coast of Languedoc-Roussillon, six planned, integrated resorts were built (the Big Six) over 20 years to accommodate 350 000 people. The resorts included La Grande Motte and Leucate-Bacares. In the Alps, increasing the capacity for skiing was the obvious answer. As with the coastal developments, the regional plan opted for the construction of large-scale, planned, integrated resorts which would include, among others, accommodation, ski runs and chair lifts. La Plagne, for example, was begun in 1963. This concept was expanded in the sixth National Plan (1971–75) as the *Plan Neige*, which aimed at creating 350 000 extra bed-spaces, bringing the total in the Alps region to 500 000. This target was achieved in little more than ten years.

The integrated resorts (stations integrées) were located at high altitudes, usually above 1800 m, to ensure a long snow season. They have a concentrated, urban-like habitat – blocks of apartments with integrated shopping centres and the functional separation of pedestrians, skiers and motorists. As Resource 3.48 shows, these resorts are set well above the settled areas of the valley floors. The French government favoured this separation of the ski tourists from the local people, as it would minimise the social and environmental impacts while offering considerable economic benefits. Conversely, the high investment costs, for example, La Plagne at £80 million, meant that most capital came from outside the region, and equally the profits leaked out from the region. Meanwhile, the skiers in their separate reserves do not spend in the villages below. This high-tech approach has been criticised, and its impact upon the beautiful and fragile Alpine environment was brought into strong focus by the developments for the 1992 Winter Olympics.

There has, however, been another quite different type of ski development in the Alpine valleys. Skiing has been grafted on to and within existing villages and economies. Called the *eastern* or *Austrian* model, it is the common form of development in the Austrian Alps. The high-tech integrated resort is known as the *western* model. Communities who saw the economic benefits and the improved transport infrastructure in valleys where the *stations integrées* were rising, while their own agricultural way of life was becoming more of a struggle, looked to the popularity of skiing as the answer. Many already had a small tourist industry: a few skiers in the winter and walkers in the summer, who stayed in local homes, guesthouses or in second homes converted from houses left empty by depopulation. Such communities have expanded their

La Plagne, a planned ski resort in the French Alps

3.47

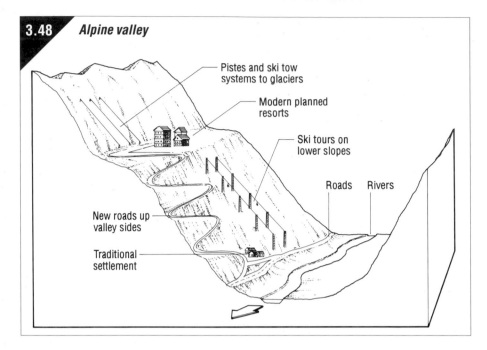

3.48 **Alpine valley**

Pistes and ski tow systems to glaciers

Modern planned resorts

Ski tours on lower slopes

Roads   Rivers

New roads up valley sides

Traditional settlement

Key understandings

◆ Alpine ski resorts can be grouped into two main models: the *Austrian* or eastern model and the *integrated* or western model. Each has a distinctive character and environmental impact.

◆ Basing development policy upon tourism has negative as well as positive economic, social and environmental impacts.

◆ Balancing economic growth with conservation and social values is a complex and delicate management process.

◆ Tourism can be a sustainable option if it is integrated within existing agricultural and social systems.

accommodation, put in new chair lifts and opened more ski runs (pistes). Where possible, they have used local capital and kept control of the business, but in their desire to remain competitive and attractive

they have sometimes run into difficulties. This case study follows the story of one such community, La Chappelle d'Abondance, as it tries to ensure the social and economic sustainability of its future.

A traditional Alpine resort: Courcheval, French Alps. Tourism integrated within an existing settlement.

Managing change in a rural community through tourism – La Chappelle d'Abondance, France

The community

La Chapelle d'Abondance, 33 km from Thonon and Evian-les-Bains, is set in the broad floor of the Abondance valley and is flanked by a series of mountains between 1800 and 2400 metres high. The population of approximately 750 people are scattered in ten hamlets, most of which are situated on the sunny side of the valley. The traditional economy has been based on farming and wood products. Over the past 40 years tourism has been built upon this foundation. By 1992, only 16% of the permanent population were employed in agriculture. A further 25% work in forestry and wood products. Approximately 45% depend at least in part on tourism. Much of the traditional environment remains a major part of the attraction of the area: 45 working farms and 1400 ha of community forest, 800 ha of which comes under national conservation regulations. The latter area fulfills the requirement to replant as much forest area as is cleared.

Alps scarred 'forever' by Olympics

3.50

Scientists say that the mountains around Albertville, Savoy, will never recover from the £1 billion preparations for the Games, which have scraped the soil from fragile alpine pastures to make smooth-running pistes. Officially protected forests have been violated and rare marshland damaged. Residents have had to be issued with gas masks because of the danger from toxic chemicals.

The Games add one more insult to the injury of the Alps, which are rapidly becoming one of the world's foremost ecological disasters. More than half the trees in this backbone of Europe are affected by acid rain, farmers are abandoning their land and landslides and avalanches are increasing under the impact of 50 million tourists a year.

One of the resorts playing host to the Olympics, Les Arcs, has already suffered a catastrophe. In 1981, 60 people died.

In all a million cubic metres of earth have been carved out of the mountainsides to prepare for the 1992 Olympics, which are sited in the buffer zone around the Vanoise National Park. Previously protected forests have lost their official safeguards and more than 60 acres of trees have been cut down.

The Games have been spread among 10 communities to try to distribute their benefits. But this has also increased the environmental damage.

At Les Saisies, the cross-country skiing runs criss-cross over a rare high mountain marshland, the home of scarce alpine plants. The digging of a biathlon arena next to the marsh threatens to disrupt its delicate water balance. Local environmentalists say it will cause tremendous damage.

The men's downhill ski run at Val d'Isere has been bulldozed out of relatively unspoiled landscale ...

The ski-jump at Courcheval is the centre of another controversy. A competition held to decide the design was won by an ecologically-friendly metallic jump, which could have been dismantled once the Games were over. It was also the cheapest design submitted. But businessmen favoured a huge concrete construction, built into the mountainside. So heavy that it threatened to slip, it was hammered in with hundreds of 100-ton piles.

A spokesman for the Games said yesterday: 'We took care of the environment question before we started the work. The mountains can be modernised and equipped and still be respected.'

But, he added, future Olympics should be subjected to environmental impact studies before work begins.

[*The Observer*, 9.2.92]

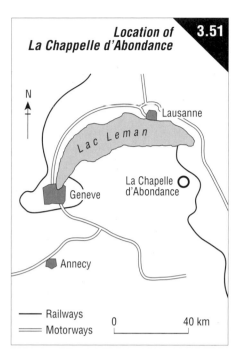

3.51

Location of La Chappelle d'Abondance

Lac Leman

Lausanne

La Chapelle d'Abondance

Genève

Annecy

—— Railways
══ Motorways

0   40 km

Until the late 1950s tourism was limited to a small number of walkers during the summer months. In 1960, because of the increasing popularity of skiing, the mayor and the local council decided to invest in the first ski lift. This was an economic success and enabled the council to carry through a steady development programme over the next 25 years. By 1985, La Chappelle d'Abondance had 9 ski lifts, 2 chairlifts and 7 ski tows, pistes (ski runs) with a combined capacity of 1800 skiers and 35 km of cross-country ski trails along the valley floor. Although the lift lanes and the pistes entailed the removal of forest, much of the wooded slopes were conserved. Ecologically-sensitive areas above the tree line were protected by designation as a Conservation Reserve.

Bedspace capacity along the valley exceeded 6000, including homes, small hotels, chalets and second homes. For example, over 40% of all bedspaces in 1991 were in local family homes. The aim was to benefit from the economic profits of tourism: more income, jobs and more opportunities to prevent emigration and to maintain social cohesion, while minimising negative cultural and environmental

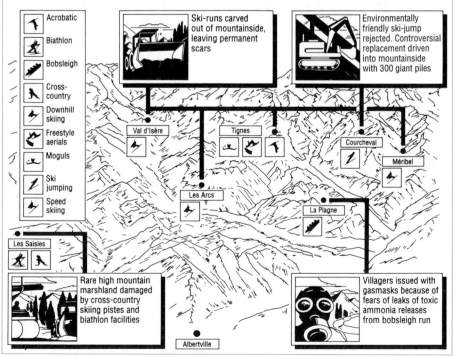

Acrobatic	
Biathlon	
Bobsleigh	
Cross-country	
Downhill skiing	
Freestyle aerials	
Moguls	
Ski jumping	
Speed skiing	

Ski-runs carved out of mountainside, leaving permanent scars

Environmentally friendly ski-jump rejected. Controversial replacement driven into mountainside with 300 giant piles

Val d'Isère

Tignes

Courcheval

Méribel

Les Arcs

La Plagne

Les Saisies

Rare high mountain marshland damaged by cross-country skiing pistes and biathlon facilities

Villagers issued with gasmasks because of fears of leaks of toxic ammonia releases from bobsleigh run

Albertville

CASE STUDY 3.5 *Change in an Alpine valley*

impacts. Accelerated cultural change is inevitable when up to 7000 visitors a week are poured into a community of fewer than 800 people.

Until the late 1980s, the integration of tourism within the economic and social structure of the valley seemed to be a success. Depopulation had ceased, unemployment was low, farms continued to raise their animals, with income supplemented from accommodation and 'farm visits' by tourists in the summer. Local wood crafts had revived through souvenir and gift purchases. Above all, the local council and community had maintained control of the tourism development and of the income. These profits supported further investment. While tourism has both summer and winter dimensions, the latter is dominant, gener-

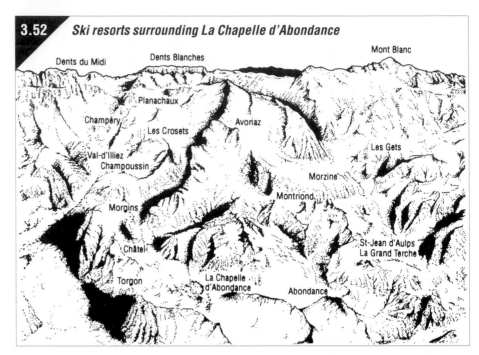

3.52 *Ski resorts surrounding La Chapelle d'Abondance*

La Chappelle d'Abondance

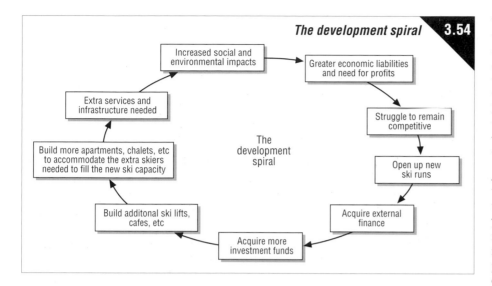

The development spiral `3.54`

The development spiral

- Increased social and environmental impacts
- Greater economic liabilities and need for profits
- Struggle to remain competitive
- Open up new ski runs
- Acquire external finance
- Acquire more investment funds
- Build additonal ski lifts, cafes, etc
- Build more apartments, chalets, etc to accommodate the extra skiers needed to fill the new ski capacity
- Extra services and infrastructure needed

ating 75% of the income from tourism.

Since 1988, however, the balance seems to have shifted. In that year the mayor, who believed strongly in the blessings of 'white gold' (snow), decided that new ski areas with all the supporting lifts had to be opened up. He argued that this was necessary to cope with growing demand, to provide more jobs for the increasing number of young people, encouraging them to stay, and to maintain attractiveness in the face of increasing competition from other resorts. A report by the French Ministry of Tourism added support to this proposal by stating that if prices for apartments and second homes were to be maintained in a ski area, improved ski facilities must be developed to keep pace with the rising expectations of skiers. In order to carry through this project quickly as a single development, rather than develop it incrementally as they had done in the past, the community looked to external investors and banks for the majority of the £7 million capital required.

Until the poor snow seasons of 1991 and 1992, the new facilities seemed to attract more skiers. However, throughout the Alps the combination of lack of snow and the eco-nomic recession has brought an alarming halt to the growth. The problem is intensified for La Chappelle, for even when the tourism income does increase, a greater proportion 'leaks' from the locality than in the past. For example, the annual repayments on money borrowed to build the new ski lift system are approximately £1 million, but income from these lifts was £600 000 in 1991 and £800 000 in 1992. The effects of this and other external payments meant that in 1991 the district council had a budget deficit of £350 000 and in 1992 of £900 000.

The community seems to have been caught in a development spiral. The council has realised that to make the new ski facilities profitable, a further 6000 bed-spaces will be required, a doubling of the 1988 capacity. This requires yet further capital invest-ment, either from local or from external sources. In turn, this will require additional investment in ser-vices such as water, electricity, sewage, and transport infrastructure. The outcome has been that by the end of 1992, the debt amounted to £13 000 per head of population and the regional authorities intervened to compel the council to increase local taxes by 30%.

The new ski developments are set on the slopes immediately above the settlement and, thus, have a strong environmental impact. The addi-tional accommodation, too, is close to the community, thereby affecting local people. This is in contrast to the earlier developments which were located on the opposite side of the valley from the settlement.

A balanced management response is urgently required: on the one hand tourism income must be maintained yet, on the other hand, tourism must not be allowed to dominate the com-munity. It seems clear that recent policy has upset the balance which existed. La Chappelle and other similar communities should avoid the trap of trying to compete directly with the huge integrated resorts. They should maintain their distinc-tive 'product' and in so doing, sustain their traditional economies and community strengths. In La Chappelle, three-quarters of the tourism income is incurred during the winter season. A profitable stra-tegy should then be to market the summer attractions more strongly. A researcher who has lived most of his life in La Chappelle sees a sustain-able way ahead:

Let's stay simple and – as far as pos-sible – authentic: this village must take advantage of its unique land-scape, handicrafts and quietness to attract children, families and groups who are looking for relax-ation and change of scene rather than for extreme sport and enter-tainment. With its accommodation stock made up of numerous self-catering flats let by locals and a few hotels, the prices are relatively cheap, and the village can well accommodate this kind of clientele. Moreover, it can encourage the democratisation of winter sport: the new skiers with a lower purchasing power could be the target of the local Tourist Office. This village must no more try to compete with huge integrated winter resorts, but keep its traditional characteristics that many tourists are looking for (Banfin, Research Dissertation, 1993).

CHAPTER 4

Living cities

Introduction

There is a two-way relationship between urban morphology and our lifestyles within it. Classic models of urban form, such as the Concentric and Sectoral models, were proposed for American cities more than 60 years ago. At that time the majority of people did not own cars, relied on public transport and lived in neighbourhoods where all kinds of services were within walking distance. The city was monocentric, had well-defined limits and strongly-defined internal patterns. Today all this has changed. In the developed world, the past 60 years or so have been the era of what has been called *Auto-Air-Amenity* cities – the three As. Cities have grown in population and geographical extent, and jobs, homes and services have been re-organised. The transformation has been so fundamental that new urban hierarchies have been proposed.

For most of us, our 'action space', that is, the geographical area over which we live our lives, has expanded. The work, home and play dimensions of our lives have become increasingly spread out, made possible by improved mobility. The result has been the outward explosion of urban areas and the proposal of new models of urban morphology. We hear new terms, such as *spread city*, *exurb* and *edge city*, introduced as attempts to describe these new forms. Two of the dominant processes in this dispersal have been *suburbanisation* and *counterurbanisation*. Low density suburbs have sprawled ever outwards and smaller towns have become ringed with housing developments despite planning controls. Families commit themselves to more travelling time and expense in order to enjoy more space, and for perceptions of greater safety, better schools and improved quality of life. These processes have attained their extreme form in North America, but even in crowded countries such as the UK, residential

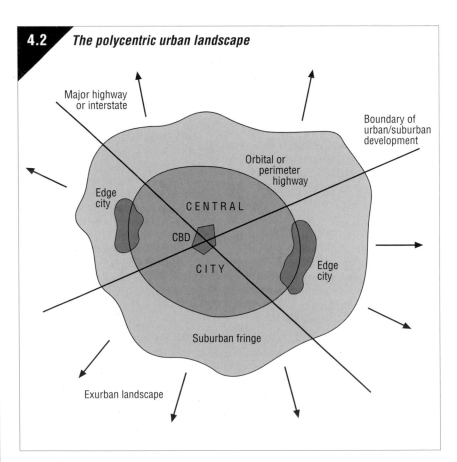

4.2 *The polycentric urban landscape*

'Edge cities' are defined as commercial areas located in suburbia that meet five tests:
1 At least 5 mill.sq.ft of office space
2 At least 600 000 sq.ft of retail space
3 A population that is higher during the work day than at other times
4 A locally recognised place of work, shopping and entertainment
5 An area that was predominantly rural or low-density residential in nature 30 years ago

4.1 **A new urban hierarchy for European cities**

Type	UK example
1 Global cities	London
2 City regions in global fringe or corridor zones	Manchester–Birmingham–Northampton corridor
3 Remote regional cities	Belfast, Glasgow
4 Regional capital cities	Bristol, Norwich
5 County towns	Durham, York
6 Specialised service centres	Reading, Exeter

[Source: Hall P. *Urban studies*, 1993]

Micheldever plan

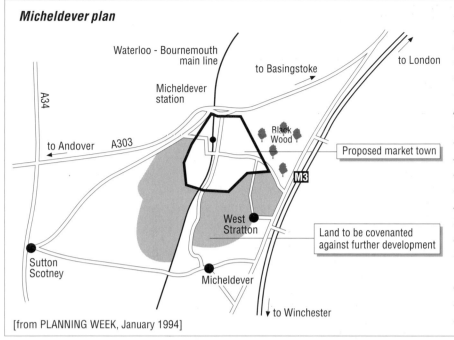

[from PLANNING WEEK, January 1994]

Hampshire is one of the counties in southern England where the confrontation between environmental conservation and development pressures is intense. Planners aim to control the further growth of cities such as Portsmouth and Southampton. Residents fight to protect smaller market towns and villages from the developers. Yet Hampshire may need to find space for 115 000 extra homes between 1991 and 2011. The preferred solution for developers is a series of new settlements such as Micheldever Station Market Town, with an optimum size of 25 000 to 30 000 inhabitants. Supporters claim that such a development would create 'a compact, human scale place with housing, employment and the full range of market town facilities'. The design would place emphasis 'on landscape and wildlife conservation and enhancement'. [Fyson, S. Homing in on Hampshire's housing targets, PLANNING WEEK, 2[2], 13.1.94]

4.3

development pressures on the countryside have been unrelenting.

The monocentric urban form with a single CBD is giving way to polycentric forms as not only homes but employment move outwards. In the UK, this has usually meant the expansion of existing towns, such as Croydon and Redditch. The true *edge city* or *suburban downtown* remains a North American phenomenon. The resulting polycentric urban form allows the ex-urban fringe to push even farther outwards, as commuters and other ex-urbanites no longer need to reach the traditional *downtown* or CBD.

There is an increasing realisation of the economic, social and environmental costs of this explosive decentralisation, and of a search for alternatives. There are signs that urban regeneration programmes and dissatisfactions with dispersed living are attracting people back to the cities. In turn, planners and developers are producing more compact urban designs. This process of re-concentration is further encouraged by the strengthening of planning controls on sprawl.

The first two case studies in this chapter, 4.1 and 4.2, set out evidence for and against the dispersed and compact city alternatives. Examples are taken from the USA and Australia to demonstrate that space is finite even in huge countries, that car-based ex-urban sprawl is non-sustainable and pays little attention to the environmental setting.

One quality claimed for compact urban designs is that a car is not needed to have an enjoyable lifestyle. Mobility is easy on foot, by bike or by public transport. Case studies 4.3 and 4.4 focus upon the issue of whether UK cities are 'livable' and attractive on these terms. For women in particular, safety has become an important issue. Case Study 4.3 explores the problems and potential solutions. Safety in moving around the city is also the theme for Case Study 4.4, which follows a Nottingham experiment into making cities 'user-friendly' for cyclists. Large, complex urban areas are especially vulnerable to extreme natural and technological events, e.g. the earthquake of January 1995, which devastated extensive areas of the industrial city of Kobe, Japan. Case Study 4.5 illustrates this vulnerability, and the complex of responses, by an analysis of Hurricane Andrew which hit the cities of South Florida in August 1992.

CASE STUDY 4.1 *Urbanisation California style*

Introduction

California, the Golden State, conjures up very special images for many people. The 'Californian Dream' usually encompasses that which is most desired in a western lifestyle. In 1991, *Time* magazine produced a special issue entitled 'California – the endangered dream'.

It is still America's promised land – a place of heart-stopping beauty, spectacular energy and stunning diversity. But faced with drought, mindless growth and a sputtering economy, can it preserve the dream? (*Time*, 18 Nov 1991).

California is, indeed, a state of extreme scale. You could drive northwards along the freeway from the Mexican border, for 1600 km before entering Oregon. You will then have passed by approximately

30 million people, encountered most of the 25 million motor vehicles, glimpsed a bewildering mixture of deserts, forests, mountains, rich orchards and farmlands and sprawling cities. For millions of Americans, the Californian dream is *economic opportunity; the freedom to jump in a car and drive to the beach or mountains; and perhaps most important of all, a house in the suburbs with a barbeque and – if you make it – a swimming pool* (Bonfante, *Time*, 18 Nov 1991). Californians see themselves as something special (Resource 4.4).

California's economic growth and prosperity have been phenomenal. Had it been an independent country, it would rank eighth in the world in terms of GNP. It is the leading American state in industrial and agricultural production. Job availability

4.4	**What Californians think of themselves**	
Perception	*Californians are*	
Trendy	73%	
Health-conscious	66%	
Money-oriented	62%	
Self-indulgent	58%	
Tolerant	57%	
Fun-loving	55%	

[Source: *Time*, 18 November 1991]

and some of the highest rates of pay in the US, along with the attractive climate and environment have attracted over 500 000 newcomers a year. The generally liberal planning regulations and power of private developers, plus apparently limitless space, have added to the spatial explosion which is threatening the

4.5

The 'California dream'

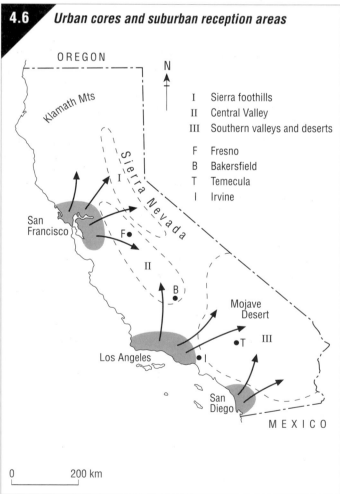

4.6 *Urban cores and suburban reception areas*

OREGON

N

Klamath Mts

Sierra Nevada

I	Sierra foothills
II	Central Valley
III	Southern valleys and deserts
F	Fresno
B	Bakersfield
T	Temecula
I	Irvine

San Francisco

F

I

II

B

Los Angeles

Mojave Desert

T

III

I

San Diego

MEXICO

0   200 km

state's resource capacity and environmental quality. Only in the last decade have varying communities throughout the state realised that they have been destroying the finite ingredients of the Californian dream: land, water, air quality, beautiful environments. Since the late 1980s, the legendary economic prosperity which has triggered 'the good life' has faded.

This case study examines the environmental implications of the massive suburbanisation which has been creeping across the state from the metropolitan cores of San Francisco, Los Angeles and San Diego. In a society where each city and county authority has considerable independence, it is very difficult to plan and to manage resources on a statewide or even regional basis. The resources illustrate how urbanisation works, how difficult it is to control, and identifies the sections of California under particular threat.

Key understandings

◆ Low-density suburban sprawl is causing severe environmental problems in California and is acknowledged as non-sustainable.

◆ Suburban sprawl in California is difficult to control because of a combination of rapid population growth, high levels of car ownership and liberal planning laws.

◆ Low-density urban development is inefficient economically, socially and environmentally.

Land conversion and suburbanisation in California

Population growth

The 1990 US population census confirms that California is the nation's most populous and ethnically diverse state. Between 1980 and 1990 the population grew by 5.6 million people, some 1.6 million of whom were legal immigrants. California has a major influx of illegal immigrants, especially from Mexico. The official population amounted to 29.3 million, but it is likely that at least 30 million people actually live in the state. A quarter of all the American population growth between 1980 and 1990, was in California. One in nine American citizens are now California residents. Only 3 million more people live in the whole of Canada.

The pace and nature of this growth are equally impressive. In 1900 the population was only 1.4 million; by 1970 it had reached 20 million. A further 10 million were added over the next twenty years. Cities such as San Diego have doubled their populations in two decades. A growing proportion of the population increase over the past twenty years has been of Latino (people of Hispanic origin – Mexico, Caribbean, Latin America), Asian and African-American populations. About 85% of all births and inward migrants to California between 1980 and 1990 came from Latino and Asian ethnic groups which, with the African-Americans, comprise over 40% of the state population. It is estimated that by the year 2000 there will be no

population majority, only a series of minority groups. Los Angeles is home to more Mexicans than any other city except Mexico City, more Koreans than any other city outside Seoul, more Filipinos than any other city outside the Philippines. Many of these distinctive cultural groups continue to generate their own communities. This population mix has significant implications for the pattern of urbanisation.

Resource 4.9 shows that the growth is unevenly spread. The three main generating metropolitan cores are San Francisco, Los Angeles and San Diego, pushing the bow-wave of suburbanisation ever outwards. Three main areas of growth can be recognised:

• the valleys and deserts east of Los Angeles and north-east of San Diego.
• the foothill zone of the Sierra Nevada between Nevada and Madera counties.

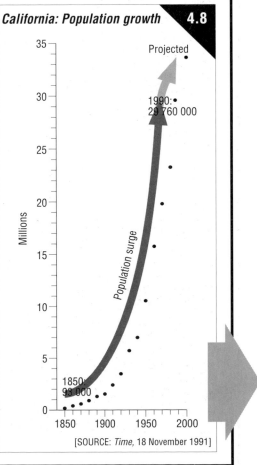

California: Population growth | 4.8

[SOURCE: *Time*, 18 November 1991]

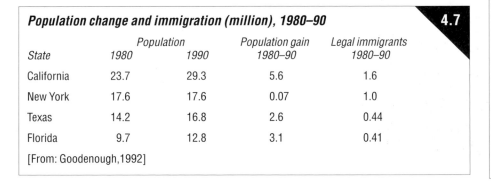

Population change and immigration (million), 1980–90 | 4.7

State	Population 1980	Population 1990	Population gain 1980–90	Legal immigrants 1980–90
California	23.7	29.3	5.6	1.6
New York	17.6	17.6	0.07	1.0
Texas	14.2	16.8	2.6	0.44
Florida	9.7	12.8	3.1	0.41

[From: Goodenough, 1992]

CASE STUDY 4.1 *Urbanisation California style*

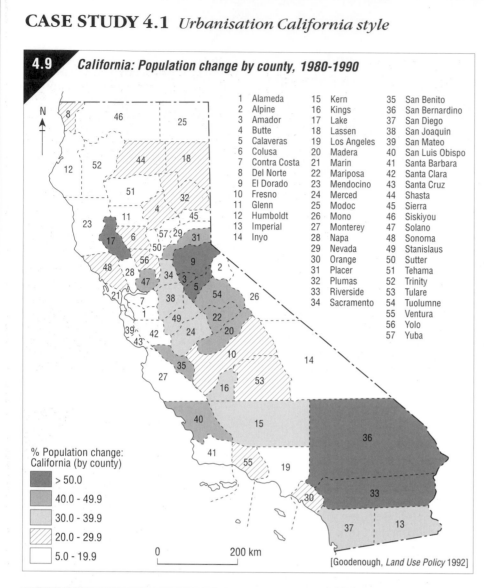

4.9 *California: Population change by county, 1980-1990*

1	Alameda	15	Kern	35	San Benito
2	Alpine	16	Kings	36	San Bernardino
3	Amador	17	Lake	37	San Diego
4	Butte	18	Lassen	38	San Joaquin
5	Calaveras	19	Los Angeles	39	San Mateo
6	Colusa	20	Madera	40	San Luis Obispo
7	Contra Costa	21	Marin	41	Santa Barbara
8	Del Norte	22	Mariposa	42	Santa Clara
9	El Dorado	23	Mendocino	43	Santa Cruz
10	Fresno	24	Merced	44	Shasta
11	Glenn	25	Modoc	45	Sierra
12	Humboldt	26	Mono	46	Siskiyou
13	Imperial	27	Monterey	47	Solano
14	Inyo	28	Napa	48	Sonoma
		29	Nevada	49	Stanislaus
		30	Orange	50	Sutter
		31	Placer	51	Tehama
		32	Plumas	52	Trinity
		33	Riverside	53	Tulare
		34	Sacramento	54	Tuolumne
				55	Ventura
				56	Yolo
				57	Yuba

% Population change:
California (by county)

- > 50.0
- 40.0 – 49.9
- 30.0 – 39.9
- 20.0 – 29.9
- 5.0 – 19.9

0   200 km

[Goodenough, *Land Use Policy* 1992]

4.10

Suburban sprawl around San Francisco

- the Central Valley, especially around Bakersfield, reflecting a spillover from the Los Angeles basin, and Fresno (population: 1980 – 359 000; 1990 – 478 000; 2000 (est) – 700 000), indicating the spread from San Francisco.

The figures in Resource 4.9 are expressed as percentages. Although the Sierra counties overall increased by 43% 1980–90, they still have only 2% of the state population. In contrast, Los Angeles county has a slow growth rate, but 30% of Californians have their homes there.

Fleeing the city – living the dream

The population growth has been absorbed in four main ways:

- by increased crowding in the metropolitan centres, especially among the ethnic and cultural minority groups, e.g. south-central Los Angeles, south San Diego to the Mexican border.
- by accreting on to existing medium-sized cities e.g. Bakersfield, Fresno.
- by moving into older neighbourhoods progressively vacated as residents move outwards to more peripheral *subdivisions* (housing developments) – what has been known as the 'white flight' of the cities by the white population, but which is becoming increasingly ethnically diverse.
- by direct movement into new subdivisions and 'exurbs' well away from existing urban centres.

It is the latter two components which have generated the explosion of low density suburbanisation outwards across California. This process has been assisted by the emergence of Edge Cities (see Resource 4.2).

The new suburban communities are built on land previously used for agriculture. They extend across the irrigated fruit, vegetable, animal feed and orchard lands of central and southern California, the grazing lands of the Sierra foothills and the interior drylands. It is estimated that up to 20 000 ha of agricultural land a year were being converted to urban

Ex-urban sprawl in Phoenix, Arizona. Low density housing spreads across agricultural land.

use during the 1980s, one-half being crop and orchard land and the other being low-density grazing land. Resource 4.12 shows the uneven distribution of this land conversion. Because the figures are percentage changes, a loss of 20% in the intensively-farmed San Joaquin county is quite different from a 20% loss in the desert and mountain Inyo county where much of the land is not used for agriculture. The figures are also are *net* figures. In most counties, new land is brought into agriculture which partly offsets the conversion loss. For example, Riverside county has been severely affected by the suburban explosion from Los Angeles and San Diego, but has also benefitted from new irrigation schemes. Its net change in farm land is, thus, minimal.

Notice the similarity if we compare the patterns of change on Resources 4.9 and 4.12. In many counties the population growth is accompanied by land conversion from agriculture. Because of the large size of individual counties, especially in the south and east, patterns are not always clear. However, the two main types of suburban growth by land conversion can be identified in the northern half of the state, around the San Francisco core. The first zone of

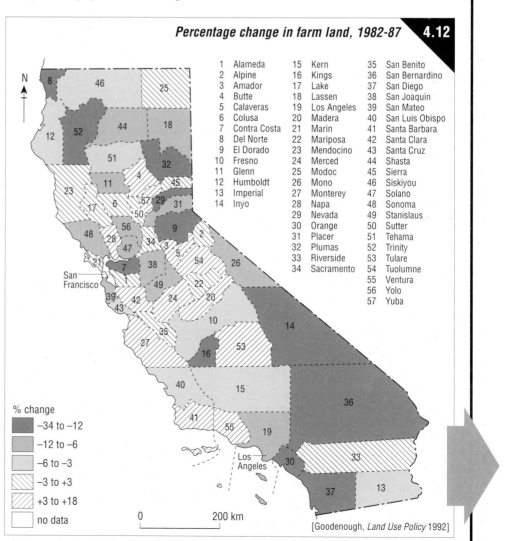

Percentage change in farm land, 1982-87 4.12

1	Alameda	15	Kern	35	San Benito
2	Alpine	16	Kings	36	San Bernardino
3	Amador	17	Lake	37	San Diego
4	Butte	18	Lassen	38	San Joaquin
5	Calaveras	19	Los Angeles	39	San Mateo
6	Colusa	20	Madera	40	San Luis Obispo
7	Contra Costa	21	Marin	41	Santa Barbara
8	Del Norte	22	Mariposa	42	Santa Clara
9	El Dorado	23	Mendocino	43	Santa Cruz
10	Fresno	24	Merced	44	Shasta
11	Glenn	25	Modoc	45	Sierra
12	Humboldt	26	Mono	46	Siskiyou
13	Imperial	27	Monterey	47	Solano
14	Inyo	28	Napa	48	Sonoma
		29	Nevada	49	Stanislaus
		30	Orange	50	Sutter
		31	Placer	51	Tehama
		32	Plumas	52	Trinity
		33	Riverside	53	Tulare
		34	Sacramento	54	Tuolumne
				55	Ventura
				56	Yolo
				57	Yuba

% change
- −34 to −12
- −12 to −6
- −6 to −3
- −3 to +3
- +3 to +18
- no data

0   200 km

[Goodenough, *Land Use Policy* 1992]

intense change is immediately adjacent to the metropolis, for example, the Solano and Sonoma Counties. A second zone of intense change is much more peripheral, as in the arc of counties from Trinity to El Dorado, across the Klamath and the Sierra foothills. This second zone suggests a 'leap-frogging' process where affluent, mobile families are willing and able to distance themselves perhaps 80 km from the work and metropolitan centres. This two-zone pattern also occurs in the south but the maps do not pick it out because both zones may lie within one county.

Resource 4.13 describes the sacrifices families are willing to make to live 'the Californian dream'. Perceived quality of life is at the heart of the motivation. They believe that they can afford larger houses than in the high-priced cities, that neighbourhoods are safer, air quality is higher and that schools are better. They also believe that neighbours and community are friendlier and that there is greater freedom. The description of life in Moreno Valley helps us to appreciate why they do it.

4.13 What suburbanisation means

Suburban sprawl has meant clogged traffic over ever greater commuting distances as residents move farther and farther from the urban cores in search of affordable homes. Take Temecula (pop. 37 000), a sudden-growth city in the so-called Inland Empire of Riverside County that has doubled in size in just five years to accommodate young families in search of relatively reasonably priced houses. The lights go on in Temecula at 4am. By 5 one can stand on the hill and ... in the darkness look down at the streams of headlights coming down the feeder roads to the Route 15 Freeway, two hours to San Diego, $2\frac{1}{2}$ hours to Los Angeles.

When Andrew Cotton leaves his computer-firm job in Irvine [a new city south of Los Angeles] at 6.45pm for the two-hour trek back to Temecula, he eats his dinner at the wheel, tries to stay awake with a book-on-tape and finally, at about 8.45, after his 20-month-old baby is asleep, spends a quarter-hour with his wife and six-year-old son. 'I keep telling myself, now, this is only temporary,' says Cotton. 'But it's been three years. My wife Jill calls herself a single parent.' At 9 the lights go out, and the alarms are set for next morning's repetition.'

[*Time*, 18.11.91]

4.14 Moreno Valley: home of the Y-chop

By Gus Lee

What is the California Dream? And whatever it is, where can it be found? In the past seven years, 118,000 modern-day pathfinders have located a form of it in Moreno Valley, a new city 70 miles southeast of Los Angeles and 42 miles from Disneyland.

This is a desert that developers turned into the mother of all real estate opportunities by diverting water from the Sacramento-San Joaquin Delta and the Oroville reservoir, far to the north. This is a place for hardworking parents, seeking picket-fenced yards, swing sets and quiet streets, for people who can endure temperatures in the 100s and can drive three hours a day to work and back.

I call these people Y-Chops – Young Commuting Home-Owning Parents – a new version of an old ideal of the American nuclear family. They have come to Moreno Valley because a home in more established California cities can cost as much as a space shuttle. In 'moVal' a typical four-bedroom house on a 7,500-sq.ft. lot costs $140,000. The affordable homes and quality of life have made Moreno Valley the fastest growing city in America.

Today three out of four working 'Mo Vallers' merge with thousands of other competitive freeway high achievers driving on gas, caffeine, ambition, ozone depletion and sleep deprivation for the two hours of freewaying to Los Angeles or the $1\frac{1}{2}$-hour drive to Orange County. This mass evacuation leaves MoVal half empty during the day. But the American urge for home ownership and its coveted symbols – a swing in the yard, idyllic neighborhoods and progressive public schools – is so powerful that the commute is accepted as part of the natural price of the Dream, a bearable surcharge on happiness, part of being a Y-chop.

Most Y-Chops are white. The evolving MoVal family has one parent commuting to work and one staying home with two children in a single-family dwelling, in a safe neighborhood with church and grandparents nearby. Many of the streets are laid out in that cookie-cutter pattern of curves and cul-de-sacs familiar from Steven Spielberg movies.

Kristin and Bo Knutson are Y-Chops who came to Moreno Valley in 1988. They were looking for a place for Kristin's parents to retire, but it was so beguilingly peaceful and appealingly inexpensive that they decided to stay. Now Kristin's parents provide a presence for Zak, 17, and help raise Alana, 1. Kristin believes that the combination of town and school is better for her children than that in their former home. She commutes three hours a day to her neonatal intensive-care nursing job at Childrens Hospital of Orange County. For the first time, the Knutsons have enough living space; at night they hear crickets. 'This is a new community', Kristin says. 'We have an opportunity to influence the future, to shape it. Older cities are set and hard to change.' The order of their home, the front-yard bougainvillea, the serenity of the neighborhood – all say, as emphatically as her words, that moving to MoVal was the right thing for her and her family.

For MoVal's Mayor, Judy Nieburger, and her staff of professional managers and energetic volunteers, the big challenge is protecting the quality of life while the population expands. Two-thirds of MoVal workers have some college education, and the percentage of residents with bachelor's degrees is increasing. Three out of four workers are between the ages of 25 and 44. They are neatly distributed among blue collar, technical, professional and management, with the vast majority full-time workers. The city has attracted a business from Asia – Borneo International Furniture – but is still seeking major American companies that will help MoVal dedicate its human energy to work and home, rather than to work, home and the freeways. Having a big employer in the neighborhood would help eliminate the Y-Chop dilemma: families need safety and community, but to attain them, one or both parents must spend a major portion of life on the road.

[*Time*, 18.11.91]

The progression of sprawl

In the UK planning policies and regulations are used as land management tools to reduce suburban sprawl. In California, the approach has been much more liberal. Individual authorities and landowners have considerable autonomy to make decisions. This gives opportunities to developers to purchase land and to get permission to change its use from farming to housing, for example. The details vary but the process of land conversion and suburbanisation seems to follow a general pattern. This is summarised in Resource 4.15. The process begins with improved accessibility, which causes land values to rise. Taxes on the land increase and, in turn, owners have to find ways of increasing their income from the land to pay these taxes. At the same time, developers notice the increased accessibility and the potential market for housing. Landowners are encouraged to sell off pieces of their land, which are then subdivided into lots of varying size and developed as *ranchettes*. Farming becomes more

difficult, more land is sold and converted and the housing subdivisions become larger, with smaller individual plots. Within perhaps ten years, farming has almost disappeared.

This process has been further exacerbated by the increasing problems of agriculture, especially where irrigation is used. Crop prices have not risen and competition is harsher. Over 80% of all water consumed in California is used for agriculture. Water is in increasingly short supply and is becoming expensive. It is constantly metered. It can be argued that because agricultural supply exceeds demand and water demands exceed sustainable supply, it does not matter if some irrigated farmland is lost. However, there has been an enormous investment in these lands and agriculture is a mainstay of the state economy, providing over 10% of the nation's farm income. Converting prime land from farming to housing in one area means drylands elsewhere need to be upgraded to irrigated lands. Is such a process economically or environmentally sensible?

Can the growth be managed?

California state laws concern development control, but local communities have extensive control over their own destinies. A city or county has autonomy in deciding on its planning policy. The principal state-level policy for land management is based upon the 1965 California Land Conservation Act (CLCA) also known as the Williamson Act. As the model of Resource 4.15 shows, one of the pressures upon a farmer to sell land for development is the increase in tax demand as the value of the land rises. The central aim of the CLCA policy is to reduce the tax demand. The farmer undertakes a contract with the state agreeing not to sell the land for conversion for a 10 year period. In return, the farmer receives a reduced tax rating. This tax rating is based upon actual farmland values, not on the much higher development land values. The city or county in which the land lies then receives the difference from state funds. Over 15 million acres were protected under this programme in the early 1990s.

The main support for such protection at state level is the California Environmental Quality Act (CEQA), passed in 1970. Only in recent years have its key powers been applied to farmland conversion. This law requires an environmental impact assessment before allowing development which causes 'significant environmental impact'. The data base upon which decisions are made is being improved by the statewide Farmland Mapping and Monitoring Programme which uses remote sensing and Geographical Information Systems (GIS) techniques. Data updates allow managers to check the effectiveness of conservation programmes.

The key weaknesses of the CLCA programme are that it is voluntary and that a landowner cannot renew the contract after 10 years or can buy himself out before the due date. The programme has been least successful in protecting those prime lands around growing

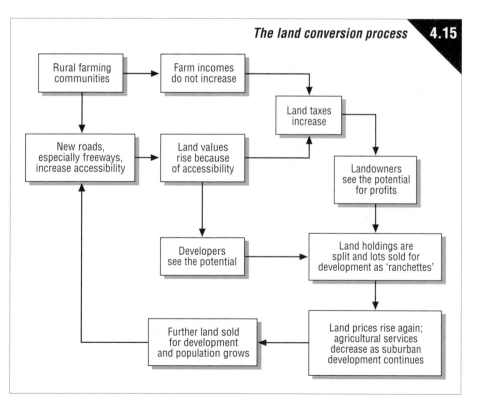

The land conversion process | **4.15**

Rural farming communities → Farm incomes do not increase

New roads, especially freeways, increase accessibility → Land values rise because of accessibility

Land taxes increase

Landowners see the potential for profits

Developers see the potential

Land holdings are split and lots sold for development as 'ranchettes'

Land prices rise again; agricultural services decrease as suburban development continues

Further land sold for development and population grows

CASE STUDY 4.1 *Urbanisation California style*

cities where development pressures are greatest. In places, developers will pay the buy-out costs. It is such a process which helps to explain the continuing rapid expansion of cities such as Bakersfield and Fresno.

The principal management tool required for each city and county is the General Plan, similar to UK structure plans. It is essentially a land-use plan based upon the *zoning* principle. The area within an authority is divided into zones according to preferred uses. Land which is zoned for farming has some protection, but an owner or developer can apply for change of use. They may succeed if:

- they make a strong enough case.
- if the authority wants the expansion.
- if the owner or developer wields enough political influence.

Land is especially vulnerable if the proposal is for very low density development, where not all of the land included would initially be lost to agriculture. However, as we have seen from the model of Resource 4.15, this fragmentation begins the process of suburbanisation.

Local management

Some of the most powerful checks to suburban sprawl have come from campaigns by pressure groups of local people. Many try to control and manage growth rather than to stop it altogether. They are not concerned solely with the protection of farmland. In American local politics, if a group of citizens can get enough signatures in support of a proposal, they can force a ballot. If this local vote is passed, it could force the council to pass legislation.

A study of 'slow growth' prosposals in 1987 showed that the three main concerns were pressures upon services, reduction in the quality of life and the need to preserve agricultural land. More than half of the California counties have recently passed such slow growth ordinances. Critics of this approach say it is elitist; campaigns by existing residents to protect themselves. The NIMBY or

Not In My Backyard syndrome can frequently be seen in planning protests in the UK. There is little doubt, however, that many communities have deeper concerns for the environment. In wealthier districts, more and more resident groups are buying open land to protect it and their lifestyles.

The combination of higher land and development costs, and increasing local resistance in zones close to existing urban areas helps to explain the 'leap-frogging' phenomenon. Developers find that they can buy land more cheaply if they target more distant districts. They also exploit the fact that many people are less inclined to join in on organised resistance. Developers can, thus, 'leap' beyond the existing suburban fringe and begin the fragmentation process.

Conclusion

There is no doubt that the low density suburban sprawl that has dominated recent Californian growth is economically and environmentally non-sustainable:

- it consumes land voraciously, putting pressure upon remaining farmlands and ecosystems.
- it has unnecessarily high infrastructural costs per person because people are so spread out.
- it is energy inefficient by causing heavy reliance upon the motor vehicle.
- it is wasteful of the most crucial natural resource in California – water. It is the limit to this resource which may form the ultimate constraint upon further growth. Already, desperate cities are buying up rural area water rights, thereby threatening agriculture. For example, one suburban Los Angeles city has purchased the water entitlement of a large cotton farm near Bakersfield and wants to transfer the water to its suburban homes.

There are increasing signs that at local level, management controls are strengthening, but the main concern is that there seems to be little co-

ordinated planning to develop overall strategies. An article published in 1992 concludes that California needs *to reorganise fragmented local government units to provide a co-ordinated public programme at the regional level. Without such fundamental political reorganisation and more widespread questioning of the growth ethic, the problems of unmanaged growth will lead to a further deterioration of the quality of life* (Goodenough, *Geography*, 1992).

[Main sources:
1. *Time*, 18 November 1991
2. Goodenough R. 'The nature and implications of recent population growth in California' *Geography*, 77(2), 335 April 1992, 123–133
3. 'Room to grow? Farmland conservation in California' *Land Use Policy*, January 1992, 21–35]

Activities

1 Describe the character of the suburbanisation in California.

2 What have been the main causes of the suburban explosion?

3 Outline the environmental and human benefits and costs of this form of settlement growth.

4 What are the main forms of land management illustrated in this case study and what are their principal weaknesses?

CASE STUDY 4.2

The compact city alternative: Australia and California

Background

Australian cities have experienced suburban sprawl as extensive as California's. In a large country with a population of approximately 20 million – less than California – this may not seem a problem. But there is growing concern at all levels in the country. In 1991, the then Prime Minister stated:

The unthinkable is starting to be thought. In some places we are running out of space. And not only running out of space, also out of air-fresh air and fresh water. The thoughtlessness of our approach to housing, the squandering of valuable virgin land and the social stress that distances and inaccessibility impose on individuals is now emerging as a major problem in our national life (Keating, P. *Housing choice and the future of the Australian city*, Public Policy Seminar, Canberra, 1991).

Sydney and Melbourne, in particular, have developed car-based, low density suburbs. They are perceived as the normal living environment, and have spread to the limits of comfortable car commuting. Key issues focus on land consumption, public investment costs of infrastructure, and private costs of mobility leading to social inequality. Only those who can afford it can enjoy this dispersed life-style.

As other countries, including the UK have found, changing the expectations of people and the shape of cities is a slow and difficult task. An Australian planner believes that *Australians in general are happy with their cities as long as they can have a reasonable house and land package and can afford the multiple car ownership it assumes.*

The sprawling low density form of modern Australian cities is the outcome of a set of interacting priorities in the decision-making of government, private developers and families. Part A of this case study argues that more compact cities make economic, social and environmental sense, but that the only way they will happen is by a significant shift in the set of priorities. Part B examines the results of research on whether living in California in more compact, integrated urban settlements does, in fact, make a difference to the amount we travel around in this car-dominated age.

City forming forces 4.17

Transport priorities

High priority is given to private car transport and is provided for in the infrastructure e.g. arterial roads and parking. During the twentieth century, the emphasis has shifted from walking *(5 km)* to public transit *(20–80 km)* to automobiles *(50 km)*.

Economic priorities

High priority is given for public investments to go into the development of suburban infrastructure e.g. roads, power, water, sewage, health and education. More investment into services is encouraged and less into industry.

Cultural priorities

Many people give a high priority to having plenty of open space. This is part of the frontier ethic of pioneering a vast new country. Australians desire and expect as much space as possible to be planned into their cities.

[After: Newman, 1992]

4.16

The 'Australian Dream': a young Brisbane couple survey the three acres on which they will build their home among the trees.

Part A: Concerns for the Australian urban environment

Resource 4.18 compares the six main Australian cities (Sydney, Melbourne, Brisbane, Adelaide, Perth, Canberra) to those in other continents. The figures show that Australian cities have broad similarities with the American cities, but are significantly different from European and Asian urban structures. The USA and Australia are both relatively young countries whose cities are very much nineteenth and twentieth century creations. For example, American and Australian cities are four times lower in overall population density than European cities and show a more rapid decline in density of population and jobs between central and outer districts. Australians use cars 10% less and public transport 15% more than their American counterparts. The use of cars for commuting in Australia is significantly higher than in Europe. Transport infrastructure reflects these patterns. European cities have only 25% of the roads and 50% of the central parking levels of Australian cities, and are six times better endowed in public transport. The figures support the idea of Australian cities as dominated by road vehicle travel and low density suburbs.

We can further analyse mass transit by comparing road provision ratio to actual usage of mass transit and roads for the cities. Resource 4.18 demonstrates this comparison. The ratio between access to mass transit and road provision can be expressed as follows:

$$\frac{\text{length of mass transit services in vehicle km/person}}{\text{length of road in km per person}}$$

Resource 4.19a plots this ratio or relative provision against car use. The scattergraph shows a clear relationship. As mass transit increases, so car usage levels decrease. There is a noticeable change in behaviour at around 20–30 km of mass transit service per kilometre of road.

How to read the graph

City A has a transit provision of 12 vehicle km/person and a car usage

Key understandings

◆ An increasing number of countries are searching for more efficient urban forms than suburban sprawl.

◆ Young Australian and North American cities have more dispersed urban forms than older European cities.

◆ The lower the population density, the lower the provision and use of public transport.

◆ More compact cities make public transport alternatives to the private car more feasible and popular.

◆ For compact cities to work, transport and land use policies must change with more public and less private transport priority, and integrated rather than segregated land uses.

◆ Accessibility may be defined in local and regional terms.

◆ Our movement patterns may be influenced both by the internal form of a community and by its relationship to external destinations.

4.18 **International comparisions of land use and transport**

	Australian cities	US cities	European cities	Asian cities
Land use				
• Urban density (total)				
– Population	13	14	54	160
– Jobs	5	7	31	71
• Central area density				
– Population12	54	92	149	
– Jobs	314	500	361	692
• Inner-city density				
– Population	22	45	91	464
– Jobs	24	30	79	296
• Outer area density				
– Population	12	11	43	115
– Jobs	4	5	17	43
Transport				
• Car use (pass.km/capita)	10,729	12,586	5,600	1,799
• Public transport use (pass.km/capita)	816	522	1,791	3,059
• Total travel (pass.km/capita)	11,545	13,108	7,391	4,858
• % Transit (of total travel)	7.2%	4.4%	24.8%	64.1%
• Walking/biking (% journeys to work)	5.4%	5.3%	21.3%	25.1%
Transport infrastructure				
• Transit service (km/capita)	57	30	79	103
• Road provision (metres/capita)	8.8	6.6	2.1	1.0
• Relative provision for transit (km of road)	7,063	5,690	40,621	242,491
• Parking spaces in CBD per 1000 CBD workers)	401	380	211	67

[Source: Newman and Kenworth, 1989]

4.19 **Transport and transit**

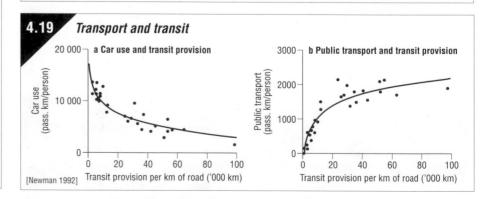

a Car use and transit provision

Car use (pass. km/person)

Transit provision per km of road ('000 km)

[Newman 1992]

b Public transport and transit provision

Public transport (pass. km/person)

Transit provision per km of road ('000 km)

level of 8000 passenger km/person. City B has a higher transit provision of 50 but a car use level of only 3000. Resource 4.19b shows that as mass transit provisions increase so does its usage levels.

Activities

1 Use Resources 4.20 a and b to establish the relationship between population density and travel mode patterns. (Look for a particular population density at which travel patterns seem to change.)

2 Use Resource 4.20c to support the hypothesis that low density cities have low levels of public transport provision, and that this provision increases as densities increase.

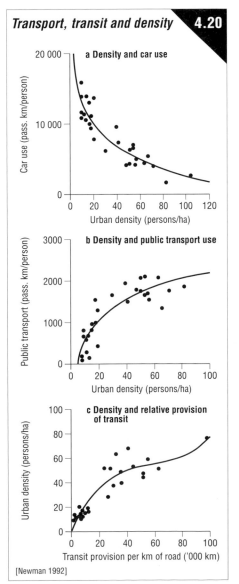

Transport, transit and density 4.20

a Density and car use

Car use (pass. km/person) vs Urban density (persons/ha)

b Density and public transport use

Public transport (pass. km/person) vs Urban density (persons/ha)

c Density and relative provision of transit

Urban density (persons/ha) vs Transit provision per km of road ('000 km)

[Newman 1992]

Advantages of the compact city

We can begin our support for a more compact urban form by summarising the disadvantages of car-dependent sprawling cities.

A study published in 1992 concluded that the issues set out in Resource 4.21 *show Australian cities are becoming less efficient economically, less sustainable in environmental terms, less socially equitable and less liveable in human terms*. (Newman, 1992). Above all, it is the economic costs of sprawling cities which arouse most criticism.

• They keep far too much capital tied up.
• They are costly to build.
• They are wasteful and expensive to maintain.

In 1991, for example, the total transport system costs in Australia were:

car system = 40c/km; rail system = 27 c/km; bus system = 23c/km. Sprawling cities waste time. The total time spent travelling per person is 310 hours/year in American cities, 274 in Australia, 235 in Europe and 203 in Asia.

It is not only in Australia that car-dependent, low density cities are criticised as environmentally non-sustainable and socially stressful. Photochemical smog from emissions, vulnerability to oil crises, atmospheric impacts from CO_2, noises and accidents are global environmental issues. The social stresses and inequalities of opportunity emphasised by suburbanisation are also world-wide. More than half of the Australian population do not drive or have access to a car. They are disadvantaged in relation to access to jobs, services, friends and leisure when cities are so spread out.

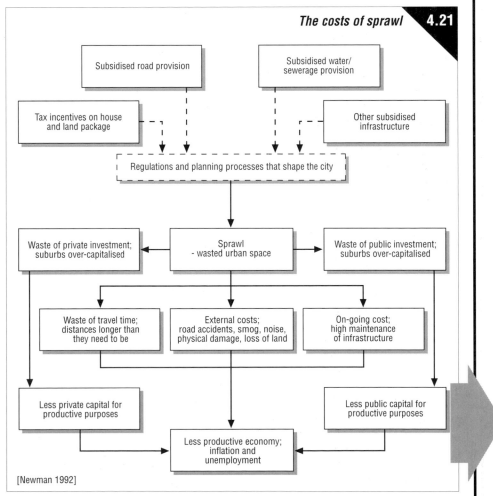

The costs of sprawl 4.21

[Newman 1992]

CASE STUDY 4.2 *The compact city alternative: Australia and California*

4.22 Technology and urban form

A Sprawl city
(facilitates continued dispersal and sprawl linked by cars)

Individual household based

Transport
- Cleaner cars
- Electric cars
- Electronic guidance on freeways

- O-Bahn buses
- Flexible buses as main transit supplementing car system

Telecommunications and computers
- Household-based office technology (fax/computer/video phone)

Other technology
- Large-scale industry (prevents re-integration)

- Large-scale water management systems

- Household-based solid waste management

B Compact city
(facilitates nodal centres or urban villages linked by quality transit)

Community based

Transport
- Electric heavy rail (spinal connections)
- Electric light rail (subcentre connections)
- Bicycles and community-based bicycle infrastructure
- Community-based car rental systems
- Demand-responsive local buses (satellite communications, smart cards) as supplement to main transit system

Telecommunications and computers
- Telecottages (community-based fax/computer/video phone centres)
- Sub-centre-based 'smart' office buildings (equivalent to CBDs)

Other technology
- Clean production systems and small-scale industry (reintegrates industry)
- Community-based water management systems
- Community-based solid waste management

Whether Australia shifts towards a more compact urban form depends upon the priorities given to housing types and transport. Resource 4.22 lists some of the options using new transport opportunities. The keys to a compact city include:

- public transport priority.
- priority to community-oriented technology not individual oriented technology.
- integration not separation of land uses within the metropolis – homes, work, services in a series of sub-cities or edge cities linked by transit and modern telecommunication systems.

The resulting city would be multi-nuclear or polycentric, still very large, but at higher densities than the existing suburbanised pattern. Jobs and services would be less concentrated, but distributed in the sub-cities, or urban villages. The need for travel is reduced.

Government at federal and state levels in Australia have begun to give priority to more compact developments. For example, the Federal government is putting $850 million into a 'better cities' programme which will sponsor higher density, transit-oriented demonstration schemes, with affordable housing near to jobs and services. In Western Australia there is a new light rail system and several high density housing schemes. In Canberra, the national capital, which is a classic example of a low-density planned city built for car use, a new town plan calls for infilling at higher densities and the development of experimental light rail schemes. The 1990 population of 280 000 was stretched over 34 km.

Part B: Do compact cities reduce car travel?

The effectiveness of compact cities, with integrated rather than segregated land uses, can be measured by whether or not they reduce the level of car travel. Many studies have shown that such layouts, supported by public transport systems have a significant effect upon the journey to and from work i.e.commuting. The complex patterns of non-work travel such as shopping and leisure are often not taken into account. A study carried out in the San Francisco Bay area of California in 1990, has addressed this question. The study was based upon an analysis of *accessibility* i.e. the ease with which interactions can take place. This concept involves how attractive the potential destinations are and the cost in time, distance and money of reaching them.

We need to understand that there are two distinct types of accessibility which influence our lives: local and regional.

Local accessibility can be defined as patterns within the local community, primarily determined by nearby activities located in small centres, and generating relatively short and frequent trips by residents.

Regional accessibility can be defined as patterns of movement beyond the community, defined with respect to large regional shopping centres, and generating relatively long and infrequent trips by residents.

This way of thinking about accessibility clearly relates to the concept of the polycentric city, as a series of communities, urban villages and sub-cities set within a metropolitan region.

The research study was based upon this hypothesis: *That the amount a person travels is influenced by both the character of the community in which he/she lives and the spatial structure of the region within which the community is set*. In order to test this hypothesis, four communities in

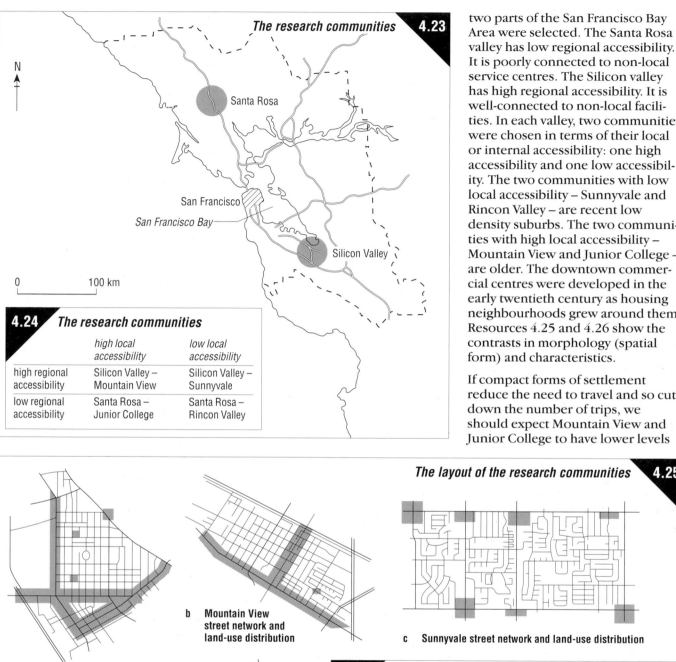

N

0   100 km

4.24 The research communities

	high local accessibility	low local accessibility
high regional accessibility	Silicon Valley – Mountain View	Silicon Valley – Sunnyvale
low regional accessibility	Santa Rosa – Junior College	Santa Rosa – Rincon Valley

Santa Rosa

San Francisco

San Francisco Bay

Silicon Valley

two parts of the San Francisco Bay Area were selected. The Santa Rosa valley has low regional accessibility. It is poorly connected to non-local service centres. The Silicon valley has high regional accessibility. It is well-connected to non-local facilities. In each valley, two communities were chosen in terms of their local or internal accessibility: one high accessibility and one low accessibility. The two communities with low local accessibility – Sunnyvale and Rincon Valley – are recent low density suburbs. The two communities with high local accessibility – Mountain View and Junior College – are older. The downtown commercial centres were developed in the early twentieth century as housing neighbourhoods grew around them. Resources 4.25 and 4.26 show the contrasts in morphology (spatial form) and characteristics.

If compact forms of settlement reduce the need to travel and so cut down the number of trips, we should expect Mountain View and Junior College to have lower levels

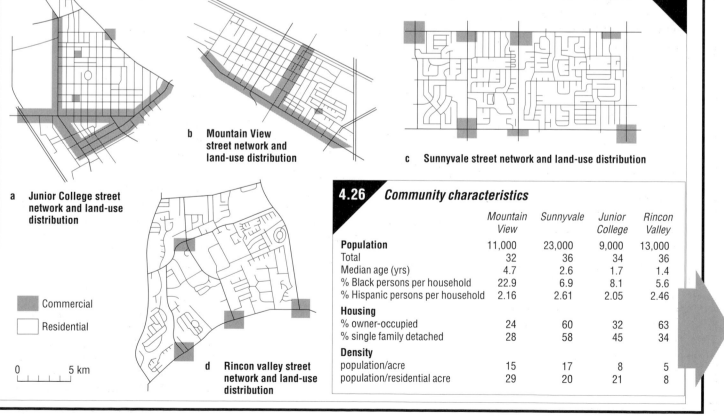

4.25 The layout of the research communities

a Junior College street network and land-use distribution

b Mountain View street network and land-use distribution

c Sunnyvale street network and land-use distribution

d Rincon valley street network and land-use distribution

■ Commercial
□ Residential

0   5 km

4.26 Community characteristics

	Mountain View	Sunnyvale	Junior College	Rincon Valley
Population	11,000	23,000	9,000	13,000
Total	32	36	34	36
Median age (yrs)	4.7	2.6	1.7	1.4
% Black persons per household	22.9	6.9	8.1	5.6
% Hispanic persons per household	2.16	2.61	2.05	2.46
Housing				
% owner-occupied	24	60	32	63
% single family detached	28	58	45	34
Density				
population/acre	15	17	8	5
population/residential acre	29	20	21	8

of car trip generation both within the community and across the region. They have high local accessibility. Thus, the community populations have easy access to services. This is supported by the layouts shown in Resource 4.25. The transport networks are in traditional rectangular grids with smaller blocks, more intersections, higher road densities, and are connected to the regional road system in the newer suburbs of Sunnyvale and Rincon Valley. The Mountain View and Junior College commercial facilities are linear and immediately surrounded by residential streets, making walking easy. This contrasts with Sunnyvale and Rincon Valley where commercial activity is focused on intersections of the arterial roads, and are less accessible on foot.

To test the hypothesis that spatial layout influences non-work travel patterns, residents of the four communities were asked how often they had walked to the local commercial centres in the past month. The results summarised in Resource 4.28 show that Mountain View and Junior College residents, who live in

layouts with high local accessibility did take walking trips more frequently. Car use for non-work local trips does seem to be reduced in more compact and integrated suburban layouts. The study concludes *that appropriately designed and well-integrated local commercial centres will in fact be used by local residents, who will walk rather than drive there for the most part* (Handy, 1992, p263).

Regional travel outside the local community

Because people tend to use regional centres less frequently than local centres, the study used a four-month period for regional visits. The results are summarised in Resource 4.29. The figures show that regional accessibility does influence trip frequency as in the Silicon valley communities. Mountain View and Sunnyvale, with their high regional accessibility, record higher trip frequencies than the Santa Rosa communities. However, if we look again at local trip generation, Mountain View scores highly there too. Thus, in this community, easy access to local facil-

ities does not appear to reduce the tendency for regional trips. It shows high levels of both local and regional accessibility. People seem to take more trips overall. The picture is different for the Santa Rosa valley communities, with their low regional accessibility. The high local accessibility in Junior College does seem to reduce regional trips to a slightly lower level than in Rincon Valley where there is low local accessibility. This supports the hypothesis that high local accessibility reduces regional travel. The study suggests that the high local *and* regional travel scores for Mountain View occur because the community is unusually accessible to a broad range of regional shopping malls.

The study findings are, therefore, uncertain. Although high local accessibility does increase the number of walking trips, it is not clear whether these replace or are in addition to local car trips. The results are ambiguous as to whether higher levels of local trips do in fact reduce regional trip levels, or that people simply travel more when both local and regional accessibility are improved.

4.27 Network characteristics

	Mountain View	Sunnyvale	Junior College	Rincon Valley
Area (sq. miles)	1.12	2.00	1.51	3.91
Road miles	21	34	27	39
No. of blocks	109	96	128	66
No. of intersections	163	255	183	208
Blocks/sq. mile	98	48	85	17
Intersections/sq. mile	146	127	121	53

4.28 Trips to local centres

	Mountain View	Sunnyvale	Junior College	Rincon Valley
Number to local centre	4.85	2.75	5.69	1.00
% respondents who took walking trips to the local centre	56	48	64	24

4.29 Trips to regional centres (trips within past four months)

	Mountain View	Sunnyvale	Junior College	Rincon Valley
No.of trips	15.92	13.97	11.01	12.16
% trips by car	92	89	82	94

Activities

1 In what ways are Australian cities distinctive from European and Asian cities?

2 Why have Australians become so concerned about the way their cities are developing?

3 Make two lists to show:
   a the advantages and disadvantages of low density cities.
   b the advantages and disadvantages of compact cities.

4 Define *accessibility* as used in this case study, and give examples.

5 To what extent do the examples in this case study support the idea that urban form is dependent upon the priorities of decision-makers?

6 From the data in this case study, evaluate the hypothesis that there is a positive relationship between accessibility and trip generation.

CASE STUDY 4.3

Making cities safer: the female perspective

Background

As geography is concerned with the ways in which space is organised, managed and used, two central concepts of the subject are *access* and *accessibility*. Because you have the right of access to a resource or facility does not necessarily mean it is accessible to you. Accessibility refers to ease of access. For example, unless ramps, lifts and support rails are provided in shops, libraries and other public places, they are not readily accessible to the elderly or the disabled.

Perception has an important bearing upon the accessibility of a place. A factor which influences the accessibility of a place to you is whether you *feel* safe in getting there and being there. Cities are increasingly perceived as threatening and unsafe environments. A private organisation called *Comedia* published a report in 1992 called *Out of Hours*, based on a survey of ten city centres in the UK. The results showed that such areas are perceived as 'no go' zones by significant sections of society. The problems of safety do not occur only in city centres. In residential districts, transport systems, leisure environments and even the home, fears for personal safety seem to be intensifying.

Any individual or section of society whose movements and activities are

Subways are quite often seen as 'unsafe' areas

constrained by fears of abuse, assault or robbery may be classified as disadvantaged. They endure reduced accessibility and quality of life because they perceive certain routes and places as unsafe. A wide range of factors influence these perceptions. Women in general perceive themselves as especially and unjustifiably restricted. This case study is based on findings of the Home Office funded 'Safer Cities Project' and a series of meetings held in a university and attended by womens'

groups and planning officers. The materials outline the issues and the main perceptions, and suggest how urban environments, including transport services, city centres, residential areas, could be managed to improve accessibility for women, that is, how urban managers could help women to feel safer. As you follow the discussion, note particularly the situations which generate fear, what might be done, what women prefer and what the potential costs are .

Key understandings

- ◆ Accessibility, ease of access, is significantly influenced by perceptions of safety.
- ◆ Women perceive themselves as especially and unjustifiably at risk in a number of urban environments.
- ◆ Locations vary in their perceived level of safety.
- ◆ Environmental planning and management can influence the reality and perceptions of fear and safety.
- ◆ There is no general agreement on the solutions.

Even where urban parks are landscaped to improve environmental quality the result might produce decreased use because the additional foliage creates potential hiding places for muggers.

Safer cities for women

Perceived risks and planning measures

Recent surveys have shown that approximately two-thirds of women are afraid to go out alone at night; many will not use public transport or city centres in the evening. A recent Nottingham study found that almost half of those who do use the city centre in the evening feel 'very' or 'fairly' unsafe. In Bradford, 60% of the women surveyed will not use public transport at night. This perception of fear which denies women the evening use of town centres, has significant economic costs. For instance, the Nottingham Safer Cities project estimated the economic loss at £24 million a year and 600 jobs for a city such as Nottingham.

The design of the urban environment could be changed to make it 'safer', but this will not work without also bringing about a shift in behaviour. Surveys claim that British town centres are dominated by noisy groups of young men who have been drinking, whereas in many European cities, young men and women 'socialise' in bars and cafes. This shared use of city centre facilities by both sexes creates a safer atmosphere. For example, the squares and streets of Athens are thronged by young Greeks until the early hours of the morning, so much so that the Greek government is trying to force cafes and clubs to close earlier. This is not primarily because of unruly behaviour, but to reduce lateness to work the following day!

In 1988, as part of the 'Action for Cities Initiative', the government launched its 'Safer Cities Programme'. Its primary aim has been *to create safer cities where economic enterprise and community life can flourish* (Trench et al, 1992). Projects have been funded in twenty cities which have been identified as having high crime rates and a range of economic problems: Birmingham, Bradford, Coventry, Derby, Hartlepool, Hull, Hammersmith, Islington, Leicester, Lewisham, Middlesbrough, Nottingham, Rochdale, Salford, Sunderland, Tower Hamlets, Wandsworth, Wirral and Wolverhampton. There were two distinct approaches to these policies: segregation, involving separate services and facilities for women; and general environmental improvements.

Segregated transport schemes for women

Buses

The idea of public transport provision for women only has been tried in several cities. The first scheme began in 1988 in Bristol, after pressure resulting from a series of rapes and violent attacks. The service provides door-to-door service during the evenings for women who cannot afford or are afraid to use other forms of transport. It is popular, and must be booked well in advance as there are only two vehicles available, both adapted for wheelchairs and operated by volunteer drivers. Priority is given to women on low incomes, ethnic minority women, disabled, elderly and young women, and those with a particularly strong fear of violence.

The similar 'Homerunner' service started in Bradford in 1989. This service has three buses and targets the same groups as the Bristol scheme, plus shift workers, who make up 60% of the passengers. It operates 6 to 11 pm, Monday to Saturday, with a flat rate fare which covers about one-third of the costs. The deficits have been made up by the Bradford Safer City Project and the West Yorkshire Passenger Transport Authority. The popularity of the service with workers has raised the possibility of sponsorship by employers.

At least seven other cities have operated door-to-door schemes. They are small-scale and demand is much greater than the supply. The researchers have found that the schemes do help women's mobility and believe there is a strong case for all local authorities to run similar subsidised ventures. Critics argue, however, that such schemes *perpetuate the notion that women must operate under some kind of curfew and thus may actually contribute to increasing women's fear of crime, discouraging even more women from using public transport* (Trench et al, 1992).

Michigan Avenue, Chicago

Cars and taxis

It is known that women have far less access to cars than men do. Even in car-owning households, they are only half as likely to hold a driving licence and to have the use of the family car. Those who do use cars frequently mention two problems:

- having to leave the security of the car in case of a breakdown.
- the vulnerability to attack in car parks, especially in multi-storey car parks.

Easier availability of car-phones and the provision of 'women only' parking bays in well-lit sections of car parks, near entrances are suggested as partial solutions.

Use of taxis is undoubtedly increasing and is a safety net for women without cars. However, some women claim to have had bad experiences with taxi drivers, especially from 'mini-cab' drivers in London. More formal licensing and registration for all forms of private-hire operators would improve control. There are London-based schemes which are run for and by women, for example, the Lady Cab service.

Making public transport safer

Many women feel that the only effective solution is to make public transport much safer. A number of towns do have imaginative and sensible schemes. These include extra staffing at rail and bus stations, conductors on evening buses, and 'hail-and-ride' minibus services which penetrate housing estates and take passengers very close to their homes. The major problem is cost. The deregulation and privatisation of the public transport system has reduced the opportunities for subsidies as local authorities have less money to spend and the private companies need to make profits. The layout of many housing estates, with peripheral main roads round the edge and narrow access roads to the houses make door-to-door pick-up and drop-off impractical.

Not all improvements need be costly, however. Moving bus stops close to shops, petrol stations or other well-lit and used locations reduces the isolation feared by women. Stockport has experimented with evening 'hail-and-ride' routes through housing estates, and has found that more people have used the buses, thereby increasing income with very little extra expense. On some London rail routes, passengers are allowed to wait in the well-lit station entrance until the train arrives, rather than waiting on a dark and perhaps almost empty platform. Tyne & Wear runs shorter trains in the evening in order to concentrate the passengers, again reducing the potential for isolation.

Environmental enhancement

Surveillance is another key to feeling safer. Surveys consistently find that women feel safer when there are a lot of people around and when they can be seen by others. This is true for city centres and residential areas. Improved surveillance can be achieved by mixing together different land uses and by the design of street environments.

This sounds like a straightforward idea. If a number of activities are mixed in one district there will be more people around for longer hours of the day and evening. This has been called the urban village idea. The problem is that one of the principles of town planning over the past 50 years has been *functional separation*. It uses zoning to segregate home, work and leisure land uses. Thus, factories and offices have been taken out of residential districts and located in areas zoned for industry and commerce. Even neighbourhood shops have left, to reappear on large 'out-of-town' developments. The CBD has become progressively dominated by business uses, many of which are empty after 6.00 pm, leaving only pubs, fast-food outlets, clubs and the few surviving theatres and cinemas. The combination of planning policy and rising land prices have displaced housing and other uses which cannot afford the high rents.

A solution, therefore, is to encourage a wider range of activities to return to central locations, for example, swimming pools and sports facilities, modern shopping malls and cinemas. Existing facilities, such as libraries and cafes, should also be encouraged to stay open in the evenings. Such changes would create a livelier, safer atmosphere for longer hours, as surveillance would be higher. It can be done, as examples from North American cities have shown, despite their more violent urban culture. For instance, one of Chicago's finest downtown streets is North Michigan Avenue. During the 1980s, apartments for 20 000 residents were built, a range of leisure activities introduced and street design improved. This created a balanced and mixed district with its core along Michigan Avenue as an *activity corridor*. However, this idea of focusing environmental enhancement along a few streets or activity corridors could lead to the perception that other areas are less safe.

In the short term, two obvious and economic strategies are to install closed-circuit television and to improve street lighting.

4.33

The isolation of public transport

CASE STUDY 4.3 *Making cities safer: the female perspective*

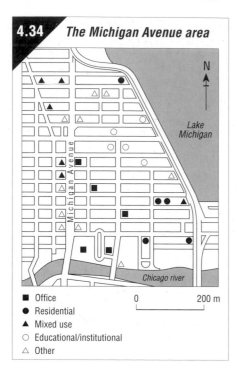

4.34 The Michigan Avenue area

N

Lake Michigan

Michigan Avenue

Chicago river

- ■ Office
- ● Residential
- ▲ Mixed use
- ○ Educational/institutional
- △ Other

0   200 m

Women's groups rejected the idea of closed circuit television. They *made it clear that they very definitely do not feel more secure in the knowledge that someone else is supposed to be watching them. This did not mean immediate help if they had a problem* (Trench et al, 1992). In contrast, research in the London Borough of Hammersmith and Fulham showed a clear reduction in women's perceptions of fear when lighting was improved. A number of cities, including Birmingham, Harlow, Manchester, Southhampton and Wandsworth, have introduced schemes for upgrading lighting in selected areas. Lighting has its disadvantages: *It may be unwise to light areas which are particularly dangerous or isolated, since the lighting may create the impression that the area is safer at night than it actually is. In addition, many people are disturbed by the tendency for groups of youths to congregate at night in well-lit spaces. The quality* and *detail of the lighting is also important: for example, women particularly dislike the intermittent lighting ... which is activated by movement, and the sudden burst of light can be very alarming. People are unable to see into the space before moving into it* (Trench et al, 1992).

Two urban components which pose particular problems for women's safety are subways and car-parks. Pedestrian subways were typical features of 1960s traffic management policies which gave priority to the movement of motor vehicles. Despite efforts to improve them, they remain barren and dangerous places. Increasing numbers of cities are removing them and replacing them with surface crossings. Some are moving the motor vehicles underground and giving the well-lit streets over to people. Birmingham has already redesigned some of its central roads to eliminate pedestrian subways. By 1992, Glasgow, Sheffield, Portsmouth and Poole had proposals and schemes for similar changes.

Car parks, especially multi-storey structures, present many problems. They are normally unstaffed, poorly lit and have many obscured areas such as stairs and lifts. Apart from improvements in lighting, the two most promising ideas are the provision of women-only sections and making it possible for women to avoid car parks by increasing on-street parking, particularly in the evening. Women-only sections would be in supervised, well-lit, groundfloor areas near the entrances. Birmingham, Leicester and Nuneaton all have schemes of car park enhancement. But as some women claim, this isolates women even more and makes them more conspicuous.

Activities

1 List *three* places or routes you are reluctant to use because you feel they are 'unsafe'. Suggest reasons why you feel unsafe in these places or along these routes. Does whether you are male or female affect your perception?

2 Draw a 'mental map' of the routes between your home and a local town or city centre. Mark on it the form of transport you use and shade or label the places and sections where you feel unsafe. Suggest the causes of this feeling and what might be done to improve your 'accessibility'. Do your feelings of safety vary at different times of the day, the week or the year? If so, why?

Project suggestion

a Identify a definable area, such as a town centre, the catchment area of a leisure centre or a kilometre grid square on a large scale map.

b On a large scale map, 1:10 000 or preferably 1:2500, mark those locations and areas which you perceive as unsafe (i) at all times, (ii) at certain times, (iii) for certain groups of people – state who they are. (You can use colour or symbol systems to differentiate these catgeories).

c On your map, mark any locations where there have been management inputs to improve safety.

d Identify types of location and situation which appear to be particularly threatening and suggest causes for this.

e For *two* locations or routes you have identified as being unsafe, propose solutions. Suggest who would have to bear the cost and carry out the improvements.

CASE STUDY 4.4 — *Can cycling be an option for the city?*

4.35

Cyclists in traffic. This is a 'hard hat' area.

Background

Ease of movement, that is, mobility and accessibility, is crucial to modern lifestyles, now that we have physically separated the key elements of our lives - home, work and play. Yet getting around our cities seems increasingly problematic. Cities are increasingly unable to cope with road traffic levels. Every day we face evidence of congestion, accidents, air and noise pollution. This awareness of the environmental, economic and social costs of the motor vehicle, is arousing growing interest in the potential of more environmentally-friendly modes of transport.

The bicycle is an obvious choice for urban mobility: it does not take up much space, it is cheap, flexible, environmentally-friendly, is good for our health and available to all able-bodied people across a wide age-range. Yet in the UK, cycling in cities has become a hazardous adventure and a mode of transport largely ignored by urban planners. Until the late 1970s, cycle networks were part of the overall town plan in only a few new towns, such as Harlow and Stevenage. Government policy was dominated by provision of roads and parking for the motor vehicle.

Cycling was seen as *a residual and declining form of transport* (McClintock & Cleary, 1993). Cyclists were forced to compete with pedestrians on paths and in forbidding subways, or with motorists on the carriageways, and were enormously unpopular with both. Only at the end of the 1970s, as government and planners faced the twin threats of daily urban 'gridlock' and the economic, environmental and political costs of restricting cars and providing public transport systems, did

Key understandings

◆ Cycling is a cheap, flexible, environmentally-friendly option for urban transport.

◆ Cycle routes have been largely ignored in urban planning and design in the UK.

◆ Cyclists must compete with other users for scarce space in crowded urban environments.

◆ Safety, sharing or segregation are crucial factors in planning cycle routes.

◆ Urban environments vary in their potential for incorporating cycle routes.

attention turn to the potential of the humble bicycle.

In 1982 the central government Department of Transport (DOT) intended to support a series of experiments to assess how cycles might be used in urban areas. The DOT invited cities to submit schemes and bid for support funding. By 1985, schemes had been approved in six cities: Bedford, Cambridge, Exeter, Nottingham, Southampton and Stockton. This case study examines the largest of these, the Greater Nottingham Network Project (GNNP), whose development was monitored by researchers until 1991. The research aimed to find out the effects of the scheme:

- Did more people use bicycles?
- Did cyclists' routes and journey times change?
- Did cycling become safer?
- Did attitudes to cycling change?
- What was the effect on other modes of transport?

As you follow the study, you may find it provides a useful basis for a field investigation in your home region.

Assessing a cycle network experiment in Nottingham

The network

When Nottingham applied to join the national DOT scheme, the city had already developed several individual cycle routes. The 20 km routes comprised four sections along the Trent river valley in the south and south-west of the conurbation. The GNNP became the main component of a broader network. The area was selected for three main reasons. It is relatively flat and conducive to cycling. It includes several university campuses with considerable numbers of actual or potential young cyclists. It is less-densely built up than the northern conurbation and has more available space for introducing cycle routes.

The scheme included the upgrading of existing footpaths, the introduction of new cycle paths, the conversion of a footbridge from steps to a ramp incline, and nine signalled road crossings. Signposted 'advisory cycle routes' along quieter back streets were added to the 20 km of cycle paths, giving a total network of 37 km. Where possible, the network followed routes already used by cyclists, in the hope that this would increase the chances of success. Three important features are

- that the network can be progressively linked to additional housing, leisure and work areas.
- it must be related to overall transport policy.
- the cycle paths can be an element in environmental enhancement schemes, e.g. 'green' corridors.

Problems which emerged

It took longer to implement the scheme than the planners had anticipated. The decision-makers held conflicting attitudes and priorities. These decision-makers included the DOT, the East Midlands Regional Office of the DOT, the County Council, the District Councils and their various departments such as Planning, Housing and Recreation. There were pressures from various special interest groups, such as *Pedal* (a group campaigning for cycle routes), local residents and groups concerned for pedestrians and the disabled. Two examples from the research findings illustrate these issues:

1 The GNNP involved crossing Nottingham's Outer Ring Road at a flyover and roundabout junction near the University. The planners wanted a signalised crossing, to be used jointly by cyclists and pedestrians. The DOT Regional Office opposed it on the grounds that it would hinder the main purpose of the junction, which was to increase the flow capacity for motor vehicles. An experimental scheme funded by the central DOT, was being opposed by the regional DOT office who were fulfilling their main purpose as they saw it, namely, to improve motor vehicle flows on trunk roads.

2 The Nottingham Recreation Department were reluctant to modify parks by adding cycle paths. The city Land Department was *keener to maximise the value of assets than to provide small parcels of land for cycle links* (McClintock & Cleary, 1993). They saw their priority as keeping land in blocks large enough to encourage developers to invest. The Housing Department was concerned over safety in residential streets and who would pay for installing and maintaining paths through housing neighbourhoods. The British Waterways Board was not keen to release land or to upgrade towpaths and was worried about complaints from pedestrians.

The need to resolve conflicts between pedestrians, cyclists and motor vehicles, was urgent. It arose because of the problem of fitting the cycle paths into an already cramped environment. Outside the main built-up area the problem was less severe. For example, along the stretch of main road between Clifton

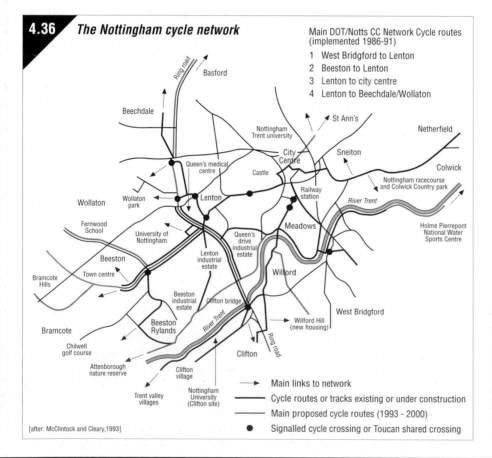

4.36 *The Nottingham cycle network*

Main DOT/Notts CC Network Cycle routes (implemented 1986–91)
1 West Bridgford to Lenton
2 Beeston to Lenton
3 Lenton to city centre
4 Lenton to Beechdale/Wollaton

→ Main links to network
── Cycle routes or tracks existing or under construction
── Main proposed cycle routes (1993 – 2000)
● Signalled cycle crossing or Toucan shared crossing

[after: McClintock and Cleary, 1993]

Average weekday cycle flows, 1985–90

	1985	1986	1987	1988	1989	1990
Nottingham	7921	6313	5920	6360	7237	5986
Cambridge	10402	NA	9684	NA	8721	9299
Southampton	NA	NA	2445	2462	2520	2278
Cycle mileage in GB (bill.km)	6.06	5.46	5.74	5.23	5.16	5.27

NA = Not available

[Source: McClintock and Cleary, 1993]

Cycling as a leisure activity

Bridge roundabout and the University Clifton site a high standard, broad cycle path was built. Due to flood risk, its route was taken partially away from the road, thus excluding the floodplain from development. Because the route was away from houses, there was little opposition from local residents. It is now popular as a leisure route because it links with shared (pedestrian/cyclist) paths along the attractive riverside. In contrast, the problems were greater between the Clifton junction and the city centre, where building and traffic densities are higher. For example, there were more road crossings, and local residents complained of danger from cyclists and of the cycle route attracting 'undesirables' into the neighbourhood.

Another reason for slow progress was delay in other road and environmental projects with which the GNNP had to be co-ordinated. The upgrading of the Clifton flyover and the pedestrianisation of city centre streets took some time to complete.

Effects of the experiment

From field observations of use and interviews with users and residents, the researchers grouped their findings under four headings:

Usage flows

To assess success or failure by whether more or fewer people cycled at the end of the project, proved difficult. The popularity of cycling is changing, both in Nottingham and across the UK. Resource 4.38 shows that the Nottingham scheme, along with the other DOT city schemes, did not record increased usage of cycles. However, the percentage fall in usage was less than that recorded nationally. Usage levels seemed to fluctuate widely from year to year for the Nottingham scheme. The researchers attributed this to the prevailing weather conditions at the times of the surveys. The user surveys were conducted over two weeks each October: in 1989 the weather was dry, whereas in 1987 and 1990 there were a number of wet days. That a higher proportion of the total cyclists used the cycle paths, was evident. They had switched from using roads, thereby improving safety. If the research had been continued through the 1990s, levels may well have increased as cycling has revived in popularity. For example, from 1992–94 there was a 50% increase in student use of bicycles at Birmingham University.

Among users of GNNP, the new facilities ranked as less important than cost, flexibility and health. Women and less-experienced cyclists in particular used GNNP more frequently, particularly for safety reasons. Time and distance was still seen as a problem, though. The GNNP routes tended to be longer than the most direct route along roads. Thus, experienced and male cyclists tended to continue to use the roads. It is a major incentive to increased use if a cycle route can cut travel time. For example, in Exeter a new cycle bridge reduced journey times by up to 40% and encouraged more people to cycle.

Accident rates

Between 1985 and 1990, road traffic densities in Nottingham increased by almost 20%. During the same period, in the northern districts of the city, cycle accidents increased. In the south and west, the area of GNNP, accidents declined slightly. Remember that *feeling* safe is equally important as *being* safe. The research showed that the new facilities *helped to make cyclists, especially female cyclists, feel safer* (McClintock & Cleary, 1993).

Attitudes to cycle use

Convenience, flexibility, independence and cost were all popular views held by cyclists. However, the research showed that cultural influences also affect usage. In districts where cycling is already an accepted part of the local culture, improved facilities quickly result in increased use. In districts such as North Nottingham where cycling has been regarded as unsafe, it may take some time to change attitudes, even when the new cycle paths are installed and signposted.

Impacts on other modes of transport

In the Nottingham survey, approximately 80% of cyclists interviewed were from car-owning households, but only 25% said they would be using a car if they were not cycling. One-third said the alternative would be to use a bus. Interviews at three major employers found that over one-half of cyclists had switched from driving a car, 23% from walking, and 14% from buses. More women had changed than men, which suggests an increase in the feeling of safety.

Lessons to be learned from the scheme

- The potential for cycle use varies according to the type of environment. For example, North Nottingham is hillier, more densely built-up and has less of a 'bike culture' than South Nottingham. It appears to have less potential for cycle use.
- Shortage of space is a critical problem to cycle routes, as cycles must compete for this resource. This issue is especially intense in the city centre. For example, the cycle route from Clifton towards central Nottingham encounters the Inner Ring Road. Once inside the CBD the multiple traffic components all clash at crucial intersections with bus lanes, general vehicle lanes, pedestrians and cyclists.
- Highway and planning authorities should consider the movement of cycles in any proposal for new developments. In Nottingham several central streets have been

Canal Street crossing, north Nottingham

pedestrianised, but cyclists have been excluded. A new *Tourist Trail*, part of the city's Heritage Tourism policy, has been created by pedestrianising the streets between the Lace Market and the castle. This was a popular route for cyclists, but after much controversy, they have been banned.

- The leisure potential of cycle paths could be realised by improved linkages of the network to the countryside, for example, along the Trent river and to Country Parks. This would encourage *non-car based recreational trips and a more 'environment-friendly' pattern of tourism* (McClintock & Cleary, 1993).
- Consultation with user groups and local people is essential from the beginning of a scheme.
- Segregation or sharing of paths and crossings by pedestrians and cyclists is one of the most sensitive issues. It must be decided by circumstances and not by cost alone. Although 75% of pedestrians interviewed said they did not object to the presence of cyclists, controversy does occur at critical points, such as subways, crossings

and narrow sections. For example, in 1987 when Beeston High Road was pedestrianised through the shopping centre, cyclists were permitted, but no specific lane was marked out. Shoppers and delivery vehicles complained. As a result, *all* wheeled traffic except vehicles for the disabled are banned between 10:00 and 16:00 hours. Crossings are especially problematic as they tend to occur at key congestion points. It is accepted that they must be shared. The new 'toucan' crossings, for example, are designed for dual use.

- Even on well-designed, clearly-marked shared paths, inappropriate behaviour by users can cause conflict.
- The signposting of cycle routes through quieter residential streets is useful, but there are problems. Parked cars can be a hazard, road surfaces may be poor and residents may object.
- Cycle paths can be an appropriate element in environmental enhancement schemes such as 'green corridors', greenways, and 'green routes' through residential areas. Finding the space and

Cyclists and pedestrians often share the same path

Cycling in China

deciding who pays and maintains them can create problems. There is the possibility that increasing the foliage reduces safety, especially for women and children.

- There must be secure, well-designed and convenient parking provision for cycles at the destination ends of networks.

Conclusions

The Nottingham research seems to show limited increases in cycle use and raises all sorts of problems. Yet it is not really impractical for cycling to be a significant part of urban life. After all, city dwellers in other countries still cycle. It is now accepted by all interest groups that there will be tightening restrictions on private car use in cities. Mass transit options are costly and take many years to develop, whereas cycle networks are relatively cheap and quick to install and are environmentally friendly.

Activities

1 Why do some pedestrians object to sharing paths with cyclists? Where is the conflict most likely to occur, and how can the problems be overcome?

2 Briefly state the main advantages of cycle use in urban areas and the main problems associated with increased use.

The mass transit option in Manchester

Project suggestion

a In your home region, select one of the following: a residential neighbourhood; a town centre or CBD; a route between a residential area and a large educational institution.

b Design and carry out a survey which covers all or some of the following: Patterns of existing cycle use; location of critical problem spots, and what causes

them; areas *not* used by cyclists; and attitudes of local people to cycling and cyclists – users and non-users.

c For all or one section of your survey area, propose a method for improving cycle use (Use plans, sketches, photos to support your written report).

In your survey design and report, use the materials of the case study to guide you.

CASE STUDY 4.5 — *Managing hazards in urban environments*

Background

Increasing numbers of people are living in zones of hazard created by natural and human processes. Hazards become disasters when they cause severe disruption to the natural processes. Disasters resulting from hazards fall into a number of types. Urbanised regions are especially vulnerable because they crowd large numbers of people and activities together and have very complex infrastructures. An earthquake in Tokyo or Los Angeles has quite a different effect from a similar event in a sparsely-populated part of Iran, for example.

Public authorities and commercial enterprises in cities where natural and technological hazards are known, have responded by setting up disaster response systems. The inhabitants are keyed in to these systems, and make their own preparations. In San Francisco, which is vulnerable to earthquakes, all schools, colleges and places of work have regular 'earthquake drills', roads are signposted as escape routes and shelters are publicised, in addition to strict building codes. Management focuses upon minimising the impact of natural hazards rather than preventing them. Costs are huge and recovery times lengthy.

Having studied a variety of disasters, researchers have concluded that human responses vary according to different types of disaster, and that responses change as time passes after the event. Communities tend to be resilient and co-operative immediately after a natural disaster. In contrast, after a technological disaster, communities tend to become more stressed and fragmented as anger, frustration and recrimination build up against the perceived culprits. Understanding this difference should help to make disaster recovery programmes more effective.

The response of the outside world to a disaster is equally complex. People outside the disaster area are fed by media images and feel the need to help. National and international agencies and organisations take the responsibility of planning and responding to the disaster. The diversity of strategies and conflicts of interests can also hamper disaster relief rather than help it, for example, the 1994 refugee disaster in Rwanda and the 1989 Exxon Valdez oil spill in Alaska.

This case study examines Hurricane Andrew, which crossed southern Florida in August 1992. It was one of the most powerful hurricanes to affect the USA this century. Its distinction as a disaster is that it is the first storm of such strength to pass directly through a large urbanised region of more than three million people. Although essentially a natural disaster, the extensive human occupation of the impact zone of Hurricane Andrew, give it some features of a composite disaster.

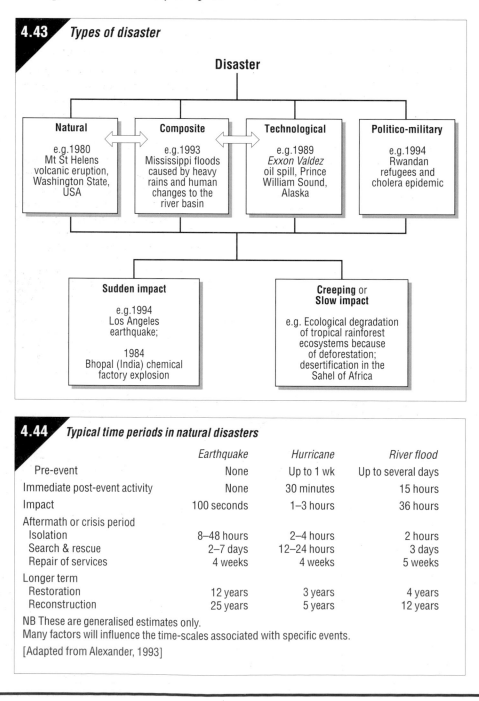

4.43 *Types of disaster*

Disaster

- **Natural** — e.g.1980 Mt St Helens volcanic eruption, Washington State, USA
- **Composite** — e.g.1993 Mississippi floods caused by heavy rains and human changes to the river basin
- **Technological** — e.g.1989 *Exxon Valdez* oil spill, Prince William Sound, Alaska
- **Politico-military** — e.g.1994 Rwandan refugees and cholera epidemic

- **Sudden impact** — e.g.1994 Los Angeles earthquake; 1984 Bhopal (India) chemical factory explosion
- **Creeping** or **Slow impact** — e.g. Ecological degradation of tropical rainforest ecosystems because of deforestation; desertification in the Sahel of Africa

4.44 *Typical time periods in natural disasters*

	Earthquake	Hurricane	River flood
Pre-event	None	Up to 1 wk	Up to several days
Immediate post-event activity	None	30 minutes	15 hours
Impact	100 seconds	1–3 hours	36 hours
Aftermath or crisis period			
Isolation	8–48 hours	2–4 hours	2 hours
Search & rescue	2–7 days	12–24 hours	3 days
Repair of services	4 weeks	4 weeks	5 weeks
Longer term			
Restoration	12 years	3 years	4 years
Reconstruction	25 years	5 years	12 years

NB These are generalised estimates only.
Many factors will influence the time-scales associated with specific events.

[Adapted from Alexander, 1993]

Hurricanes are a regular part of natural ecosystems in southern Florida, which have adaptive mechanisms to allow them to recover. Despite elaborate hazard management plans, cities and human systems have not adapted sufficiently to withstand and recover from such sudden and violent surges of energy. The case study follows three major phases of the episode: the pre-event phase, the event, and the initial post-event phase. The views and reactions of the local population and the management agencies are illustrated. The key groups involved are individuals and local communities, local, state and federal (national) government agencies, voluntary charity and aid organisations, commercial enterprises and corporations, and the media.

Key understandings

◆ Hurricane Andrew was one of the most powerful storms of the century and the first in America whose path lay directly across a major urbanised region.

◆ Hurricanes are a component of the natural environmental systems of south Florida. Ecosystems have adaptive mechanisms for recovery.

◆ Despite established procedures, the human system of south Florida is imperfectly adjusted to hurricane impacts.

◆ One of the key problems in disaster response and management is the multiplicity of agencies involved.

◆ Management of extreme events falls into three main phases: pre-event, event and post-event.

◆ Post-event responses to disasters change rapidly over time, and the recovery times of natural and human systems may last many years.

Coping with 'The Big One'

Hurricane Andrew may have been abnormal in its impact but was typical in its life history. During the 'hurricane season' between June and November, at least 60 low pressure waves containing warm, moist, unstable Tropical Maritime air move westwards across the Atlantic. Only a few escalate to become hurricanes. Resource 4.45 tracks Andrew's 12-day journey from West Africa to Louisiana.

Phase 1: Pre-event management and response

Florida is 'hurricane country' and it has a well-established management system. The crucial role in the period before the hurricane reaches Florida is played by the US Meteorological Service and the National Hurricane Centre at Coral Gables, Florida. This federal government agency monitors the progress of the storm and passes information on to the state government agencies and the media. The monitoring involves three stages: *detection,*

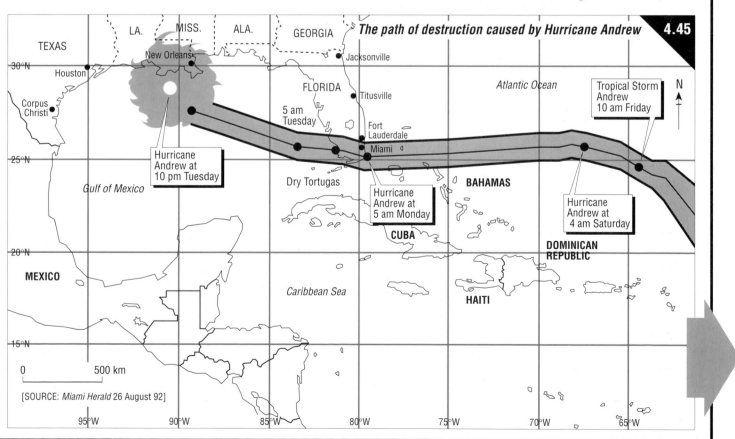

The path of destruction caused by Hurricane Andrew   4.45

TEXAS, LA., MISS., ALA., GEORGIA, FLORIDA

New Orleans, Houston, Corpus Christi, Jacksonville, Titusville, Fort Lauderdale, Miami, Dry Tortugas

Atlantic Ocean

Tropical Storm Andrew 10 am Friday

Hurricane Andrew at 10 pm Tuesday

5 am Tuesday

Hurricane Andrew at 5 am Monday

Hurricane Andrew at 4 am Saturday

Gulf of Mexico

BAHAMAS

CUBA

DOMINICAN REPUBLIC

MEXICO

Caribbean Sea

HAITI

0   500 km

[SOURCE: *Miami Herald* 26 August 92]

95°W   90°W   85°W   80°W   75°W   70°W   65°W

30°N   25°N   20°N   15°N

N

CASE STUDY 4.5 *Managing hazards in urban environments*

4.46 Pre-event responses

Friday 14 August
The US National Hurricane Centre(NHC) record the presence of a low pressure wave moving slowly westwards from the West Africa coast on to the tropical Atlantic Ocean.

Sunday 16 August
The storm has intensified sufficiently for the NHC to list it as a tropical depression with winds exceeding 30 mph.

Monday 17 August
Winds increase beyond 40 mph and it is designated as tropical storm Andrew.

Tuesday 18 August
Daily conferences on Andrew begin at NHC to decide upon the level of response, such as warnings through the media. Andrew's presence appears on the television weather forecasts.

Wednesday 19 August
The meteorologists note that the storm is moving west once more and is intensifying.

Friday 21 August
The NHC issues urgent warnings that Andrew continues to strengthen rapidly.

Saturday 22 August
7.00 am: The NHC designate Andrew, now some 800 miles east of Miami, as a hurricane as winds exceed 75 mph.

2.00 pm: The NHC are now convinced that the hurricane is heading directly for southern Florida cities. The official warning reads: The westward movement is expected to continue through Sunday, increasing the threat to south and central Florida. Interests in that area should monitor advice on this hurricane.

5.00 pm: The state authorities announce a 'hurricane watch' status which puts all public agencies on emergency standby. All police, fire and health service leave is cancelled. Hourly media hurricane bulletins are issued.

Throughout the day supermarkets and other stores are besieged by people stocking up with emergency rations, water and batteries. Long queues build up at petrol stations as people fill their tanks. Hardware stores, lumber yards and DIY warehouses report huge sales as people buy materials to protect the windows of homes and business premises. Prices rise for many commodities as businesses cash in on the demand. This, the crowds and the mounting tension cause anger, frustration and occasional outbreaks of violence.

Sunday 23 August
Throughout the day evacuation orders are issued by the state and county authorities for communities living on the offshore barrier islands and Keys. Television and radio give constant updates, and repeat advice on how to prepare. The county's ten emergency shelters fill up with more than 20 000 people and more than 70 000 others leave their homes. The sick and frail, plus women in advanced pregnancy are moved into hospitals and nursing homes which become full to overflowing.

Monday 24 August
3.00 am: The NHC report the hurricane as 40 miles east of Miami, with winds of 140 mph, and hurricane-force winds across a zone up to 150 miles wide.

4.30 am: All police and fire personnel are ordered off the streets. In effect, the cities are shut down.

5.20 am: The NHC are unable to track the details of the hurricane as its headquarters at Coral Gables are hit by gusts exceeding 164 mph, at which point all the recording equipment is destroyed.

tracking and *land fall prediction*. In turn, the state government and local authorities make decisions and use the media to communicate guidance and instructions. The central dilemma for these public agencies is *when* to put out warnings, *to whom* and *at which level* of severity. To broadcast information too late and too mild might create disaster; too soon and too severe would provoke panic. Both scenarios could lead to accusations afterwards.

For individuals and families the first key decision to make is when and whether or not to stay at home. If families decide to stay, then they need to prepare. There are well-known and published state guidelines on what to do in case of a hurricane and well-signposted 'hurricane escape routes' in case of evacuation. Advice is given on how to secure the house, with pointers to the strongest and safest places to shelter. Bathrooms and wardrobes near structural pillars and walls are usually safest. Homes are built without storm cellars in Florida, mainly because of the high water table in this flat, low landscape.

Resource 4.46 takes us through the week leading up to Andrew's arrival in southern Florida. The level of activity increased as it became more certain that a hurricane was heading directly towards a fully-urbanised region.

Phase 2: The event
Throughout Sunday evening and Sunday night the wind and rain built up, but the actual hurricane lasted at most three hours, depending upon the location in relation to the storm centre. Resource 4.50 illustrates the variation in hurricane experience in terms of duration and wind direction. The sheer power and roaring, screaming noise made by winds of over 140 mph are impossible to describe, but Resource 4.48 takes us through the experience of two families.

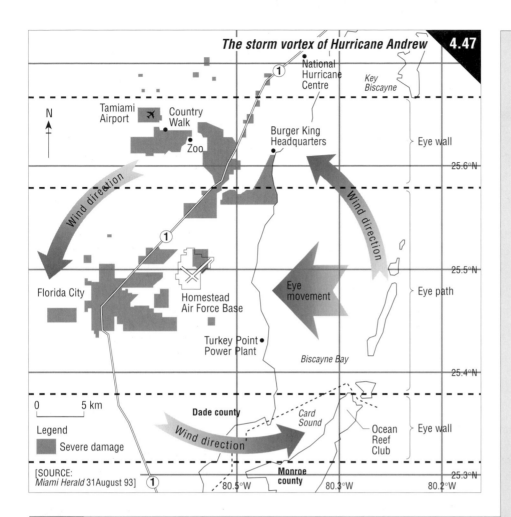

The storm vortex of Hurricane Andrew | 4.47

Tamiami Airport
Country Walk
Zoo
National Hurricane Centre
Key Biscayne
Burger King Headquarters
Eye wall
25.6°N
Wind direction
Wind direction
Florida City
Homestead Air Force Base
Eye movement
Eye path
25.5°N
Turkey Point Power Plant
Biscayne Bay
25.4°N
Dade county
Card Sound
Ocean Reef Club
Eye wall
0   5 km
Wind direction
Legend
Severe damage
Monroe county
25.3°N
[SOURCE: *Miami Herald* 31 August 93]
80.5°W   80.3°W   80.2°W

4.48 | **Living through a hurricane**

The Whiteman family

Saturday

Judi Whiteman, a Dade county resident for 40 years, knew that supermarkets would be packed, and she was at hers before 7 am. She loaded up with 30 gallons of drinking water, canned food, batteries and other items recommended for a hurricane. On the way back she filled up with gas. Her husband Richard, began putting up the strong storm shutters on their 4-bedroomed house.

Sunday night/Monday morning

Behind their strong shutters, Judi and Richard hadn't been too worried. They watched the news till 11.30 pm then slept till 4 am, when the loss of electricity woke them up. They stumbled out into the living room to see water dripping down. Then they noticed the doors were buckling. They threw themselves against the doors. Suddenly, the wind blasted the doors open. Richard was thrown against a wall; Judi was blown into a hallway. A 15 ft board flew across the room like a spear. The expensive shutters were snapping, French doors blew out. The ceilings in the living room collapsed. The Whitemans retreated to a bedroom. The ceiling there began to fall. They retreated to a closet [fitted wardrobe], crouching in six inches of water, with a mattress over them. In a moment's lull they could hear on the tiny battery television they had carried with them, the news that 'The worst is yet to come'. Then they heard neighbours shouting. The house next door had collapsed and the six people needed shelter. The Whitemans invited them in and they hid in closets and bathrooms.

7.30 am: As the winds steadied the Whitemans emerged to find that their house was totalled [mostly destroyed].

The Marks

Sunday morning

As the announcement was made that the barrier islands would have to be evacuated, Frank Marks began preparing his home in South Dade county. As a scientist, he knew that because hurricane winds churn anticlockwise around the eye, his greatest problem would be the east and north-east bedroom windows. He boarded up all the windows. He moved all the valuables to an upstairs closet [wardrobe], placed them up high, then pushed a dressing table against the closet door. Downstairs he protected sliding glass doors with a bookcase, weighted down by a barbecue grill. He decided the safest place would be the family room, because its only window faced west. All furniture was placed in the centre of the room, along with mattresses. If necessary, their 'escape hatch' would be a small washroom and toilet off the family room. All emergency provisions – flashlights, batteries, a sleeping bag – went in there.

Sunday night/Monday morning

Frank gathered everyone in the family room. The children slept for a while but when the winds began screaming everyone woke up. Suddenly there was a loud pop. A window had blown out. The house began shaking 'like a bulldozer was pounding it'. Frank yelled for everyone to get in the small bathroom. Into this cramped space squeezed five adults, two kids and Max, the cocker spaniel. Frank sat on the sink, his feet braced against the door to keep the wind from blowing it in. He was awed – 'I've never felt anything like it' – and afraid.

7.00 am: Frank, who is a hurricane expert, came out to find that only one window had broken. It was upstairs on the north-east side. All the family valuables, tucked away in closets protected by dressers were 'bone dry'.

Phase 3: After the event

Like all disasters, Andrew generated a complex set of responses and management programmes with varying time-spans. Despite the well-established management procedures in Florida, responses to the hurricane by state and federal agencies were subject to much criticism. On 7 September 1992, the magazine *Newsweek* included an article entitled *What went wrong?* with the subheading, *Hurricane Andrew was hardly a surprise. So why did politicians and government agencies seem unprepared to deal with the storm's damage?*

Day 1

The first day was dominated by chaos, not through panic, but because of the severity of the destruction. Across a 40 km zone north-south and a 30 km east-west zone, roads were blocked, all electricity was cut off, phone lines were down and water supplies disrupted. This breakdown of communications and services prevented co-ordinated response by the various agencies. At individual and local community level, an initial feeling of being stunned and helpless was quickly followed by either despair or a surge of energetic resourcefulness. There were many examples of people helping each other and of spontaneous neighbourhood co-operative efforts. Another response, localised but ominous, was an outbreak of looting, especially in shopping centres of less wealthy areas.

This scenario was to be repeated throughout the following weeks. We need to distinguish between those who were affected by the hurricane and the organisations and agencies responsible for disaster response. The number of agencies and organisations caused tensions and confusion. There were local, state, federal government and the military groups, private sector providers, such as power and phone companies, and voluntary bodies such as the Red Cross. Storm impact was spread across several district and county authority areas. Homestead, Florida City and Coral Gables, for example,

4.49 Fraying nerves add to trauma

Two days of shock are yielding to a fresh and delicate phase that will test the already frayed nerves of Andrew's victims. Operating on little sleep and much uncertainty about the future, many survivors are adding frustration to their catalog of post-storm emotions. Pain and doubt grew, along with the casualty totals.

"The first day, residents were pretty stoic. They were just happy to be alive," said Florida City Manager Dick Anderson. "Now, people are increasingly worrying about where their next meal is coming from, how they are going to feed the kids, where can they find Pampers, those kinds of things."

President Bush announced $10 million for Florida to provide as many as 5,000 short-term jobs for clean-up. The sum comes atop the $57 million directed to South Florida this week by the Federal Emergency Management Agency.

The evidence of growing impatience started to appear in the queues for food and water, where people have fainted from dehydration. As relief workers work around the clock to solve complex logistical puzzles, no system yet exists to distribute supplies that have arrived.

There just aren't enough structures," said Florida City Mayor Otis Wallace. The closest available shelters for people in Homestead are more than a dozen miles away. Many people are afraid to leave their homes unprotected.

'Food first'

"The first thing that would give them a sense of hope is a definite place where people can eat with their kids every day," Anderson said. "Food first."

Gov. Lawton Chiles was irritated: "Well, we've got 120,000 C-ration meals that are here somewhere, but we don't know where the hell they are."

The county fire department is airlifting workers into previously inaccessible areas and high-risk locations.

"It's the next phase," said David Paulison, Dade's fire chief. "We're at the point now where we can go and search for people who are trapped, whether they are dead or alive.

Reports of looting diminished significantly Wednesday. The county reported 35 arrests in a 24-hour period, compared to 100 on Monday night alone. The loosely enforced 7 p.m. to 7 a.m. curfew remains in effect.

Grant Peterson, associate director to the Federal Emergency Management Agency, said his office is setting up a half-dozen disaster-relief application offices in South Dade "as fast as humanly possible," but the effort has been hindered by a lack of structurally sound office space with electrical power.

FEMA will reimburse the county for 75 percent of its costs for repairs, debris removal and structural damage to county facilities.

[*Miami Herald*, 27.8.92]

Day 3: Frustration

1 What are the positive and negative responses of
- the people?
- the public agencies?
- the private organisations?
2 What are the main problems to emerge?
3 What claims are being made by individuals and managers?
4 Summarise the situation on Day 3.

---

are separate cities. The state co-ordinating powers are based in the state capital, Tallahassee, in the distant north-west of Florida. A yawning gap opened up between the wealthy and poorer families and communities. The Coral Gables inhabitants had money, insurance cover and influence, while the poorer inhabitants of Homestead, for example, had little insurance cover and were disadvantaged in a number of social and economic ways.

Day 2

Priorities for families were shifting by the second day. Fundamental concerns began to focus on shelter, safety, health, and food in an effort to survive. Shelter was a priority, especially for the more than 100 000 people whose homes had been destroyed or badly damaged. People stood guard over their homes and businesses for fear of looters. The lack of piped water and dislocation of drainage and sanitation systems

Officials debate reasons for delay

Chiles will preside today over a meeting of all local, state and federal agencies in an effort to focus better on the developing problems.

A force of 3,500 U.S. soldiers, dispatched by a president to rescue South Dade, reached town Friday to cope with a still untamed disaster.

The first of 8,000 soldiers in a revved-up relief mission arrived to discover a tangle of new complications. Dozens of agencies and organizations strained to match a sudden abundance of supplies with a similar abundance of victims.

Homestead and Florida City, the worst-hit areas, are suddenly overstocked with food, but have no effective distribution system. Good Samaritans hauling goods by the truckload are arriving at random locations, adding to the growing logistical thicket.

It was The Aftermath, Day 5.

Dade schools set an opening date of Sept. 14. Search teams neared the end of their weary hunt for storm victims. Police reported just two looting arrests.

At County Hall, Manager Joaquin Aviño created a task force to reconsider Dade's building code in the wake of a hurricane that left an estimated 63,000 homes destroyed and 175,000 or more homeless.

South Dade's highways turned into a mad cavalcade of activity, a rolling circus of overloaded trucks shuttling southward with siren-sounding escorts.

As they rolled and stopped, accordion-like, on the steamy, jammed roads of south Dade, they passed the two most popular signs of the times.

The first gives a homeowner's name, address and name of insurance company.

The second: LOOTERS WILL BE SHOT.

Or, a spray-painted variation spotted in Perrine: WARNING! MAD DOG WILL EAT LOOTERS!

[*Miami Herald*, 29.8.92]

Day 5

NOTE:

- Chiles is the state governor of Florida and has overall responsibility for decisions within the State.
- Joaquin Avino is Manager (Chief Executive Officer) of Dade County.

1 Who are involved in responding and what are they doing?
2 What and who are arriving?
3 What are the main problems indicated?
4 What evidence is there that there are too many organisations involved?

---

brought a real threat of illness and disease. In the more heavily-affected districts, food and drink supplies were desperately needed. All shops were shut and many roads were impassable.

For the public agencies, the priorities were search and rescue, impact assessment and communication. The dead and injured were still being recovered, hospitals were full and temporary facilities in clinics, halls and tents were being organised. Extra medical staff arrived from all over Florida and beyond. Fragmentary impact assessment information was being collated at the disaster centre in Miami, from field reports and helicopter over-flights. Co-ordination was hampered because electricity, telephone lines and the roads were still out of action. Some key understandings were emerging which would form the basis of decision-making during the following weeks. This included the location and scale of the impact

zone, the character of the damage, the variation of damage within the impact zone, the realisation that local and state agencies could not cope, and that federal support was essential. The two most important federal government responses were:

- the involvement of FEMA, the Federal Emergency Management Agency. This national agency's sole purpose was to organise and co-ordinate disaster relief.
- the impact area was declared a National Disaster Area, thereby qualifying southern Florida for federal government relief funds.

Resources 4.49 to 4.61 contain a selection of materials from the main South Florida newspapers. They demonstrate the importance of the media in achieving the task of communication and dissemination of information in the aftermath of a disaster. A series of questions have been compiled for each set of extracts to help you interpret the information.

4.51 *Assessing Andrew's Damage*

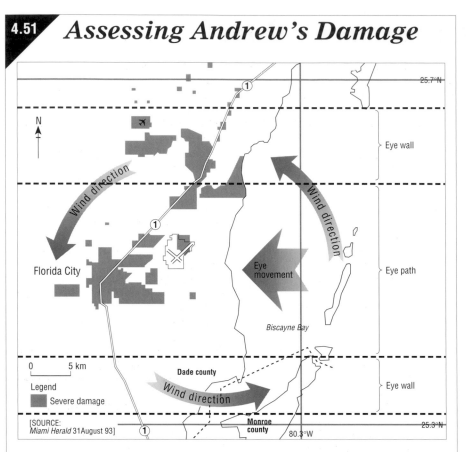

Eye wall

Eye path

Eye wall

Florida City

Eye movement

Wind direction

Wind direction

Wind direction

Biscayne Bay

Dade county

Monroe county

0   5 km

Legend

Severe damage

[SOURCE: *Miami Herald* 31 August 93]

25.7°N

25.3°N

80.3°W

The first block-by-block assessment of Hurricane Andrew's rampage reveals a scatter-shot pattern of destruction beyond the eye's center, reaching random neighborhoods far from devastated Florida City.

"There were storms within the storm," said Dr. Bob Sheets, director of the National Hurricane Center in Coral Gables. "Like bubbles in oatmeal."

The map's darkest blotches show Andrew's obvious targets: Cutler Ridge, Homestead, Florida City, Country Walk and pinpoint areas some 20 miles away also hammered by the deadly winds.

Beyond the eye, Andrew spun off a series of small, violent storms that destroyed isolated neighborhoods. The winds inside these compact tempests often reached those speeds closer to the storm's center – 140 miles per hour.

"You had tremendous damage inside these cells," Sheets said. "The air just came crashing down."

Andrew stormed ashore at 4:55 a.m. due east of Homestead Air Force Base and rolled westward blowing sustained winds of 141 miles per hour. The area hit hardest were on the outer edge of the 10-mile-wide eye wall – Homestead, Florida City, Cutler Ridge and Goulds. The reason: they bore Andrew's gales almost continuously because the eye never passed over them.

"If you were in Cutler Ridge, barely inside the eye wall, then you had the highest winds almost continuously," Sheets said. "Time is a big factor. It will just wear strucures down."

[*Miami Herald*, 31.8.93]

Day 7 *Where things stood at the end of Week 1*

1   **Impact assessment**

   a *Who appear to have been mainly responsible for collecting information?*

   b *What factors have they taken into account when assessing impact?*

   c *How will this map of impacts assist the management of response?*

   d *How have the characteristics of the hurricane influenced the distribution of damage?*

4.52 Dade leaders consider plans for the future

More than 60 of Dade County's most powerful leaders listened Sunday to reports of progress and problems in getting the storm-battered county back on its feet.

Their consensus: Dade County is emerging slowly from the nightmare of Hurricane Andrew, but its devastated communities need lots of help to rebuild and retain their business base.

Top issues

The group hit on several key issues, but made no firm plans on tackling unresolved issues, such as:

• Keeping federal troops in Dade beyond their anticipated monthlong stay.

• Reorganizing the volunteer relief effort in South Dade. Several leaders, urged that people wishing to help should contact official relief agencies before heading down to the disaster zone.

• Preventing an outbreak of infectious diseases in the disaster area. "We are sitting on a public health time bomb," said Ira Clark, president of Jackson Memorial Hospital.

• Keeping more than 50,000 jobs from being lost because of the devastation. "We already had a serious problem before the storm with 100,000 people out of work," said Bill Collum, president of the Greater Miami Chamber of Commerce.

• Changing a perception outside of South Florida that Hurricane Andrew wiped out Miami and Miami Beach, when those popular tourist areas were not hard-hit by the storm.

"The message should go out to the world that we were spared. We are open for business," said Miami Mayor Xavier Suarez.

• The possibility of generating money for reconstruction by imposing a 1-cent sales tax for two years. Metro Mayor Steve Clark, who made the proposal, said the tax would raise about $250 million in reconstruction aid.

[*Miami Herald*, 31.8.92]

---

2   **Official responses**

   a *In what way is the message of the headline different from the central concerns of earlier days?*

   b *Who are the key decision-makers quoted? (NB: Metro refers to Dade Metropolitan County)*

   c *What are the key issues identified?*

   d *Why and for whom are these issues of particular importance?*

TeleHerald's Community Bulletin Board

READERS HELPING READERS

Need food, water, shelter, transportation? Trying to find a friend or relative? Seeking volunteers? Or volunteering goods, services, or shelter? We are offering our TeleHerald phone system and the pages of The Herald as a free bulletin board.
Call. Leave your name and phone. We'll print all that we can.

MISSING PERSONS

• Wesley Watters, 296–9688, looking for Pamela from H & R Bloch, offering you and your boyfriend shelter.
• Friends of Debby and Ross Stopp, (904) 893–4337, please call collect.
• Annabelle Foster, 435-0286, looking for nephews in Homestead.
• April Smith, are you OK? Call Nancy San Martin, 261-2482.
• Charlene Blackshear, 633-0605, looking for Rose in Homestead.
• Cliff Crittenden, call Pat at 592-6936 or 592-1702. Pee Wee wants to help.
• Metro-Dade police will look for missing people in unincorporated Dade who have not been heard from since the storm. Call 595-6263.
• The Red Cross can help families find missing relatives. Call 326-6602.

PETS

• Call 1-800-US-STRAY if you lost a pet during the storm, or found a pet after the storm. Officials will try to match the calls and reunite the original owners with their pets.
• The Florida Hurricane Pet Relief and the

---

3 The role of the media

For several weeks after the hurricane, newspapers carried special pages of information. This resource illustrates a tiny selection from a single day. They signify an impressive element of the response: a great upsurge of human caring, sympathy and a desire to help.
a What role is being played by the newspaper?
b Who is advertising? Why?
c How do these items support the ideas that all aspects of normal life have been disrupted, and that so many people want to help?

Friends of Dade County Animal Services offer free rabies shots and care for sick and injured animals at the following sites: Dade County Animal Services, U.S. 1 and 84th Ave., Miami; and a field unit at Campbell Square Shopping Center, 790 N. Homestead Blvd.

TEMPORARY SHELTER

A limited number of free apartments are being made available temporarily to homeless victims. If you need a place to live, or if you have properties you are willing to offer to hurricane victims, you can:
• Call the Greater Miami Apartment Association at 868-9579 or the Broward-Palm Beach Apartment Association at (407) 998-8486.

WATER

Residents in Dade should boil or purify tap water before drinking it. Water must be boiled for three to five minutes or purified.
• Zephyrhills Spring Water, Florida's largest bottled water company, is donating 30,000 gallons of spring water a day to storm victims. Five tankers are distributing water at Homestead Middle School, 650 NW Second Ave., Homestead; Convention Center, across from City Hall, Miami Beach; Richmond heights Middle School, 150 15 SW 103rd Ave., Miami; North Shore, 73rd Street & Collins Avenue, Miami Beach; and Cutler Ridge Mall, 112th Avenue at 211th Street (the southwest corner behind Sears)
Hours are 10 a.m. to 6 p.m. Bring your own containers.

SANITATION

Metro-Dade residential garbage collection has resumed for households north of Flagler Street. Garbage collection will resume for most households south of Flagler Street – but not in areas where street access is limited. The county has opened six disposal sites for residents to dump limited hurricane debris, including tree trimmings, furniture and burnable debris. No garbage, construction or demolition debris, such as concrete roof or floor tiles, will be accepted.

TRANSPORTATION

• Metrobus: Service is limited but free. Metrorail: Resumes limited service today. Free. All stops will be served, but in order to observe the curfew, the hours of opening will be from 7 a.m. to 11 p.m.

• Special Transportation Services, the county's program for disabled residents, resumes limited service today. it will run from 7 a.m. to 7 p.m. north of Kendall Drive, and only for "essential trips" – such as to the supermarket.

PEOPLE OFFERING HELP

• Agnes Wasner can provide shelter, 456-2992.
• Anna Couceiro has a room for mother and child, 1930 Washington Ave. Hollywood, 922-7850.
• April Munoz, 432-0539, has small apartment for up to three people.
• Hammocks Middle School staff and students: free food and shower, call Aaron Adler at 433-8841.
• Carrie Oliver has shelter for up to four people, 785-9452.
Cynthia Lawson has room for family of three and can pick up, 983-1731.

INSURANCE

Contact your agent as quickly as possible. If you can't reach your agent, here are emergency claims numbers for major insurers in Florida:
• Aetna Life & Casualty, 1-800-238-6225
• American Reliance, 1-800-252-4655
• Allstate Insurance.

MEDICAL EMERGENCIES

• Centro Medico Latino Americano, 650 SW 12th Ave., Miami, is open with doctors, nurses, first aid, and X-ray capability.
• Miami Children's Hospital and the Cuban and Greater Miami pediatric societies are sending teams of physicians to the Homestead area to treat children needing medical assistance. Today they will be at Homestead Middle School, 650 NW Second Ave. Miami Children's also has a 24-hour hot line to answer medical questions from parents. Call 669-6450.

POSTAL SERVICES

Mail that carriers can't deliver is being stored at local post offices and can be picked up at the counter. Questions: Call 470-0750 between 8 a.m. and 10 p.m.
There is no mail delivery south of Kendall Drive, where the Postal Service has set up five pickup sites. Residents can pick up government checks and other mail starting today.

[*Miami Herald*, 31.8.93]

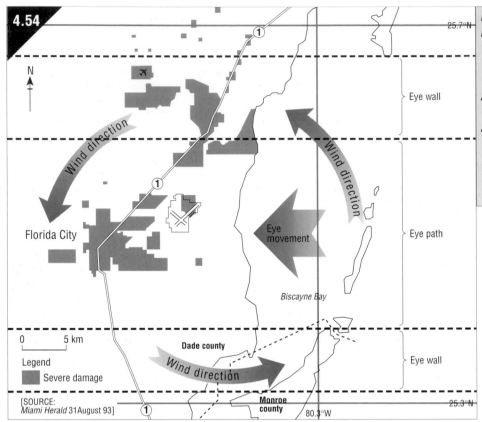

Day 9: The use of zones for disaster management

1 Why do you think the managers have decided to organise their response through a four-zone structure?
2 What factors would influence the drawing of the zone boundaries?
3 Within Zone 4, what aspects of need are given special focus? Why are these services located where they are? (Think of supply access and accessibility for those in need.)

The public agencies, assisted by the Salvation Army and Red Cross, had set up tent cities, giving shelter to more than 20 000 people, kitchens and supply outlets. Co-operation and co-ordination between state and federal agencies were improving. Over 20 000 troops were in the impact zone.

Language barrier keeping relief from many

4.56

Despite a massive relief effort in Florida City and Homestead, Guatemalan, Haitian and Salvadoran immigrants are still short of food, medicine and information.

Hundreds are not getting help or venturing far from home for three reasons: They do not speak English, they are afraid of the military, or they fear immigration authorities.

"We don't know where to go to get information," said one undocumented Salvadoran man.

"We just stay here. We don't know anything about the tent cities or the Red Cross. We have no papers, so we don't want to get help."

Haitians have it worse. Only a few volunteers speak Creole, and even fewer can help with paperwork. Some Haitians in Florida City still don't know where to get food.

Over Radio Continental, 1430 AM, Spanish-language staffers tried to get the word out from a trailer in an open field. Soldiers helped them put up their antenna after the hurricane destroyed the station. Many in the neighborhood credit Continental for saving lives.

Alfredo Gallegos reads out the list of shelters and food distribution locations and encourages listeners to get medical attention and move into tent cities. Aware that most war-weary Salvadorans and Guatemalans panic when they see military uniforms, he tries to persuade them that U.S. soldiers are there to help.

Gallegos also passes on information about financial aid and immigration problems.

[*Miami Herald*, 5.9.92]

End of week 2:
Harsh realities emerge

Late in the second week, criticism, frustration, desperation and anger were becoming more apparent, especially among the more vulnerable and disadvantaged communities, and despite the increasing provision of temporary and replacement 'mobile homes'. Such communities rely heavily upon state and federal agency support. The extracts of Resources 4.56 and 4.57 illustrate these issues.

1 Who are the groups identified and in which towns do they live?

2 What are their main problems and why are they occurring?

3 List the organisations involved and what their role appears to be?

4 Who are receiving most criticism and why? What are the potential solutions?

Victims to FEMA: We've been ignored

4.57

Federal disaster relief officials, criticized for slow response to the ravages of Hurricane Andrew, Monday faced some of their harshest critics – residents of unincorporated Dade County who complained their neighborhoods have been ignored.

The Federal Emergency Management Agency, which is coordinating hurricane relief efforts, sought residents' advice on what kind of help to provide.

What they heard, during community meetings in Perrine, Modello and a farmworkers' group office in Homestead were complaints about the lack of information about the relief efforts.

"Communication is the key," said James Marshall, president of the Richmond Heights Homeowners' Association. "We're not getting anything down here. There is nowhere to cash checks in Perrine. People are suffering."

"There's a whole lot of resources but no coordination," Hanna said. "We keep hearing that all these resources are going to the Red Cross and the Salvation Army, and we're not seeing any of it here."

Amelia Olson, a Leisure City resident, said word about help comes through the grapevine because her neighborhood lacks power for radios and TVs.

After the Perrine meeting, local residents stayed behind to discuss their needs. Their main request: that FEMA set up small command posts in Perrine and nearby neighborhoods to make it easier for residents to find out what kind of help is available.

Based on those concerns, FEMA is drawing plans to improve responsiveness. FEMA officials said they want the meetings to lead to neighborhood teams that can give out information and respond quickly to request for aid.

[*Miami Herald*, 8.9.92]

4.58

Temporary and replacement mobile homes, Homestead

4.59 *SHODDY WORK*

Metro-Dade officials vowed Friday to discipline builders and county inspectors whose negligence contributed to the devastation from Hurricane Andrew and moved to ban some building materials that failed to hold up in the storm.

The Board of Rules and Appeals, a panel of architects, engineers and contractors that oversees the South Florida Building code, called on the Metro Commission to impose an immediate ban on the use of pressed board and staples in roofs. Structural engineers say the widespread failure of those materials during Hurricane Andrew played a key role in the devastation of many homes.

The county's chief building official also vowed to investigate any past negligence that may have contributed to the collapse of homes. County inspectors who failed to do their job may be fired, while contractors and sub-contractors who performed shoddy work could have their licenses withdrawn.

Earlier this week, the national Wind Engineering Research Council issued a report blaming poor construction for much of the damage caused by Andrew.

Those flaws have angered thousands of people left homeless in the wake of the storm and raised concerns about the rebuilding effort.

Code violations will result in disciplinary action. The county's construction trade Qualifying Board is empowered to fine, suspend licenses or reprimand contractors.

In cases where intentional or willful violations of the code can be proven, the county will work with the State Attorney's office.

Dade State Attorney Janet Reno said her office is checking whether criminal charges can be filed against contractors who acted negligently.

FLYING CONCRETE

Condominiums at Naranja Lakes were torn apart by concrete tie beams, each weighing nearly a ton. In the hurricane, flat roofs acted like huge wings pulling the beams aloft. Held to walls only by mortar, but strapped tightly to trusses, the beams sailed off their perches and ripped through houses. Left unbraced, walls collapsed. Three people died.

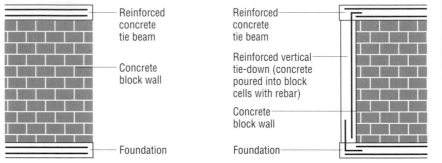

Wrong and right
The structure of the wall at left is substantially weaker than the one at right. Vertical tie-downs anchor tie beams securely to the foundation. Naranja Lakes condos originally cost between $13 000 and $17 000. An engineer estimated that developers saved about $200 per unit by not installing tie downs.

Several major insurance companies, stung by the losses from hurricanes Andrew and Hugo, are pushing for stricter enforcement of local building codes.

"There's a lot that can be done and should be done to ensure that we're building structures that can stand up to a hurricane and other natural disasters," said Harold Covey, executive vice president of State Farm Fire and Casualty Co.

In the past year, several companies – including State Farm – created the Natural Disaster Loss Reduction committee – to provide assistance in the formulation and enforcement of local building codes, and development of building materials. The reasoning behind their effort is to limit the losses insurers face after a major disaster such as Andrew.

[*Miami Herald*, 5.9.92]

Into week 3: Counting the cost
The crucial question of who could, would and should pay for the repair or replacement of a home or business, loomed. Families were concerned about home insurance. Cities such as Homestead contain a high proportion of low-income families who either rent, or who have little or no insurance cover. Most landlords have no responsibility for rehousing their tenants, and owners without insurance can rarely afford to repair or rebuild. Even homeowners and landlords with full insurance found that with claims running into billions of dollars, some insurance companies were reluctant to pay out. The companies claimed that the damage was due to shoddy construction or slack inspection standards by county officials, and that owners should sue the construction companies or the county authorities. For many families and businesses, finding the people responsible is opening up a legal nightmare.

4.60

**Houses are still damaged.
Homestead, January 1993**

Experts predict slow recovery

Andrew's punch will push up unemployment, already more than 10 percent, by another percentage point. Many families and businesses will deplete savings or go deeper into debt to finance rebuilding. And many jobs may disappear forever as some businesses never reopen.

That picture emerges from economic studies of other U.S. disasters – all of which were minor compared to Andrew.

Earlier estimates put the damage at $20 billion – more than three times the cost exacted by Hurricane Hugo, which brutalized Charleston and the South Carolina coast in 1989.

To put that in perspective: If everyone in Dade County put every cent of his or her income toward rebuilding, it would take nearly nine months to raise $20 billion.

RETAIL
No gain. There will be great bursts of activity in building products and in furnishing as businesses and homeowners replace lost possessions.

But economic research by the University of South Carolina following Hurricane Hugo, which hit Charleston hard, showed that retail sales simply shift after a catastrophe. they don't grow.

GOVERNMENT
Government units usually fare much better than individuals or businesses. Essentially, they are reimbursed fully for their losses by taxpayers.

However, the news isn't all good. Governments often receive initial windfalls of disaster assistance monies. But a University of South Alabama study of Mobile, Ala.,

following Hurricane Frederic, found eventual cleanup costs exceed the gains. That could create the possibility that taxes, will have to be raised. In addition, the federal government may decide not to reopen Homestead Air Force Base, which pumps $500 million into the local economy annually.

CONSTRUCTION
Initially, a boost. Bruce Thomson, a labor market analyst for Florida's Department of Labor and Employment Security, estimates that up to 7,000 construction jobs will be created in the months ahead. That's about half of the construction jobs lost in the recession.

But the news may turn negative over the long-term. Continuous employment in the construction industry is dependent on a strong economy. But once the rebuilding bills are paid, the Miami economy will be weaker, not stronger.

TOURISM
The one bright spot following the storm. The county's most popular tourist attractions – the Deco district, Key Biscayne, Doral and Coconut Grove – were spared. The experience of other cities, such as Charleston, suggests that advertising campaigns must be mounted quickly to reassure potential visitors, however. Helping matters, there are still months to clean up before high tourist season.

BANKING
Smaller community banks in the South Dade area may suffer. Many businesses and individuals will have difficulty repaying loans, and the real estate that backs many loans is likely to drop in value. In addition, the pool of qualified borrowers – where banks make most of their money – has like been reduced by the hurricane.

[*Miami Herald*, 31.8.93]

The next phase: Looking to the future

The realisation that recovery would be slow as well as costly, hit south Florida communities and businesses hard.

1 What is the issue? Who, according to the extract, is to blame?

2 Why was the damage unnecessarily severe?

3 Why will the issues raised delay the settlement of claims and, hence, the ability of owners to complete repairs for months and even years?

4 A second dimension of the issue is typical of a society's response as it begins to look ahead, that the disaster must not happen again. What solutions are suggested for the future?

Profit and loss in the tourism industry

Tourism is Dade county's No. 1 economic engine, and for the county to rebuild, tourists and the money they bring are integral cylinders. Dade's 8.4 million annual visitors help pump $7.2 billion into the economy and account for one in three Dade jobs.

"We had the best tourism year in the history of this country before this unexpected visitor came to town," said Merrett Stierheim, president of the Greater Miami Convention and Visitors Bureau.

"We don't want him to score a double victory by allowing the world to think our beaches and tourism centers have been destroyed."

Already, Stierheim has appeared on each of the three major television networks and has traveled to several cities to hold news conferences. Since the storm, the bureau has produced more than 3,000 two-minute promotional videos and circulated them to tour operators and travel agents around the world. Tours are already under way with travel writers, film producers and travel agents.

Bureau employees have contacted every major tourist professional they can think of – from international consulates to foreign tour operators – to tell them Miami is up and running.

Even the film and fashion industry, a significant part of Dade's tourism industry, has kicked in. Dade County's film office has taken out ads in film and fashion trade publications, and it's planning a tour for fashion writers and production executives.

Despite the bureau's efforts, some tourist and business groups are canceling or redirecting their trips to places like Tampa and Orlando.

Meanwhile, some of the large hotel chains – now virtually booked for months with relief workers, military personnel and South Dade residents who are temporarily homeless – have a different challenge.

The Hyatt Coral Gables, for example, is sold out through September with relief workers. That leaves little room for the business groups and tourists who already had reservations.

WHAT'S OPEN

Here is a list of some tourism-related closings and reopenings in Dade County because of Hurricane Andrew.

Attraction	Re-opening date
Biscayne National Park	Unknown
Coral Castle	Unknown
Everglades National Park	Unknown
Fairchild Tropical Garden	Unknown
Florida Pioneer Museum	November
Parrot Jungle	Opened Saturday
Metrozoo	Unknown
Redland Fruit & Spice Park	Unknown
Seaquarium	November
Weeks Air Museum	Unknown

Source: Greater Miami Convention & Visitors Bureau
[*Miami Herald*, 13.9.93]

4.62

Closed shopping mall in Homestead, January 1993.

Slow recovery: Resources 4.61–4.64

1 What evidence is given to suggest that recovery may be slow?

2 For (a) the short-term and (b) the long-term, what are the gains and losses suggested by the forecasters? (Construct your answer in the form of lists.)

3 a Why is tourism so affected by the hurricane?

  b What strategies are being used to promote tourism? Why? Is such a publicity campaign likely to be truthful?

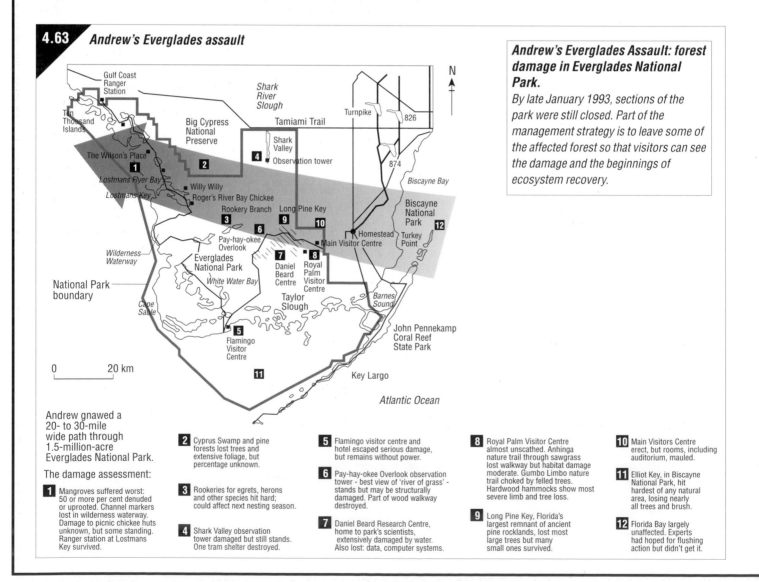

4.63 *Andrew's Everglades assault*

Andrew's Everglades Assault: forest damage in Everglades National Park.

By late January 1993, sections of the park were still closed. Part of the management strategy is to leave some of the affected forest so that visitors can see the damage and the beginnings of ecosystem recovery.

Andrew gnawed a 20- to 30-mile wide path through 1.5-million-acre Everglades National Park.

The damage assessment:

1 Mangroves suffered worst: 50 or more per cent denuded or uprooted. Channel markers lost in wilderness waterway. Damage to picnic chickee huts unknown, but some standing. Ranger station at Lostmans Key survived.

2 Cyprus Swamp and pine forests lost trees and extensive foliage, but percentage unknown.

3 Rookeries for egrets, herons and other species hit hard; could affect next nesting season.

4 Shark Valley observation tower damaged but still stands. One tram shelter destroyed.

5 Flamingo visitor centre and hotel escaped serious damage, but remains without power.

6 Pay-hay-okee Overlook observation tower - best view of 'river of grass' - stands but may be structurally damaged. Part of wood walkway destroyed.

7 Daniel Beard Research Centre, home to park's scientists, extensively damaged by water. Also lost: data, computer systems.

8 Royal Palm Visitor Centre almost unscathed. Anhinga nature trail through sawgrass lost walkway but habitat damage moderate. Gumbo Limbo nature trail choked by felled trees. Hardwood hammocks show most severe limb and tree loss.

9 Long Pine Key, Florida's largest remnant of ancient pine rocklands, lost most large trees but many small ones survived.

10 Main Visitors Centre erect, but rooms, including auditorium, mauled.

11 Elliot Key, in Biscayne National Park, hardest of any natural area, losing nearly all trees and brush.

12 Florida Bay largely unaffected. Experts had hoped for flushing action but didn't get it.

The Sheraton Biscayne hotel
The Sheraton Biscayne hotel is the largest and most expensive along this stretch of coast. In January 1993 it still stands empty and unrepaired, with its landscaping destroyed, and sand banked up to the main building. January to April is peak season for Florida tourism, so 1993 was a 'write-off' for this section of the coast.

Review

- Several distinct but overlapping phases to the disaster can be identified.
- Impacts and ability to recover varied not only geographically (over space) but socially and economically, depending where you were, and who you were.
- Disaster response in an urbanised region is extremely complex because of the variety of agencies involved. Thus, even in a 'hazard region' such as south Florida, and in a wealthy and advanced nation such as the USA, disaster impacts can be severe and long-lasting.
- It has become clear that a disaster has only a limited 'shelf life' in the public and media consciousness. Agencies, politicians, the public and the media pass on to other high profile issues. For example, the 1993 Mississippi floods displaced south Florida from the headlines and from FEMA's focus.

Activities

1 Outline the main reasons why the response to Hurricane Andrew was complex. Suggest ways in which it could have been made more efficient.

2 Was Hurricane Andrew a natural, technological or composite disaster? Give reasons for your answer.

3 To what extent does the following extract, written as a general description of the aftermath to a disaster, reflect what happened after Hurricane Andrew hit?

During the initial phase of recovery, victims' lives are organised in artificial patterns. Temporary shelter dominates, and eating arrangements may be communal instead of private. Social cohesion tends to be reinforced under the duress of the disaster, which represents a common enemy to be faced by all survivors. However, as long-term effects begin to predominate, old inequalities reassert themselves and often become accentuated. The long term may be a period in which the authorities, faced with many other problems, lose interest in the disaster area … The complexity and variety of society mean that there is no standard timescale for reconstruction: the length of time it takes to overcome the effects caused by disaster may vary by as much as four times, depending on the size of the affected population, the availability of resources and the level of organisation.

(Alexander. D, *Natural Disasters*, UCL Press, 1993)

CHAPTER 5

Managing urban regeneration

Introduction

Cities not only grow outwards, but also change internally. The pace of this change appears to be accelerating, especially in areas where industries pass through product and technology cycles. As a result, one of the biggest challenges facing urban managers is what can be done for the parts that 'wear out' or become redundant, and who should do it. No country can afford to leave significant obsolescent industrial sites derelict. Economically, such areas are not producing income and they lower the environmental quality of life. They are a waste of space.

As modern industry changes its character and its locational needs, it will leave vacant spaces. Redevelopment needs to take these aspects into account because cities are places both for living in and making a living in. Urban regeneration is high on the planning agenda in industrial cities throughout the world, as old industries die or change their character, and as new industries emerge. At the heart of the problem lie the questions of *money:* who should provide it and for what. In capitalist societies market forces and the profit motive are powerful energies. Urban land has high value and is expensive to redevelop. Putting in modern infrastructure is costly and does not yield a direct profit, nor do environmental improvements such as landscaping and public open space. We also need to agree on what kind of urban landscape we want. The role of government and the public sector in relation to the private sector is crucial.

The case studies of this chapter examine how the complex relationships among government, local councils, local communities and private developers vary, and how this influences the outcome. Who made the decisions and what their motives were, are key understandings. Case Studies 5.1 and 5.2 analyse mega-projects on derelict dockland sites. Ports are the critical interface between land and sea transport, but the locational and organisational needs of these 'break-of-bulk' points have changed fundamentally over the past 35 years. This has left traditional docks abandoned, often in the heart of urban areas. Dock facilities are space-

A derelict industrial landscape

consuming, and when they close down they leave behind large sites in attractive waterfront locations. This has led to some exciting revitalisation schemes which combine commercial enterprises and economic profit with social and environmental benefits. However, in such complex and hugely costly schemes, conflict and controversy are inevitable. Case Study 5.1 uses two UK examples, London's Docklands project, given high profile in recent years because of its apparent failure, and Salford Quays, a less publicised project in Manchester's inland docks, with a different balance between private and public sectors.

Industrial regions whose wealth was created around traditional heavy industries such as coal, iron, steel and chemicals,

have endured long-term structural decline, for example, the Rust Belt of the north-east United States, the Ruhr in Germany, the Clyde Valley and South Wales. A result of this decline has been the emergence of serious concentrations of derelict land, much of it difficult to redevelop. Central government and local authorities have introduced policies to attract investment and development on to such sites on almost any terms.

Case Study 5.3 examines the Merry Hill regional shopping centre in the Black Country, West Midlands. (The economic condition of the Black Country is the subject of Case Study 6.1.) Built on the site of an old steelworks, it highlights the costs as well as the benefits of such policies. Case Study 5.4, again from the Black Country, illustrates a different approach to a very difficult site. The Saltwells Nature Reserve places environmental and social benefits above economic revival, and shows how such an approach can be an effective element in an urban regeneration programme.

Seattle waterfront: warehouses are redeveloped as tourist attractions

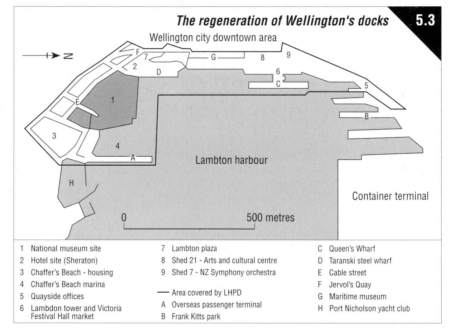

The regeneration of Wellington's docks **5.3**

No.		No.		Letter	
1	National museum site	7	Lambton plaza	C	Queen's Wharf
2	Hotel site (Sheraton)	8	Shed 21 - Arts and cultural centre	D	Taranski steel wharf
3	Chaffer's Beach - housing	9	Shed 7 - NZ Symphony orchestra	E	Cable street
4	Chaffer's Beach marina			F	Jervol's Quay
5	Quayside offices	—	Area covered by LHPD	G	Maritime museum
6	Lambdon tower and Victoria Festival Hall market	A	Overseas passenger terminal	H	Port Nicholson yacht club
		B	Frank Kitts park		

Wellington (pop. 392 000) is the capital city of New Zealand and an important port. In contrast with some other waterfront cities around the world, Wellington has retained its dock facilities, thanks to its deep-water harbour. However, as new roll-on, roll-off facilities have been developed, the commercial heart of the port has shifted eastwards. By the end of the 1970s, the abandoned old docks had left a 20 ha site available next to the Downtown district. During the 1980s, discussions between the city council, the Harbour Board (who owned the land), the business community and local community groups, resulted in a redevelopment plan. When completed it will be 'a place for people', like the successful Sydney waterfront scheme which links the CBD to the famous Opera House. According to the development plan, it will be 'an integrated, harmonious development between the city and the sea, with appropriate commercial, maritime, recreational, educational, cultural and residential uses. It is managed by a consortium of public agencies and the business community.

CASE STUDY 5.1 *Government policy and urban regeneration*

Background

During the second half of the nineteenth century the explosive growth in world industry and trade was assisted by advances in transport technology. On land this was 'the age of rail', while on the oceans, ships increased in number, size and speed. The outcome was the building of extensive docks with associated warehousing, rail freight yards and industries for the processing of raw materials, in coastal cities such as London, Liverpool, New York and Rotterdam. These great ports formed the crucial 'break-of-bulk' points in the global land and ocean transportation system. Inland ports were created using rivers and canals large enough to carry ocean-going ships, for example, St Louis (USA), Duisberg (Germany) and Manchester.

The ocean-rail system remained the basis of world trade until the 1960s. By the 1970s, however, patterns of trade had shifted. Old industries faded and new countries and trade alliances developed. Ships became larger and standardised containers required different dock handling and storage facilities. On land, road steadily replaced rail. For example, in the UK, the city of Liverpool declined as the trade balance and the decline of the cotton industry swung towards Europe, favouring east coast ports. London's ageing docks, although near to the European markets, could not accommodate the massive oil tankers, nor the huge bulk-carrier and containerised ships. On land these older port cities lacked the road transport infrastructure to provide good access and accessibility.

By 1980, these out-dated docklands made up some of the largest areas of derelict land in inner cities. Their decline also brought high unemployment to long-established communities, such as London's East End. These areas became part of 'the Inner City Problem' and a focus of government policies. Both the public sector (government) and the private sector (commercial investors and developers) perceived the enormous potential of such large sites with water frontage. During the prosperous years of the mid 1980s, a number of large-scale projects emerged across Europe and North America. Experience has exposed the complexity and huge costs of such mega-projects. Some have been harshly criticised for emphasising economic profit at the expense of social and environmental needs. London's Docklands and Manchester's Salford Quays are two such projects. The core questions which need to be addressed are whether the central government-private sector relationship has worked. The major beneficiaries need to be identified. Key influential groups to consider are central government, local councils, private developers and local communities.

Key understandings

◆ London's Docklands is the largest urban regeneration project in Europe.

◆ Large scale urban regeneration is complex and to succeed, requires a balance of involvement between central government, local government, the private sector and local communities.

◆ In Docklands, central government through its agency, the LDDC, has acted as 'facilitator', encouraging the private commercial sector to carry out the development.

◆ Criticisms concerning Docklands centre on the lack of an overall plan, an underestimation of the infrastructure needs of a massive project, a narrow perception of 'regeneration', the under-involvement of local authorities and communities, and over-reliance on 'market forces'.

◆ In the Salford Quays development, the driving force has been the local authority, which has achieved a different balance of development.

Part A: London's Docklands – success or failure?

The policy context

The massive Canary Wharf complex in London's Docklands has become a symbol of the apparent 'failure' of free-market approaches to urban regeneration. The largest regeneration scheme in Europe failed to attract businesses and caused the collapse of its major developer, the Canadian company, Olympia and York in 1992. Yet Canary Wharf itself is only the most high-profile element for the revitalisation of east London's declining and disused dock complexes. This is not simply a private enterprise project. Its foundation is one of the most important government policies of the 1980s for energising urban regeneration: the Urban Programme and Urban Development Corporations (UDCs). The problems and successes of Docklands are the outcome of the relationship and power balance between central government and the speculative property market.

UDCs were created in 1980. The Local Government, Planning and Land Act 1980, enabled the Secretary of State for the Environment to identify and designate Urban Development Areas (UDAs), each to be run by a UDC. The primary objective of a UDC was *to secure the regeneration of its area ... by bringing land and buildings into effective use, encouraging the development of existing and new industry and commerce, creating an attractive environment and ensuring that housing and social facilities are available to encourage people to live and work in the area* (Local Government Act, 1980, N6, S136).

This fundamental shift of policy transferred much of the initiative for urban renewal away from local authorities. In their place, a UDC is an agency under direct central government control, whose main purpose is to encourage private sector investment and development. A UDC does *not* replace a local authority; it takes over the single function of development control. With a maximum 10 year life-span, it works as a temporary emergency planning agency.

The main functions of a UDC have been:

- the acquisition of land.
- the clearing and preparation of sites.
- the upgrading of local infrastructure and services.
- the marketing and sale of prepared sites to private developers and businesses.

A UDC works as a facilitator not a developer. It acts as a 'pump primer' by using public funds to attract private investment.

Setting up the UDC

The London Docklands Development Corporation (LDDC) was established in October 1981 as one of the first UDCs (along with Merseyside). It received its funding from annual grants from central government and from the sale of land to private developers. The LDDC aimed to stimulate regeneration of the four components of the disused London docks: Wapping; Surrey Docks; the Isle of Dogs and the Royal Docks. In 1981, 80% of the designated UDA was owned by public bodies such as British Gas, the Port of London Authority, the Central Electricity Board and Local Authorities. Of the total area of 1800 ha, 1000 ha was classified as derelict.

During the first two years the LDDC energetically acquired most of this land much more rapidly than normal because:

- a UDC could bypass many planning procedures, e.g. a land purchase did not require a public enquiry.
- it had money available (in 1981-82 it received £50 million, which was to rise to £300 million by 1991).
- central government could put pressure on the various owning public bodies to sell.
- as development controller it could override the objections of the local authorities.

Canary Wharf, London Docklands: an urban regeneration megaproject in trouble.

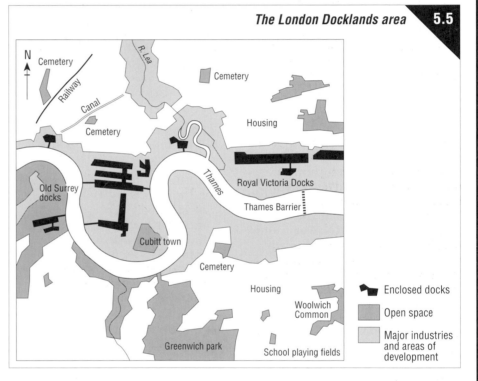

The London Docklands area 5.5

Enclosed docks

Open space

Major industries and areas of development

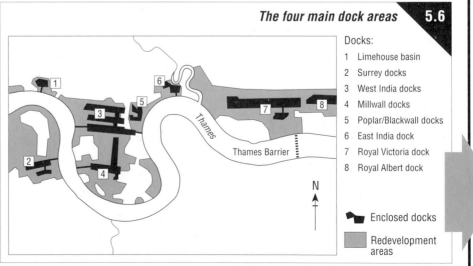

The four main dock areas 5.6

Docks:
1 Limehouse basin
2 Surrey docks
3 West India docks
4 Millwall docks
5 Poplar/Blackwall docks
6 East India dock
7 Royal Victoria dock
8 Royal Albert dock

Enclosed docks

Redevelopment areas

CASE STUDY 5.1 *Government policy and urban regeneration*

This last factor was especially important because the local authorities in Docklands already had co-operative projects under way through their Docklands Joint Committee (DJC). In 1976, for example, they had drawn up the Docklands Local Plan, which provided for 23 000 new homes over 20 years, half of these being council rented properties for the working class communities of east London. The LDDC overrode and largely ignored this plan.

Phase I, 1981–86

We can make sense of this new approach by the LDDC if we place it in the context of broader government policies of the early 1980s. In *housing*, the result was a shift in the balance of new homes by type of tenure. Instead of the DJC priority for council rented property, the LDDC allocated 80% of housing to private ownership. The 'prestigious' waterfront location meant high land prices. So most housing became expensive to buy, and beyond the means of many local people. To make this land available, the LDDC took over land which Newham and the other councils had previously allocated for 'social' or council rental housing schemes. As a result, the Dockland scheme failed to solve local housing problems.

In *infrastructure* the LDDC went ahead with four well-publicised schemes. Publicity was seen as important in order to raise the 'image' of Docklands.

- The Docklands Light Railway (cheaper than an underground route) to link with the rest of London.
- A new road into the Isle of Dogs.
- The short take-off and landing airport (STOL) in the Royal Docks.
- The laying of optic fibre cables to new developments to provide high-speed computer links.

As this newly-assembled, prepared land and infrastructure began its development in the mid-1980s, it coincided with a property and *service industry* boom. The strongly-marketed image of Docklands and its

5.7 *External energies directing LDDC policy*

1 A Conservative government belief in home ownership; cut-backs in council home building; Right-to-Buy policy; stimulation of private sector house building.
2 Encouragement of prosperous classes to move back into inner city areas to live.
3 Increased control by central government; reduced control and influence by local authorities.
4 Reduction of public sector spending; increased reliance on and encouragement of market forces and private sector initiatives.
5 Economic recovery from the 1982 recession and increasing availability of investment money.
6 Post-1983 house property boom especially in south-east England.

excellent location near the existing financial heart of London made the area attractive. The first centre of development in the Isle of Dogs was further boosted by its designation as an Enterprise Zone in 1982. This eased planning regulations even more, and gave additional funds and tax relief.

All seemed set for success, but by 1986 a number of serious issues were arising:

- The local councils felt ignored, yet the impacts of the Docklands development were spilling over into their areas of responsibility. Traffic congestion increased and waiting lists for housing grew.
- Local communities were realising how few benefits were coming their way, despite earlier promises

from the LDDC and the developers. For example, the new housing was far too expensive for them. They did not have the necessary skills for many of the jobs being created. The quality of the jobs which were available to locals was poor, being either part-time or low paid service jobs. Many 'new' jobs were, in fact, transfers. By the end of 1986 approximately 7500 jobs had been created in the LDDC area since 1981, but only 2500 were new jobs. More than 5000 were transfers from elsewhere. Above all, the local people felt strongly that their opinions were not being sought. They were not being involved in the regeneration of their own neighbourhoods.

Poor quality industrial premises on the Isle of Dogs

- The transport infrastructure improvements were seriously inadequate. The DLR was delayed by technical problems and had a design capacity of only 6600 passengers an hour, while forecasts were for an eventual 30 000 people a day using the line. Traffic jams at junctions where the Docklands roads joined the main network became a significant factor in deterring firms from locating in the projects. The STOL airport was running into technical and environmental problems (noise and safety). There was still no overall transport plan for the LDDC area and its connections with the sub-regional network.
- There were growing complaints about the standards of design. A review of the Isle of Dogs development concluded *that the first wave of commercial development completed by 1986 was either*

free-standing 'pavilion' buildings unfortunately juxtaposed with one another and separated by only security fences and car parking, or monotonous, light industrial sheds. ... A clutter of office blocks whose diverse and conflicting styles and haphazard arrangement turned the Isle of Dogs into an 'architectural zoo' (Oc.T. & Tiesdell.S., TPR, 1993).

Phase II: 1987–89

Despite the rising criticisms, the LDDC claimed in 1987 that Docklands had attracted £2.2 billion of private capital for only £0.25 billion of public investment. However, the Canary Wharf proposals seemed to mark a new beginning: a high-quality, high-image project, the largest single development in Europe. Yet its sheer scale, with its 240 m tower centre-piece, meant that the fate of the whole Docklands

5.9 **Main objections by the Docklands Forum**

1 Inadequate measures to secure jobs for local people
2 The huge local housing demand which was largely ignored within the plan
3 Massive underestimation of the required transport infrastructure
4 The design and environmental impact of the enormous bulk of the development

development came to rest on the Wharf's success or failure .

Central government saw the Canary Wharf project as a 'flagship' for its economic policy and philosophy. It encouraged the LDDC to sell the land at well below market value, overrode local objections and refused to set up a public inquiry, the normal procedure with such planning controversies. The final key to softening local opposition was the developers' forecast that up to 60 000 jobs would be created. Despite these claims and the government pressure, building did not begin until 1988.

Phase III: Post 1990

The delay has proved to be crucial. From 1989 the property market began to fail and by the time the offices and other commercial space became available, demand had fallen. For example, the LDDC income from land sales was £115 million in 1988-89, but in 1989–90, it only reached £24 million. The combination of the poor transport network, the falling income from sales and rents, the massive interest charges on the financing of the project and the deepening economic recession caused recurring crises from 1990 onwards. The main developers of Canary Wharf, Olympia & York, collapsed in 1992, and only in late 1993, was a 'rescue package' developed by a consortium of banks to secure the financial future. As late as mid-1993, half of the office space was still empty and the building programme remained incomplete. The Corporation 'land bank' stood at almost 600 ha.

Canary Wharf has 10 million sq.ft. of office and other service space, equivalent to about 20% of the total space in London's existing financial district, i.e. the City. The ambitious design sets the buildings around public spaces such as squares and boulevards, all within the water frame of the docks and the river.

The master plan was rapidly approved in 1985, in the face of strong opposition from local authorities and the Docklands Forum, the organisation which represented local community interests.

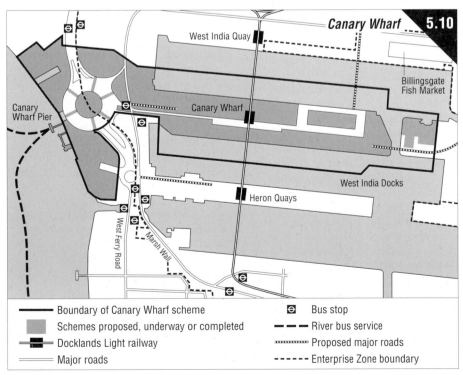

Canary Wharf **5.10**

West India Quay
Billingsgate Fish Market
Canary Wharf Pier
Canary Wharf
West India Docks
Heron Quays
West Ferry Road
Marsh Wall

———— Boundary of Canary Wharf scheme
▨ Schemes proposed, underway or completed
▬▬ Docklands Light railway
═══ Major roads

🚏 Bus stop
– – – River bus service
∙∙∙∙∙∙ Proposed major roads
- - - - Enterprise Zone boundary

CASE STUDY 5.1 *Government policy and urban regeneration*

The problem has been complicated because the developers had agreed to provide part of the funding for the required transport improvements. When they were unable to do so, the government refused to make up the shortfall, and so schemes were further delayed. It was a catch-22 situation: clients would not rent premises until the transport system was improved and the transport system would not be improved until the developers received sufficient income from rentals. In November 1993, the government finally agreed to help fund the improvement of the transport infrastructure, the development of the eastward extension of the Jubilee underground line to the Docklands. By increasing the accessibility of Docklands, the government hopes that the development will become more attractive to companies and government departments. The LDDC is spending almost £2 billion on a road programme from Limehouse through Poplar and across the mouth of the River Lea into the Royal Docks.

Reflection – are there lessons to be learned?

There is no doubt that the Docklands Development has some impressive achievements. By 1992, almost 22 million sq.ft (2 million m²) of commercial and industrial space had been completed. Yet criticisms have emerged which illustrate the complexity of urban mega-projects:

1 That central government by its connection with the LDDC, negotiated directly with the private sector and reduced the role of local councils and communities. There has been little direct involvement by central government. The strategy has been 'Leave it to the private sector', to investors, developers and construction companies. The government role has been to assist not direct by freeing up the planning system, and by 'pump priming' with some initial funding and facilities. The idea was that the energies of market forces would bring economic benefits which

Occupied commercial premises in the London Docklands Development area

would trickle down to local areas. The LDDC, the key government agency, has for too long been restricted to this non-directive role.

2 That the government and LDDC vision of urban regeneration has, until recently, been too narrow. Regeneration was seen to be essentially about physical and economic change, to erect new buildings and attract new businesses. This ignores the social dimensions of change and the need to involve the local communities in the decision-making process from the start. There were already local authorities and local organisations in existence. The planning process could have, and should have, benefitted from them at all stages.

3 That there was neither an Environmental Impact Assessment (EIA) nor an overall plan within which individual projects could be fitted and evaluated. The LDDC as the planning body, saw its role as restricted to acquiring, preparing and making land available to private developers. A detailed structure plan, developed from consultation with local authorities and communities, and with central government was needed. This could have ensured more

coherent and carefully-phased development, higher quality of design, fundamental changes in infrastructure within Docklands and in the surrounding sub-region, and the introduction of this infrastructure at the time of the development and not as 'crisis management' afterwards.

Overall, the message from Docklands seems to be that effective regeneration should be a *partnership* among central government, local councils, local communities and the private sector. This is achievable, as examples from the Netherlands and the USA show (see Case Study 5.2: San Francisco). Since the problems began to surface in Docklands in the late 1980s, the LDDC and the local councils, such as Newham, have shown more co-operative attitudes and tried to make partnerships. The Conservative government, on the other hand, has been reluctant to be seen as interventionist, because of its philosophy and because of the financial implications of becoming directly involved.

[Main reference: Oc T. and Tiesdell S. 'The London Docklands Development Corporation (LDDC), 1981–1991', *TPR*, 62(3), 1991, 311–330]

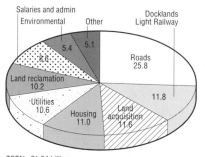

a Allocating the funds %

Salaries and admin
Environmental
Other
Docklands Light Railway
5.4
5.1
8.6
Roads 25.8
Land reclamation 10.2
11.8
Utilities 10.6
Housing 11.0
Land acquisition 11.6

TOTAL: £1.34 billion
(cf. £9.0 billion invested by the private sector).

b The jobs balance sheet

Total jobs attracted	41,421
Transfers from elsewhere	24,862
New jobs created	16,862
Jobs lost in Docklands	20,532
Net change of jobs in Docklands	3,670

c Employment profile trends (%)

1981			*Jobs attracted 1981–91*	
1 Other manufacturing	29.0		1 Banking, finance and business services	23.7
2 Transport and communications	20.8		2 Other manufacturing	19.2
3 Distribution, hotels etc.	15.5		3 Distribution etc	14.7
4 Other services	10.5		4 Construction	14.0
Total jobs	27 213		Total jobs	41 421

d Unemployment

July 1981	Jan 1983	Jan 1985	Jan 1987	Jan 1989	Jan 1991
3553	4570	4983	4877	3264	3900

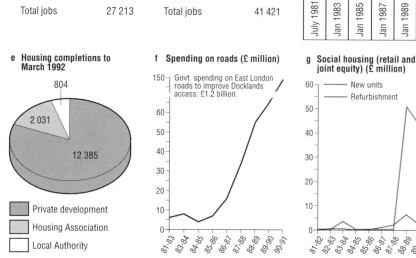

e Housing completions to March 1992

804
2 031
12 385

- ▨ Private development
- ▨ Housing Association
- ☐ Local Authority

f Spending on roads (£ million)

Govt. spending on East London roads to improve Docklands access: £1.2 billion.

150
60
50
40
30
20
10
0

81-83 83-84 84-85 85-86 86-87 87-88 88-89 89-90 90-91

g Social housing (retail and joint equity) (£ million)

— New units
— Refurbishment

60
50
40
30
20
10
0

81-82 82-83 83-84 84-85 85-86 86-87 87-88 88-89 89-90 90-91

Activities

1 Outline the process of urban regeneration adopted by the government and the LDDC, and suggest why this has been criticised as being too narrow.

2 What is meant by the *trickle down* approach to regeneration?

3 Why do you think the LDDC never produced an overall structural plan, and what difference might such a plan have made?

4 What factors have led to the problems and criticisms of Canary Wharf?

5 Use the data of Resource 5.12 to assess the success or failure of the Docklands Development.

6 Outline the roles of the LDDC and the central government in the Docklands Development.

7 Why do the local communities feel let down by the redevelopment process? How could a genuine partnership approach have improved their quality of life?

Part B: The Salford Quays Project

The Salford Quays project, begun in 1984, is by many measures more successful than London's Docklands. A 1990 report claims that *Salford Quays has achieved a worldwide reputation for regenerating an area that had seemed almost beyond revitalisation* (Colenutt & Tansley, *First Year Report of the CLES Monitoring Project on UDCs* 1990). One of the key differences from the London project has been the strong control retained by the city council. This control and interest has played a significant part in the relative success of Salford Quays. Salford City Council has negotiated a partnership arrangement with a private developer, Urban Waterside plc. The city reclaims and services the land, and then disposes of sites for private development. The development plan has been drawn up by consultants appointed by the council. As an inner city area, the site qualifies for a range of government (Department of Environment) and EU grants. It has attracted considerable public sector funds. For example between 1984–94, it received £22 million from Derelict Land Grant funds and £17 million from Urban Programme funds. The aim has been that for every million pounds of public investment, £4 million of private investment will be attracted.

The city has been skilful in retaining some control. It accumulated the land, agreed to pay for the infrastructure and it attracted funds. Yet the council acknowledged the power of the developer and market forces by keeping the plan flexible. The 1985 plan avoided too precise a land-use allocation, allowing for a flexible approach to development opportunities. The plan indicated a range of activities that would be acceptable, such as small-scale commercial activities, leisure pursuits and housing. It also indicated those activities which would be discouraged, for example, offices over 1500 m², and heavy industry.

The Manchester Ship canal, along which the Salford Docks were built, opened in 1894, and as late as 1960 was carrying 18 million tonnes of cargo a year. By 1980, the canal was little used and the docks virtually closed. The Salford Quays Project, started in 1984 and still in progress ten years later, is an excellent example of a large scale inner city regeneration scheme.

5.14 | **Salford Quays expenditure, 1992–94 (£'000)**

Public sector	1992–93	1993–94
Derelict land grant	1069	631
Urban programme	548	199
European Regional Development Fund (EU programme)	390	730
Other	1	49
Total	2008	1609

Total spent on infrastructure to April 1994: £35.5 million

Private sector: Total development expenditure to April 1994: £250 million

[Source: Salford Planning department]

This flexibility is illustrated by the 1987 increase in densities permitted in the plan, a response to the boom in commercial development. The presumption against buildings taller than four storeys and larger than 1500 m² was removed. The increased densities and greater traffic generation have been accommodated within the original transport plan. This identified another key difference from the London's Docklands, where inadequate transport capacity has proved a crucial weakness. Furthermore, the project has coincided with the building of Manchester's Metrolink, a light rail transit system, with a route through the Salford Quays.

A further illustration of the local focus has been the employment policy. The Council has emphasised that benefits should go to the people of Salford. Because the majority of new jobs are in the service sector, the city has set up training and education schemes to equip local people with the appropriate skills, for example, a job link-up with the new Copthorne Hotel. By late 1993, over 4000 new jobs had been created.

The relatively low priority given to housing inside the project has been disappointing, however. By the end of 1991, barely 500 units had been completed, funded by Housing Associations for affordable rentals.

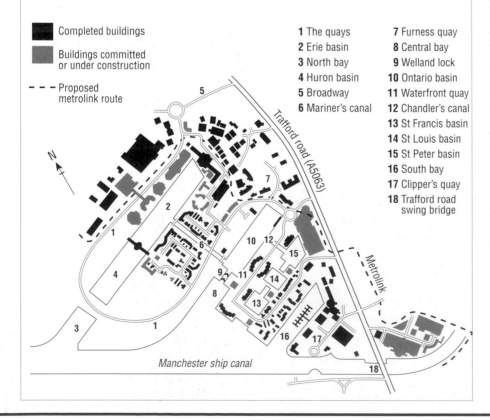

■ Completed buildings

■ Buildings committed or under construction

- - - Proposed metrolink route

1 The quays
2 Erie basin
3 North bay
4 Huron basin
5 Broadway
6 Mariner's canal
7 Furness quay
8 Central bay
9 Welland lock
10 Ontario basin
11 Waterfront quay
12 Chandler's canal
13 St Francis basin
14 St Louis basin
15 St Peter basin
16 South bay
17 Clipper's quay
18 Trafford road swing bridge

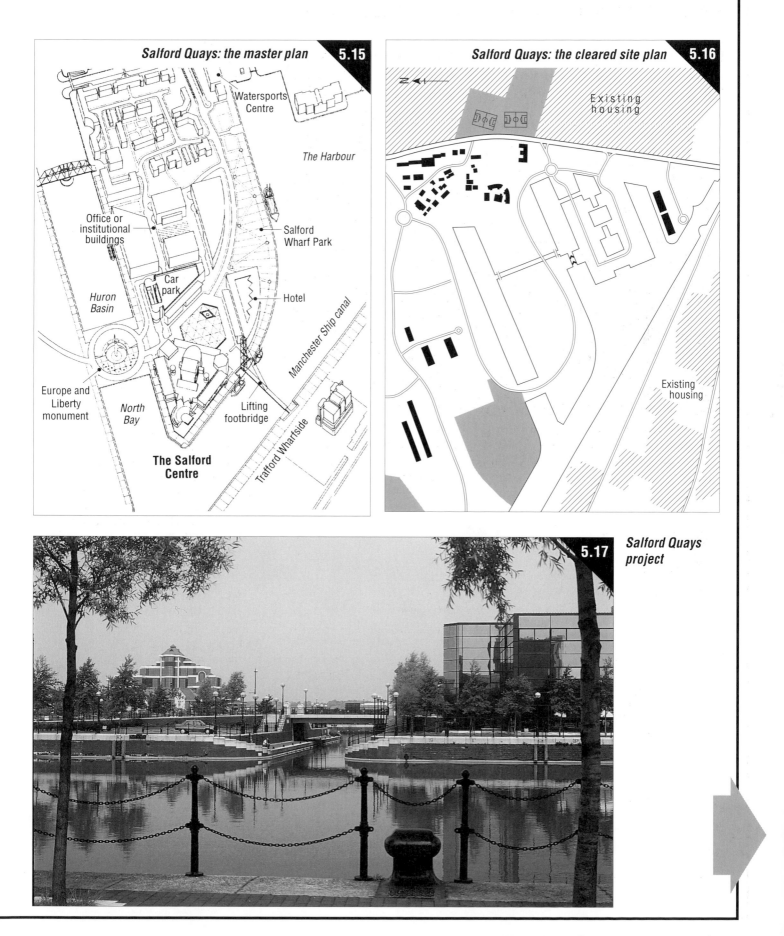

Salford Quays: the master plan 5.15

Watersports Centre

The Harbour

Office or institutional buildings

Salford Wharf Park

Huron Basin

Car park

Hotel

Europe and Liberty monument

North Bay

Lifting footbridge

Manchester Ship canal

Trafford Wharfside

The Salford Centre

Salford Quays: the cleared site plan 5.16

Existing housing

Existing housing

5.17 *Salford Quays project*

CASE STUDY 5.1 *Government policy and urban regeneration*

However, the Council has been able to set up housing schemes in the surrounding areas convenient for the Quays. Emphasis inside the project has been on the creation of a high-quality environment, using the water areas as the centrepiece. Water quality has improved, especially since the docks have been separated by dams.

In 1993 a watersports complex was opened, one of the several facilities aimed at improving the quality of life for local people. There are ambitious plans, too, for a high-quality cultural and leisure complex if funding can be raised by a partnership between the private and public sectors. The progress of this project for concert halls, restaurants and shops has been slowed down by the economic recession of the early 1990s.

Activities

1 In what ways is the Salford Quays project similar to and different from London's Docklands project? How do these characteristics help to explain the relative success of the Salford scheme?

2 Why is it more difficult to develop high-quality facilities and environments for leisure than to attract office and other commercial developments to projects such as Salford Quays?

The Salford Centre

CASE STUDY 5.2 *Avoiding a 'Docklands' disaster*

Background

During the nineteenth century, America attracted millions of immigrants and grew to be a great industrial and trading nation. The majority of the migrants entered and the goods exited through three great ports: New York on the east, New Orleans on the south and San Francisco on the west. Even after the transcontinental railway network was complete, San Francisco remained a large port, sustained by the Panama Canal and later, by the growth of the Pacific trade. In recent decades, ports such as Long Beach (Los Angeles) and Seattle have challenged San Francisco's supremacy.

As in other traditional ports, the older docks of San Francisco, with their extensive rail marshalling yards, have become redundant. San Francisco, set around its huge bay, is a very beautiful city, and the centre of one of the most rapidly growing metropolitan regions in North America. In consequence, it has become a 'honeypot' for American, Japanese and Hong Kong investors. Large waterfront sites such as derelict rail yards and docks are, therefore, extremely attractive.

This case study examines the evolution of one such waterfront site, Mission Bay. San Francisco is a distinctive city, with a tradition of intense and successful community involvement in social and physical development. For example, innovative and radical policies for the treatment of minority groups have been established. Community participation has been a vital element in influencing the character of the Mission Bay project, especially as regards the balance between housing and industry, the layout of neighbourhoods and the creation of jobs for local people. Construction began only in 1992 after a seven-year planning process. This involved detailed negotiations between the San Francisco city council, the developer and community action groups. The United States is a capitalist society in which

San Francisco

market forces wield considerable power, yet community participation has been significant.

Key understandings

- ◆ Large sites in central locations are rare, have high value and are environmentally sensitive.
- ◆ Community or open planning is an approach which involves all interested parties at each stage of the planning process.
- ◆ Decision-making which involves co-operation and consensus is complex and time-consuming.
- ◆ Effective planning must create a balance between economic, social and environmental values.
- ◆ Mixed land-use developments can be economically viable even in high land value locations.

Balancing private profit and public benefit: the case of Mission Bay, San Francisco, California

Setting

Mission Bay is a 127 hectare site only 1.5 km from downtown San Francisco. It is a rare, valuable and sensitive site, unusually large for such a location, near an expanding CBD, and with the attractiveness of facing directly on to one of the world's most famous bays. It possesses, therefore, an enormous developmental potential in terms of investment and profit for a developer. Equally, it sits within a city of great civic pride. The council is proud of the fine city which they have seen rebuilt since the devastation of the 1906 earthquake. There are many active citizens groups who act as 'watchdogs' over proposed developments.

CASE STUDY 5.2 *Avoiding a 'Docklands' disaster*

Consequently, decision-making processes for major projects such as Mission Bay become very complex. The Mission Bay Plan (MBP) attempts to overcome this complexity:

The Mission Bay Plan is the outcome of a landmark process in which the private developer funded a public agency [the City of San Francisco] to take the lead in planning a major mixed-use urban development. San Francisco's planning department opened the planning process to a large number of actively involved citizens and community organisations, and itself played an active role in all elements of analysis, design, planning and negotiation.

As a result, the plans for this new urban community enjoy substantial public support in a city where any form of change, especially land use development, is quite controversial. A massive effort involved 30 city agencies, several regional agencies, and state and national agencies (Bash, 1992).

Site history

The Mission Bay site is part of the extensive infill area along the shores of San Francisco Bay. It is not built on solid, hard-rock geology, but on material laid down within the past century. This creates problems in terms of load-bearing strength and construction costs of massive buildings, and the response of materials

to earthquakes. Seismic waves cause the materials to lose their internal strength and their ability to support weights. It had been these infill areas along the bay which suffered greatest structural damage in the 1989 earthquake.

The original purpose of the infill was to build rail freight yards and warehousing as part of the Port of San Francisco. By the 1980s, the rail yards had closed but some commercial buildings were still in use. The location was an unsightly mixture of derelict land, out-of-date buildings and poor-quality infrastructure. At this time there were increasing pressures for extensions to San Francisco's prosperous CBD.

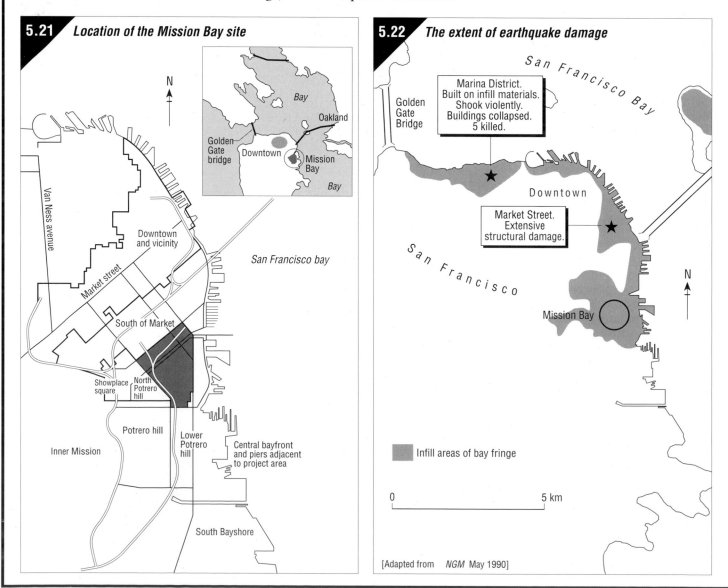

5.21 *Location of the Mission Bay site*

5.22 *The extent of earthquake damage*

Marina District. Built on infill materials. Shook violently. Buildings collapsed. 5 killed.

Market Street. Extensive structural damage.

Infill areas of bay fringe

0   5 km

[Adapted from *NGM* May 1990]

This encouraged the landowners of Mission Bay to make two planning applications for a second downtown which would focus on a series of 40-storey office towers. The proposals aroused such strong community opposition that they were rejected by the city council.

The Mission Bay plan

In any development project, the owner of the land is a crucial factor. The Mission Bay site was owned by private railway companies and the San Francisco Port Authority, a combination of the private and public sectors. In 1984 the rail companies formed a land development corporation. This corporation became the developer with whom the City of San Francisco has formed a partnership. The final plan, agreed in 1991 after seven years of discussion, consultation and negotiation, is summarised in Resource 5.23. The essential characteristic is that it is not dominated by office towers. It is to be a high-density, mixed land-use development, in which 23 000 people will live.

If this project is completed as planned, it will be a remarkable achievement on such a large, high value site in a capitalist country with notoriously liberal planning policies. From the developer's point of view, a higher proportion of commercial office space would be where they expect to gain most profits, not from community facilities or open space. Resource 5.23 sets out how land ownership is divided and illustrates why a co-ordinated plan between city and developer is essential. An important element of the plan is a land exchange of 30 ha between the Port Authority and the developer.

Despite its central location, the MBP is not a commercial 'downtown' development. As the Plan states: *Mission Bay is conceived as a traditional city neighbourhood*, identified by these characteristics:

- A residential population large enough to provide a set of local neighbourhoods and support for community and service facilities.
- High housing densities, typical of neighbourhoods in inner city locations.

- An assortment of housing, including subsidised housing, to create a social mix, and mechanisms within the plan to ensure that this happens.
- Shopping streets threaded within the community to encourage 'street life', rather than isolated shopping malls.
- All housing to be easily accessible to public transport and to parks.
- Street systems to be well connected to freeways and transit routes.
- A variety of job opportunities within Mission Bay to reduce commuting levels.

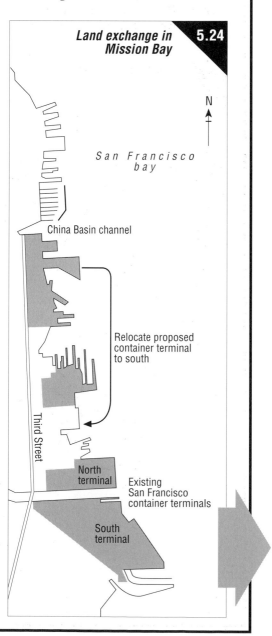

5.24 Land exchange in Mission Bay

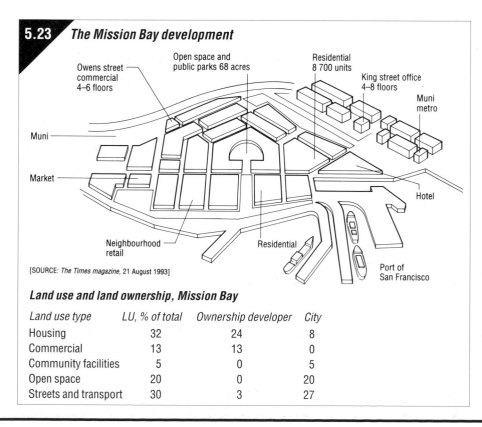

5.23 The Mission Bay development

[SOURCE: *The Times* magazine, 21 August 1993]

Land use and land ownership, Mission Bay

Land use type	LU, % of total	Ownership developer	City
Housing	32	24	8
Commercial	13	13	0
Community facilities	5	0	5
Open space	20	0	20
Streets and transport	30	3	27

CASE STUDY 5.2 *Avoiding a 'Docklands' disaster*

5.25 *Players, pressures and priorities*

The City of San Francisco
The council realises it cannot afford to develop the site itself. Still, it wants a high-quality development which will yield jobs, tax income and improve the quality of life for local people. The council knows, too, that it must agree to a scheme which allows a commercial developer to make attractive profits, while being acceptable to community groups.

The Developer
The developer sees the vigorous rejection of earlier office-dominated proposals. It realises that it must put forward a scheme for mixed land uses if it is to gain the support of the community and the council. It must also press for a scheme which yields as good an economic return for the huge capital investment as possible.

Community action groups
They are totally opposed to purely commercial, high-rise office complexes. They want community involvement in decision-making and community benefits in the outcome. They know they need the city council support and have considerable skills in campaigning, lobbying and putting forward their own proposals.

How the decisions were made

From the start, a key to the plan was the acceptance by all three leading 'players' that a partnership was the only way the project could be accepted and funded.

The central tension focused around cost and funding. The figures involved are huge. If the two elements, development costs and building costs, are combined, the MBP will consume at least $2 billion. As in any project, each 'player' wants to pay as little as possible while achieving the maximum gains in terms of their objectives. Resource 5.26 shows the result of seven years of negotiation and trade-offs between the developer and the council regarding the development cost element of the project. (The community action groups are primarily concerned with getting the land use mix and the quality of environment they want, rather than with who will pay for them.) Notice how much

'planning gain' the city have extracted from the developer. 'Planning gain' is persuading the developer to provide certain non-profit elements in return for permission to go ahead with its development. For example, the city will agree to more office space (profit-making) if the developer gives more land to the city for public open space (non profit-making).

In Mission Bay the developer will pay 78% of the development costs ($250 million out of $320 million), including half of the community and cultural facilities. The City of San Francisco is to pay little in comparison, as it has squeezed most of the public sector contributions from other state and federal agencies. The developer has not been as generous. Companies who buy buildings in Mission Bay will be charged a special tax to help cover the cost of the community and cultural facilities.

Creating the community

Housing
The bid-rent curve which economic geographers use to explain land-use zoning within a city is based on the idea that land uses vary in their ability to pay rent for a site and building. Thus, commercial businesses will dominate central locations with high land values such as Mission Bay. Housing will usually consist of small zones of elite apartments and homes. By these economic criteria, the MBP is distinctive in three ways:

- the size of the residential population.
- the dispersal of homes through the project rather than being zoned into one section.
- the mix of housing types for different socio-economic groups.

The MBP will contain 8500 housing units at an average density of 210 units per hectare (about 10 times that of a suburban housing estate of detached houses). To achieve these densities, most housing will be of

5.26 *Funding the Mission Bay project (in $ million)*

Element	Total	Developer	City	Federal grants
Basic infrastructure	100.2	69.1	–	31.1
Rail transit system	24.9	2.0	–	22.9
Open space	31.1	31.1	–	–
Community facilities	23.9	12.9	2.0	9.0
Fees	62.8	59.5	3.3	–
Land exchange with Port Authority	16.5	16.5		

[From: Bash, 1992]

3–4 storeys, with up to 10-storey blocks near to the taller office buildings. Over 3000 of the housing units will be subsidised (30% by the developer; 70% by the city) to provide housing for less affluent households. To ensure that the housing element is actually built, the plan requires a fixed number of housing units to be built for every unit area of office space completed.

Open space

Where land prices are high there is always pressure to reduce the area given over to non-profitable uses such as open space. The 28 hectares of open space planned for the MBP is unusually high, a reflection of the pressures exerted on the developer by community groups and the city council. Parks will line 3 km of the bay shoreline and be set within neighbourhoods, linked by paths, bike lanes and jogging trails. The system will cost the developer $31 million to build. The city will then maintain it.

Community facilities

The developer will provide 1.25 ha of land and build a theatre and cultural centre at a cost of $4.5 million. A further $8.5 million will be spent on facilities such as a recreation centre, fire station, health clinic and child care facilities.

Commercial development

For the developer, this is the heart of the project, where the profits will be made. The key locational criterion for labour-intensive service industries is accessibility. Staff and clients need to be able to get to and from the premises easily. Also, businesses may be less sensitive to noise from traffic than is housing. Thus, in the MBP, the 450 000 m² of offices will be along a light rail transit line, with direct access to a freeway. It will have 4800 parking spaces. Most office space is likely to be taken up by companies with headquarter offices in the expensive downtown. They can place their clerical and data-processing departments in the near-by, but less expensive MBP, while retaining

their prestige downtown head offices. The 84 000 m² of other commercial and light industrial premises are to be located alongside a freeway, i.e. a location less suitable for housing or open space. The 70 000 m² of retail space will mostly be along two streets, one with vehicular traffic and one pedestrianised. This is to encourage people to shop on foot and to integrate the shops within the community.

Transport

Space and funding for transport infrastructure are two further elements which often get 'squeezed' in high cost mega-projects because transport routes and parking spaces do not, directly, make money. The MBP places considerable emphasis on an internal network and external links with the urban region. This is to reduce the proportion of people who commute by car to 53%, well below the norm for American cities. The huge expenditure on mass transit systems will connect with the existing BART (Bay Area Rapid Transit) network. To help fund this *the developer will pay a City Transit Impact Development Fee of $54/sq.m. of office space, totalling $424 million* (MBP, 1991). There is to be a new light railway and existing commuter routes will be upgraded and new stations added. The road network will be linked to the freeway system by new access ramps very early in the development process. This contrasts with London's Docklands where crucial links between the internal and external networks have been added much later. One objective of the integration of housing with other landuses is to encourage local people to walk to shops or work, or to use transit lines rather than drive.

Economic development and the community

A major criticism of many mega-projects is that they are dominated by large external corporations and by commuters. Too little attention is paid to local people and small enterprises. To try to improve the

opportunities for such people, the MBP has set up an economic development fund. This is financed jointly by the city and the developer *to achieve substantive economic participation in the project for disadvantaged minority-owned businesses, women-owned businesses and locally-owned businesses, and for minorities, women and economically-disadvantaged San Francisco residents, especially those living near Mission Bay* (MBP, 1991). This programme of 'affirmative action' is a tribute to the efforts of community action groups and the commitment of the city council.

Activities

1 What is meant by *open* or *community* planning?

2 Who are the main 'players' in the Mission Bay project and what are their key objectives?

3 Why did the various groups accept that the only way was to form a co-operative partnership?

4 Why do you think it took seven years from the original planning application to the acceptance of the MBP? (There are positive and negative reasons.)

5 List the significant features of the MBP which distinguish it from many such central projects?

6 Use the evidence from the Mission Bay project to illustrate the concept of 'planning gain'.

7 Discuss the advantages and disadvantages of a community-based approach to large-scale city redevelopment projects.

CASE STUDY 5.3 *Impacts of regional shopping centres*

Background

There is no doubt that large, multi-store shopping malls, retail warehouse parks and off-centre complexes have changed the nature of shopping and the structure of the shopping hierarchy. These massive developments have created attractive, accessible environments which promote shopping as a leisure activity through the inclusion eating outlets, multi-screen cinemas, childrens' play areas, fitness centres and even ice-rinks. Although North America is the 'home' of these mega-malls, the phenomenon is world-wide. In Brasilia, the planned capital of Brazil, the central indoor shopping complex is packed with thousands of people on Saturday nights from 5 to 11pm. More than half of the week's trade is done then, and for many people it is the major social event of the week. In Bangkok, Thailand, downtown indoor centres are crowded in evenings and at weekends.

In Britain, multi-store centres are a significant element of the modern

5.27

The Galleria, Dallas, Texas

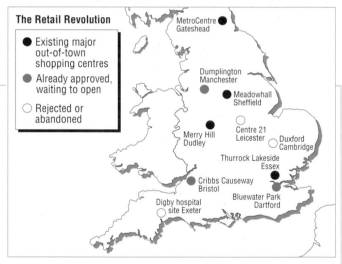

The Retail Revolution

- ● Existing major out-of-town shopping centres
- ● Already approved, waiting to open
- ○ Rejected or abandoned

MetroCentre Gateshead

Dumplington Manchester

Meadowhall Sheffield

Merry Hill Dudley

Centre 21 Leicester

Duxford Cambridge

Thurrock Lakeside Essex

Cribbs Causeway Bristol

Bluewater Park Dartford

Digby hospital site Exeter

5.28 *Giant that never got off the ground*

By Dominic Kennedy

Cambridgeshire County Council signalled its approval for out-of-town shopping as early as 1985, and by the end of the decade three proposals were on the table.

The favourite was on farmland owned by one of the Cambridge colleges, at Duxford, nine miles south of the city centre next to the M11. Grosvenor Developments and Tesco Stores were behind the proposed "sub-regional shopping centre", with space for 4,500 cars, which would be the largest of its kind between Brent Cross in north London and the MetroCentre on Tyneside.

"There was popular outrage among the residents when the full implications became clear to them," said Lawrence Wragg, a merchant banker and chairman of the pressure group South Cambridgeshire Against Rural Extinction (Scare).

The Duxford site was to include one or two department stores, a food supermarket, other shops, restaurants, a food court and a petrol station. The plans included a community service element, a modest swimming pool with a hall. It did little to stifle resistance.

At its peak, Scare had nearly 2,000 members. Pensioners gave their spare time to work for the campaign, companies allowed the group to use their photocopiers free, and schoolchildren organised sponsored walks which helped to raise £20,000 to fight the proposals.

For the four-month long enquiry which began in 1991, the campaigners hired a planning consultant to put their case. Two rival schemes to the north and east of Cambridge were considered at the same time as Duxford.

By then, though, the retail boom was over. The county council realised there was no need for such a large development and argued against it. The enquiry inspector chose Duxford as the best of the three schemes.

John Gummer, the Environment Secretary, announced last week that he was rejecting the proposal because of the damaging effect it could have on the vitality of Cambridge, and because of transport problems

The MetroCentre in Gateshead is regarded as the largest of its kind in Europe. Other schemes described as "regional or subregional shopping centres" are Lakeside at Thurrock, Essex, Meadhowhall in Sheffield and Merry Hill in Dudley.

There are three sites with planning permission for similarly large developments, designed to attract shoppers from several counties: Bluewater Park at Dartford, Kent; Cribbs Causeway, Bristol; and the Dumplington project near Manchester.

Three other ambitious proposals have been abandoned. Centre 21 in Leicester was ruled out in favour of a smaller shopping centre.

Plans for the Digby hospital site in Exeter were abandoned when the district council decided to concentrate on city centre shops instead.

[*Times* 8.2.94]

urban environment, both on out-of-town 'greenfield' sites and inner city 'brownfield' sites. Wherever they are located, their land demands and traffic create considerable environmental impacts, both positive and negative. This in turn, generates strong planning controversies. Out-of-town centres take up agricultural and greenbelt land, while city sites cause congestion of neighbourhood roads. On the positive side, they add shopping choice and quality for the consumer and can act as a powerful vehicle for urban regeneration. For example, both the Metro Centre in Gateshead and the Meadowhall Centre in Sheffield are located on derelict industrial sites. They attract inward investment, other businesses, create jobs and have a valuable multiplier effect on the local economy. Little wonder then that many city councils have been keen to attract development companies who are interested in investing the huge sums required. There is, however, evidence that the boom may be over and that government policy may be changing (Resource 5.28).

On the other hand, because of the large consumer population needed to make such a centre economically successful, it must be highly accessible to a large urban area. It must fit into a regional system with an already established shopping hierarchy and saturated road network. (Note the contrast here to a number of North American examples where the complexes are one element of entirely new urbanising areas, i.e. areas without existing service systems and infrastructures.) Councils, existing businesses and local people are increasingly realising that the arrival of a new regional shopping centre may be disastrous for established downtown business districts, and may accentuate traffic problems. This case study outlines the results of an Environmental Impact Study (EIS) carried out in 1993 on the Merry Hill Centre in Dudley, West Midlands. The materials allow us to assess the benefits for the consumer, the scale of the project, its role in urban regeneration, the impacts on the regional shopping hierarchy and the effects upon the surrounding traffic system. The EIS also addresses whether or not planners should encourage another such development in the West Midlands.

Are mega-malls a good thing? The impact of the Merry Hill Centre on the West Midland shopping hierarchy

Description

The retail complex of Merry Hill Centre in Dudley was built between 1986 and 1989. As late as 1994, however, additions such as the Waterfront leisure and office development were still being made. In October 1994, the developers announced a further project to enlarge the Centre by up to one third. The complex lies at the heart of the Black Country and is an element in the vigorous urban and economic regeneration programme for that industrial district. It is located on land once occupied by the Round Oak Steelworks which closed in 1982. The steelworks left behind a large derelict site, adjacent to one of the last remaining farms in the area. Although built by private developers, Merry Hill has benefitted from the Derelict Land Grant scheme and from its position within an Enterprise Zone (EZ). It, therefore, qualified for central

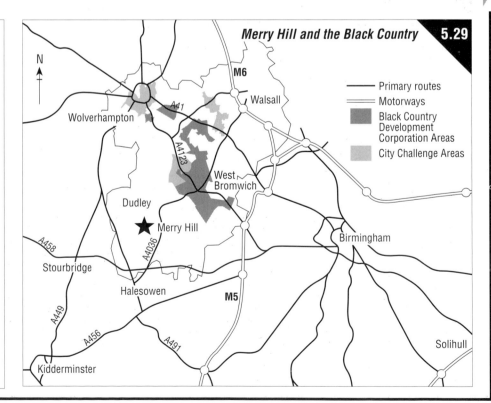

Merry Hill and the Black Country 5.29

Key:
— Primary routes
= Motorways
■ Black Country Development Corporation Areas
▨ City Challenge Areas

CASE STUDY 5.3 *Impacts of regional shopping centres*

government support funding and a relaxing of planning regulations.

Merry Hill was developed in five stages, beginning as a set of retail warehouses and ultimately adding the main internal shopping malls. As a result of this piecemeal development, there are poor linkages between the various elements, despite the internal monorail. Car parks are also dispersed. The Centre is, however, popular and appears to be economically successful, with an annual turnover exceeding £300 million. It covers of 1.39 million sq. ft. of retail floor space, and contains several key 'anchor' stores, such as Marks & Spencer and Sainsbury's. In addition, there is a food court, two fast food restaurants, a multiplex cinema and a car park capacity of 10 000 vehicles. In early 1993, average weekday visitors totalled around 50 000, rising to 72 000 on Saturdays. At least 90% arrive by car although special bus services serve surrounding districts and towns. By February 1993, the Centre employed 3370 people. Almost 80% are female, and 69% of the jobs are part-time.

Employers do not have difficulty with recruitment.

Catchment area

Approximately 450 000 people live within a 15-minute drive of Merry Hill. This zone covers Dudley and parts of Wolverhampton, Sandwell and west Birmingham. The 15–30 minute drive zone extends across the remainder of the Black Country, much of Birmingham and the towns of Kidderminster and Bromsgrove, and includes 1.3 million people. Bus travel speeds are lower and the 40-minute bus isochrone is roughly coincident with the 15-minute car isochrone.

5.30

Merry Hill Centre

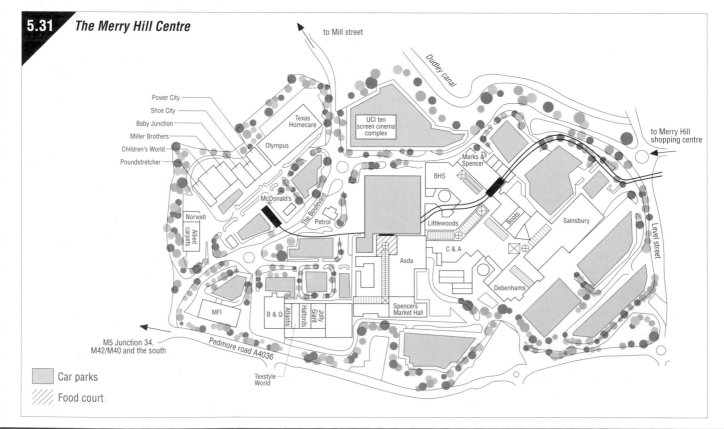

5.31 *The Merry Hill Centre*

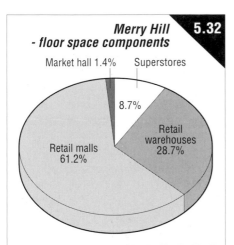

Merry Hill - floor space components `5.32`

Market hall 1.4%
Superstores 8.7%
Retail warehouses 28.7%
Retail malls 61.2%

A February 1993 survey showed that the main catchment zone lies mostly within the 30-minute drive isochrone. It captures 1.85 million people. There is a core zone of more intensive use which coincides with the 15-minute isochrone and includes 492 000 potential customers. Within this core zone, Merry Hill accounts for approximately 40% of the 'comparison shopping' expenditure, such as clothing and footwear, and in the wider main zone, around 15%. For bulk household goods, such as furniture and carpets, Merry Hill gets 19% of the core zone expenditure and 7% of the main zone spending. The figures are 14% and 4% respectively for superstores. In the wider 'main' zone, Merry Hill is directly within the catchment areas of the established major centres of Birmingham and Wolverhampton. Resource 5.35 shows the visit frequencies.

Impact on existing centres

The 1993 EIS examined the impact of Merry Hill upon 12 existing centres. The results are summarised in Resource 5.36.

Dudley town centre has been the most severely affected. For example, for 'comparison goods' it lost 70% of its market share between 1989 and 1993. This contrasts with the other major centres in Birmingham, Walsall and Wolverhampton, where market share falls were below 15%. Birmingham and Wolverhampton, in particular, are seen as 'robust and successful centres' which have benefitted from recent environmental improvement schemes. The EIS concludes that for Dudley:

The centre has lost major multiple retailers. There has been an increase in vacancies; there has been a decline in retailing in the centre; there has been a decline in rentals and there has been a

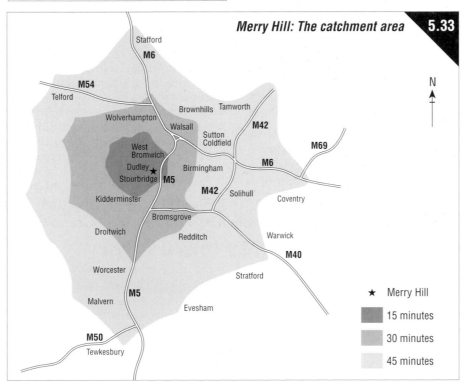

Merry Hill: The catchment area `5.33`

Stafford
M6
M54
Telford
Brownhills Tamworth
Wolverhampton
Walsall
Sutton Coldfield
M42
M69
West Bromwich
Dudley ★
Stourbridge M5
Birmingham
M6
Kidderminster
M42
Solihull
Coventry
Bromsgrove
Droitwich
Redditch
Warwick
Worcester
M40
M5
Stratford
Malvern
Evesham
M50
Tewkesbury

N

★ Merry Hill
■ 15 minutes
■ 30 minutes
■ 45 minutes

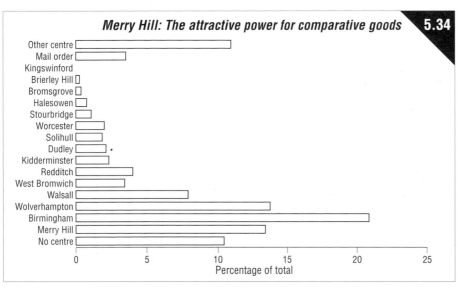

Merry Hill: The attractive power for comparative goods `5.34`

Other centre
Mail order
Kingswinford
Brierley Hill
Bromsgrove
Halesowen
Stourbridge
Worcester
Solihull
Dudley
Kidderminster
Redditch
West Bromwich
Walsall
Wolverhampton
Birmingham
Merry Hill
No centre

0   5   10   15   20   25
Percentage of total

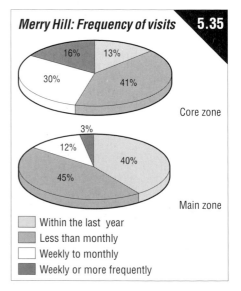

Merry Hill: Frequency of visits `5.35`

16% 13%
30% 41%
Core zone

3%
12% 40%
45%
Main zone

☐ Within the last year
☐ Less than monthly
☐ Weekly to monthly
☐ Weekly or more frequently

CASE STUDY 5.3 *Impacts of regional shopping centres*

marked decline in shopping flows (Tym & Partners, 1993).

Between 1988 and 1993 Dudley lost the following major stores, all of whom have relocated in Merry Hill: Littlewoods, Marks & Spencer, BHS, C & A and Sainsbury's. Other stores which have left include Mothercare, Next, Burton and Curry's. The loss of all these important stores *has significantly downgraded Dudley's position within the shopping hierarchy* (Tym & Partners). Resource 5.39 shows the harsh reality of this drift.

The loss of such key 'anchor' stores leads to a spiral of quantitative and qualitative decline. Where vacant units do attract new tenants, they are often low-quality, discount retailers. In 1993, for example, the former BHS and Sainsbury units were both used as indoor markets. Dudley is undergoing what the EIS describes as a 'cycle of readjustment' in response to Merry Hill: *the town centre operates as a secondary*

5.36 Impact of Merry Hill on existing shopping centres

Centre	Status	Impact	Centre	Status	Impact
Dudley	Town centre	Severe	Walsall	Sub-regional centre	Slight
Stourbridge	Town centre	Significant			
Halesowen	District centre	Significant	Bromsgrove	District centre	Slight
Kidderminster	Town centre	Significant	Kingswinford	Local centre	Slight
West Bromwich	Town centre	Significant	Wolverhampton	Regional centre	Slight
Brierley Hill	Local centre	Some	Birmingham	Regional centre	Slight
Cradley Heath	Local centre	Some			

centre attracting local customers buying low quality or discount goods (Tym & Partners).

Interviews with retail companies, estate agents, shop owners and shoppers established that the main criticisms of Dudley town centre are:

- Ageing built environment.
- Difficult access associated with the scatter of car parks around the centre.
- Poor pedestrian movement with the central area.

- Regular congestion of the road network.

Two policy alternatives face the Dudley council. They could accept the positioning at a lower level in the retail hierarchy, and attract investment at modest levels appropriate to such centres, or they could fight to attract investment to accomplish a major redevelopment. The latter would create a high-quality environment which should attract major retailers and, in turn, more shoppers. To persuade developers to

5.37 Death of the High Street as big stores leave town

By Simon Hinde

It is a familiar high street that could be almost anywhere in Britain. The household names such as Marks & Spencer, C & A and British Home Stores have departed, replaced by a shoddy collection of charity stores and struggling family businesses.

The traditional town centre is in near-terminal decline. Nearly one in eight of its shops lies empty, a rise of about 50% over the past seven years, as the recession compounded a trend towards out-of-town shopping.

The charge has been led by the nation's top stores. Ten years ago, 80% of Sainsburys were in high street locations; today, only half are. Even Marks & Spencer, the barometer of the country's retail mood, now takes one-eighth of its turnover from out-of-town

stores compared with just one-eightieth in 1986.

This weekend Currys, the electrical retailer, publicised plans to close 100 of its 330 remaining high street branches. It will, however, increase its total floor space at far lower rental and staff cost by opening an additional 40 out-of-town superstores this year. "Electrical retailing has been driven out of town by the cost of space on the high street," said John Clare, managing director of Dixons, the chain's owner.

Research by Verdict, the retail analyst, has revealed that 25% of retail sales are now from out-of-town locations, compared with 5% in 1980. "In some high streets as many as half the shops are empty," said Richard Hyman, its chairman.

As the big names leave, they take many of their most affluent customers with

them. Independent, often family-owned food shops such as butchers, bakers, grocers and corner shops have suffered particularly badly, with the number of small food retailers declining by nearly one-third over the past decade.

David Harbourne, secretary of the Independent Food Retailers Confederation, said his members were struggling to compete with supermarkets, leaving town centres drained of their vitality. "We are the heart and lungs of a town centre. Take us away and the centre is doomed," he said.

Dudley, the historic town at the heart of the Black Country, has suffered more than most. In 1989 two local property entrepreneurs opened the Merry Hill shopping centre on its outskirts; it has wrought such devastation on the town centre that locals have dubbed it

"Merry Hell".

The famous names to have joined the exodus away from the town centre include British Home Stores, Burton, C & A, Currys, Littlewoods, Marks & Spencer, Next, Rumbelows, Tesco and Sainsbury. Their replacements include amusement arcades, charity shops, discount shops and an indoor market selling cut-price goods.

Other shops remain empty. Before Merry Hill opened, about one in 30 shops in the town was empty. Today the figure is nearer one in four.

Stephen Schwartz, manager of Trueform on Dudley High Street, has watched a reduction in the range of customers shopping in the town centre as the range of shops decreased. "There are still a lot of old people and some youngsters, but many young families

Dudley town centre retail floorspace changes, 1989–92				**5.38**
Type	1989	1992	1989–92 change	
A Convenience	95 100	71 400	-23 700	
B Comparison	545 000	475 800	-69 200	
C Vacant	65 500	162 800	+97 300	
Total A + B	640 100	547 200	-92 900	

Stourbridge town centre retail floorspace changes, 1989–92				**5.39**
Type	1989	1992	1989-92 change	
A Convenience	75 100	89 400	+14 300	
B Comparison	186 500	180 800	- 5 700	
C Vacant	34 250	22 150	-12 100	
Total A + B	261 600	270 200	+8 600	

invest the huge sums required in a region whose forecast economic growth rate is low, is a problem.

The complexity of the shift of fortunes in existing centres as a result of the arrival of Merry Hill, can be illustrated by examining trends in two other centres in the core zone: Stourbridge and Brierley Hill. The EIS concluded that Stourbridge has been 'significantly' affected but the figures of Resource 5.39 seem to contradict this conclusion. Vacant space fell and overall occupancy rose.

Merry Hill Centre from the air

and middle-income customers now drive to Merry Hill," he said.

While Dudley's problems are extreme, they are not unique. Traders in Stroud, Gloucestershire, estimate that half of their number went to the wall after Tesco and Waitrose opened supermarkets on the outskirts. About one in five of the town's shops is unoccupied, while the Merrywalks shopping centre, an unappealing 1970s relic, is half empty.

"If you walk down the high street, you see far too many empty shops, charity shops and 'here-today-gone-tomorrow' discount stores. The big names have gone and there are no long-stay companies coming in to replace them," said Peter Woodward-Gregg, head of Stroud chamber of commerce.

Discount shops have thrived spurred on by the recession. Companies such as Poundstretcher, What Everyone Wants and Ethel Austin have all extended their empires rapidly.

[*The Sunday Times* 12.6.94]

The negative impact identified by the EIS was in fact *qualitative* rather than quantitative. It showed a 43% decline in 'comparison shopping':

The concern regarding Stourbridge is the town's inability to attract major multiple retailers. The town itself had a population of 54,661 in 1992, equivalent to that of Kidderminster. However, whereas Kidderminster has attracted Littlewoods, Owen Owen, Safeways, Iceland, W.H.Smith, M & S, Woolworth's, Sainsbury, Boots and Waitrose, [in Stourbridge] Owen Owen closed down in 1990 ... Closures have included Olivers and

Dewhurst, with Victoria Wine becoming a coffee shop and Christian Centre in 1991–92. The Curry's outlet is now a Sue Ryder charity shop, and Next downgraded its store to Next Directory in 1992. The impact of Merry Hill on Stourbridge has largely taken the form of a qualitative reduction in retailing (Tym, 1993).

Brierley Hill is the local centre closest to Merry Hill and has suffered significantly in quantative terms. The EIS is pessimistic over its future. Yet interviews with shopkeepers and traders, who do not compete with Merry Hill, found that they were benefitting from the increased 'passing trade' on their way to and from Merry Hill. Nonetheless, the EIS finds *clear evidence of retail decline*, a low-quality built environment including traffic congestion, a lack of investment and weak local economy. Even as a 'local centre' in the retail hierarchy, its future does not look bright despite the shopkeepers' optimism concerning the 'passing trade'. Asda and Do-It-All remain, but MFI relocated to Merry Hill in 1986, with its site used for ten pin bowling in 1993.

The town centre lacks a perceptible shopping core which will attract and appeal to local shoppers (Tym & Partners, 1993). This is a local social issue as Brierley Hill is a long-standing community of considerable strength. The decline of its focal retail area may well be influential in a loss of community feeling.

The implications for future planning policy in the West Midlands

Any development requires planning permission from the local authority Planning Committee before it can proceed. The Planning Committee considers the application against local needs and the existing structure plan. It also operates within a framework of law, regulations and guidelines established by central government, especially the Department of the Environment (DOE).

The EIS of Merry Hill used such a set of guidelines, namely Planning Policy Guidelines number 6 (PPG.6). In the left-hand column, Resource 5.42 sets out the five criteria against which a major development proposal such as Merry Hill should be measured. The right-hand column summarises the EIS findings, should another such centre be proposed. The conclusion is clearly that another 'Merry Hill' cannot be justified in the West Midlands at present.

[Source: Tym R. and partners, *Merry Hill Impact Study*, HMSO, 1993]

Activities

1 What role has Merry Hill played in urban regeneration in the Black Country? (Remember to define what you mean by *urban regeneration*.)

2 What factors have influenced the impact felt by other existing town centres?

3 For any two of the affected centres, summarise the changes that have taken place in retail provision and what the environmental impacts have been.

4 Discuss the effects of Merry Hill upon the shopping hierarchy of the West Midlands conurbation.

5 Summarise the arguments *for* and *against*

  a Merry Hill.

  b proposals for another such development in the region.

6 In the Spring of 1994, the government published planning guidelines aimed at restricting out-of-town growth and reviving traditional High Streets. Use Resource 5.43 to give reasons for the new policy, and Resource 5.44 to suggest why it may be hard to achieve.

5.41 Brierley Hill town centre retail floorspace changes, 1989–92

Type	1989	1992	1989–92 change
A Convenience	77 300	76 600	-700
B Comparison	110 300	97 200	-13 100
C Vacant	3 000	18 300	+15 300
Total A + B	187 600	173 800	-13 800

5.42 Policy implications of Merry Hill

Criteria given in ppg6 to be taken into account when considering a planning application for a major scheme.

Such centres would not normally be appropriate in areas where:

1 There is unlikely to be a significant growth in population or retail spending.

2 Continued investment in nearby town centres is likely to be seriously jeopardised.

3 There would be a loss of Green Belt or important open space or countryside or high quality agricultural land.

4 Public transport could not adequately serve a wide population.

5 The effect on the road network and on the overall level of car travel would be unacceptable.

EIS conclusions for the West Midlands after Merry Hill

1 There is unlikely to be significant growth in the population of the West Midlands and, in the short term, it is improbable that there will be substantial growth in consumer spending.

2 On the basis of the perceived impact of Merry Hill, a similar scheme elsewhere in the West Midlands is likely to jeopardise investment in one or more centres such as Dudley.

3 A development of a site such as Merry Hill would not entail loss of Green Belt or agricultural land. There are vacant urban 'brownfield' sites available in the conurbation, although most of these are identified for industrial type uses.

4 Merry Hill is not well served by public transport in the same way that Birmingham and Wolverhampton are. Further out of town, developments in the region might have better access by public transport than Merry Hill but it would be difficult to replicate the level of service achieved in the major centres, especially those which will be served by LRT (Light Rail Transport being planned from Wolverhampton to Birmingham).

5 Access to Merry Hill by private car is perceived to be getting worse due to congestion. A similar new scheme would need to have better road access and, in turn, traffic generated by new development would have to be capable of being absorbed by the wider road network.

5.43 Gummer seeks to make life difficult for the motorist

By Nick Nuttall, Environment correspondent

John Gummer, the Environment Secretary, yesterday stepped up his campaign against the explosive growth of the car by signalling tough new restrictions on parking spaces, out-of-town industrial parks and the development of housing on the edges of villages and small towns.

Planning policy guidance 13 makes it clear that developments which increase the need for cars should be resisted in favour of ones that encourage the use of buses, railways, walking and cycling. "The Government recognises that forecast levels for traffic growth especially in urban areas cannot be met in full and that new road building or the upgrading of existing highways may be environmentally unacceptable," it says.

The guidance also spells out for the first time to planners the Government's commitment to see people living, working and playing at the heart of public transport networks which are, in the main, in the inner cities. It urges local authorities to resist building local roads if better links between new developments and public transport can be made instead.

Reducing car travel would reduce emissions of carbon dioxide, the gas linked with global warming, and deliver other environmental benefits.

The document urges councils to make life difficult for the motorist. New office, retail and housing schemes should have severely limited parking spaces. In the past planners have tried to match the level of parking with the number of people working or living in a building.

The moves were yesterday welcomed by environmental groups. Fiona Reynolds, director of the Council for the Protection of Rural England, said: "This document spells out very clearly that the Government is committed to development that takes place in urban areas as opposed to more suburbanisation of the countryside. It has now made this a formal objective of policy and gives local authorities practical advice on delivering it."

[Times 16.3.94]

5.44 *Stores look for new ways to drive customers out of town*

The board of Sears has given the green light to plans to extend its out-of-town Sportsworld chain. It is looking to add up to 60 new stores to its existing three sites over the next three years.

The decision is partly an attempt to steal a march on Sports Authority, the American out-of-town operator owned by K Mart, which plans to expand in Britain. But the fact that both Sears and K Mart are jostling for position flies in the face of the current belief that the growth of out-of-town retailing has ground to a halt. Recession, a slowdown in the pace of retail park development, and more importantly the Government's latest planning guidelines aimed at rejuvenating the high street have all prompted critics to write the sector's obituary.

Out-of-town retailing is indeed at the start of a new chapter, but it is unlikely to be the last. The explosive growth it enjoyed during the 1980s may be over, but the market is enjoying renewed buoyancy. Stores selling computers, office equipment, sporting goods and shoes are opening up alongside the more familiar DIY, food and electrical outlets. Established names such as Marks and Spencer and John Lewis as well as new formats such as warehouse clubs and factory outlet mails are adding to this impetus.

The fact remains that the lifestyle changes that fuelled the rise of out-of-town retailing over the past decade or so still hold good today. These include the move in population away from cities and towns, the rise in car ownership and the increase in the number of working women. All these factors have conspired to increase the importance and popularity of the one-stop, once-a-week shopping that favours out-of-town developments.

It is not just consumers for whom out-of-town shopping still holds appeal. What attracted retailers such as B&Q, Tesco and Currys to the sector in the 1980s still holds true in the 1990s. The fundamental appeal is that the out-of-town format enables retailers to benefit from economies of scale. They can sell larger volumes of product than on the high street – and at lower cost. In the new retailing environment of low growth, low inflation and intensifying competition the economics of out-of-town retailing is becoming increasingly attractive.

Paula Alexander, head of corporate affairs at Sears, is in little doubt. "The lower rent is still a major component," she says. "Our research shows that out-of-town rents are at least 50 per cent lower than on the high street.

Furthermore, consumer desire for lower prices will not go away.

Sportsworld stores offer prices up to 15 per cent lower than those of high street sports retailers, yet achieve net margins considerably higher than those of Sears Olympus high street outlets. These returns are partly driven by the product mix. The big out-of-town stores – typically 25,000 sq ft, against 2,000 sq ft on the high street – enable the chain to display a wider range of merchandise, much of it higher margin.

While the high street outlets tend to be dominated by low margin footwear, the out-of-town stores have the room to carry more extensive lines of more profitable sports goods such as games equipment, sportswear, fitness machines and camping and outdoor products.

Ms Alexander says: "You have to give people a reason to get in their car and drive to your store. People are not just looking for lower prices when they shop out of town, what they really want is authority. They want to be secure in the knowledge that when they get to that store they don't need to shop anywhere else." Having chosen to sell golf bags, Sportsworld stocks about 25 types. Out-of-town retailers have to satisfy the demand for depth and width of range.

Retailers – and indeed consumers – are still attracted to the fact that out-of-town developments provide easily accessible, purpose-built stores with plenty of adjacent car parking. Useful features if you are buying a three-piece suite, and ones that are hard to find in city centres. The recent publication of new planning guidelines for local authorities by the Government raised fears that the construction of out-of-town developments will be halted. This reaction now seems over-stated. John Gummer, Environment Secretary, was more aggressive than many had expected but senior officials in his department have reassured the retail lobby that although the development of large out-of-town shopping centres such as Meadowhall, in Sheffield, and Lakeside, in Essex, has come to an end, the smaller retail parks still have a future. Many of these are on the edge of town centres, not in the green belt, and already have planning permission.

The lure of out-of-town retailing is proving strong even for fashion retailers, for whom the format was widely believed to be unworkable. When it comes to shopping for fashion, the thinking goes, consumers like to make comparisons not just on price but on "style". However, the belief that the high street is the only place for fashion retailers is beginning to be challenged. Shoe City, Sears' out-of-town shoe superstores, were originally set up as a clearance operation but the company now believes they have greater potential. It is trying out a new store format, which offers all of British Shoe Corporation's high street brands from Saxone to Roland Cartier under one roof. Far from confusing consumers, the format seems to be working. "Customers want to go somewhere where they can buy the kids' shoes, perhaps a pair of synthetic court shoes for work and then a smarter pair for the evenings," Ms Alexander says.

New entrants to the out-of-town sector such as Shoe City and Sportsworld now have sales of £1.4 billion, according to Verdict. It believes these new players will drive the increase in out-of-town sales during the next few years, which it forecasts will grow by 11 per cent a year, reaching £55 billion by 1997. As Mr Hyman says: "There's no question, out-of-town retailing is here to stay and set to grow."

[Times, 29.3.94]

CASE STUDY 5.4   *The management of derelict land*

Background

In the UK, the official definition of derelict land is *land so damaged by industrial or other development that it is incapable of beneficial use without treatment* (DOE, 1982). There are no figures available for the UK as a whole, but the most recent survey taken for England in 1988, showed that there were approximately 40 500 hectares of land which can be said to be derelict. Of this total, 32 000 hectares are recorded as 'justifying reclamation', that is, worth spending money on to restore to a productive use. Some 65% of this reclaimable area lies in urban areas. These figures represent a serious waste of precious space in a small, densely-populated country, and is an unacceptable lowering of environmental standards.

The regional variations depend upon the size of a region, its history of industry and land use, and recent policies of reclamation. For example, the north-west and south-west regions have the highest totals, but for quite different reasons. In the north-west, the decline of the Lancashire coalfield and cotton industry, along with the ageing urban fabric of cities such as Manchester has left much dereliction, most of which is reclaimable. A study of Manchester illustrates the impact of urban redevelopment policies and economic change by identifying three phases of dereliction:

1 The massive slum clearance programme of the late 1950s to early 1970s, where demolition outspaced reconstruction. In 1984, over one-third of all derelict land was on former housing areas.
2 In 1962 the south-east Lancaster/north-east Cheshire (SELNEC) Highway Plan proposed a set of four ring roads. The subsequent delays and cutbacks caused continuing 'planning blight' in areas threatened by the roads programme.
3 From the late 1970s, Manchester suffered accelerated economic decline. Three of the city's inner wards lost 60% of their jobs, 1971–85.

In the south-west region, in contrast, the largely rural dereliction is dominated by sterile and toxic mining spoil from china clay and copper mining. This is very difficult and expensive to reclaim, hence, the high proportion of land which is regarded as 'not justifying reclamation'. Also, not having an urban location, there are fewer land pressures and opportunities for economically-rewarding redevelopment. Reclamation schemes would be primarily for conservation and amenity reasons, and so, less able to yield profits directly.

Factors affecting the potential are where the land is located and what state it is in. Apart from the demolition of housing, each type of industry brings its own form of dereliction. For example, railway property may be available in elongated strips, quarries as partly-infilled holes, and military land may

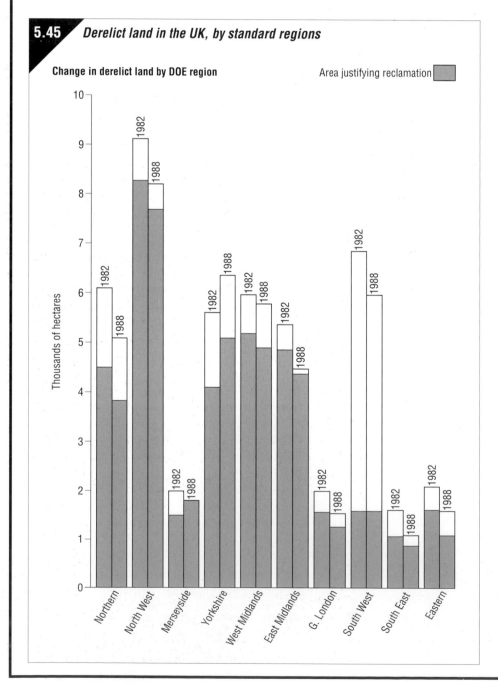

5.45   **Derelict land in the UK, by standard regions**

Change in derelict land by DOE region   Area justifying reclamation ▨

have safety hazards. A further vital factor is *land ownership*. Reclamation schemes are easiest if the sites are in large blocks owned by a single owner and the ownership is by the local authority. Unfortunately, ownership is often fragmented among a variety of private owners. Indeed, for approximately 15% of derelict land the owner is 'unknown'.

This case study examines the Black Country, a part of the West Midlands region which covers the four urban boroughs of Dudley, Sandwell, Walsall and Wolverhampton. It has some of the most concentrated areas of urban, industrial dereliction in the UK, but also has some of the most effective reclamation policies. These policies illustrate the *partnership approach* and distinguishes between 'end uses' (the use after reclamation). There are 'hard' end uses, such as housing and industry, and 'soft' end uses, which include open spaces and nature reserves. There is an increasing emphasis upon the latter as part of the campaign for the

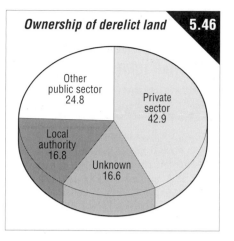

Ownership of derelict land 5.46

- Other public sector 24.8
- Private sector 42.9
- Local authority 16.8
- Unknown 16.6

'greening' of urban areas. In 1994, the Black Country published its *Nature Conservation Strategy*. This ambitious plan indicates *how the Black country's natural heritage could be conserved for future generations to enjoy* (B.C.N.C.S., 1994).

The case study is in two parts. There is a focus on derelict land strategy for the Black Country, and followed by a look at the Saltwells Local Nature Reserve, developed on abandoned industrial site.

Key understandings

- ◆ Derelict land is a widespread problem in industrial cities.
- ◆ Reclamation of derelict land is complex and costly, and must be supported by strong, careful plans and policies from local authorities.
- ◆ Effective reclamation schemes involve co-operation between various interest groups and agencies in the private and public sectors.
- ◆ Conservation and recreation may be important end uses from reclamation schemes.

Greening the Black Country

People's strong need for nature, which may be a very deep emotion: the need for something green and wild or a place to go for sanctuary and solitude, a place to experience 'wilderness' in the city. The need for such places … lies at the heart of the livable city. (Elkin et al, Reviving the city, Friends of the Earth, London, 1991).

Industrial dereliction in England, 1988 5.47

	% of total
Group 1 Iron and steel; Metal products and metal finishing; Non-ferrous metals; Transport equipment manufacture	30
Group 2 Chemical works; Petroleum refineries Petrol stations	12
Group 3 Gas works; Power stations	10
Group 4 Textiles; Leather works; Wood treatment	13
Group 5 Docks; Canals	9
Group 6 Other industries (including warehouse, brick works, saltworks, sewage works, pit head buildings, food processing)	- 26

[Source: DOE 1989]

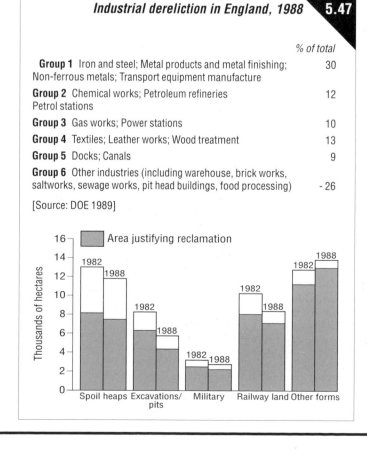

Area justifying reclamation (bar chart, Thousands of hectares, values for 1982 and 1988)

- Spoil heaps: 1982 ≈ 13, 1988 ≈ 11.8
- Excavations/pits: 1982 ≈ 8.2, 1988 ≈ 5.7
- Military: 1982 ≈ 2.5, 1988 ≈ 2.5
- Railway land: 1982 ≈ 10, 1988 ≈ 7
- Other forms: 1982 ≈ 13, 1988 ≈ 13.7

5.48

The reclamation of derelict land in the Black Country, West Midlands

Policy context

Central and local governments have had policies on derelict land since the 1940s, but the basis of the present policy is the 1982 Derelict Land Act. Through this policy, the central government Department of the Environment (DOE) has allocated money either directly to local councils for approved schemes, or through other government programmes, such as the Inner City Partnership Programme and the City Challenge. The Derelict Land Grant (DLG) varies according to local needs. It ranges from 100% in Assisted Areas (areas targetted by government for regeneration) to 50% grants elsewhere. By 1991, £70 million was being paid out annually. The DLG programme does seem to have helped local authorities tackle their derelict land problems, since the total area of derelict land declined by 11% between 1982 and 1988. It is important to remember that the totals shown in Resource 5.46 are *net* figures, the balance between new derelict land appearing and land being reclaimed.

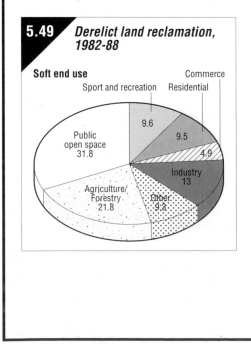

5.49 *Derelict land reclamation, 1982-88*

Soft end use

Sport and recreation
Commerce
Residential
Public open space 31.8
9.6
9.5
4.9
Industry 13
Agriculture/ Forestry 21.8
Other 9.3

Part A: Black Country Derelict Land Management Strategy

The Black Country is one of the two components of the West Midlands conurbation, the other being Birmingham. It consists of a series of towns which grew as independent nucleations on the coal, iron and steel, and metalworking industries of the nineteenth century. As the towns expanded, they merged to become a 'conurbation'. More recently, they have been organised into four boroughs: Dudley, Sandwell, Walsall and Wolverhampton. For the past thirty years the old coal, iron and steel industries have been in decline. Since the 1970s the engineering and metalworking industries have also endured accelerated decline. The outcome has been one of the highest concentrations of derelict land in the country.

Since the 1960s, each of the four local authorities has had its own policy for the management of derelict land. The Merry Hill development in Dudley represents the 'hard' end use for reclaimed land (See Case Study 5.3, p146). At the same time, the council have pioneered several 'greening' projects, including the Saltwells Wood reserve. This would be a 'soft' end use approach. (See Part B of this case study, p158.)

In the mid 1980s, central government agreed to fund a series of urban derelict land projects in England based on the 1982 Derelict Land Act. The four Black Country boroughs realised that they stood a better chance of obtaining funding under this programme if they put forward a combined proposal. They called this plan the Black Country Derelict Land Strategy (BCDLS, hereafter referred to as 'the Strategy'). It was approved by government in 1986. The reclamation of derelict land needs to be an ongoing programme, not a 'one-off' project. The Strategy is operated and funded as a three-year rolling programme. A three-year plan is approved and

funded, but is reviewed annually and adjusted. This allows for flexibility while providing a longer term framework. For example, in 1992 the three year plan for 1993–96 was approved and published. The Strategy works through a hierarchy of an overall plan of goal, strategic aims, and objectives or priorities.

In 1988, nearly 5% of the surface area of the Black Country was recorded as derelict, an area of almost 1800 ha. This was an increase of 17% since 1982. Of the total, about one-third is general industrial dereliction, 13% old quarries, mining shafts and spoilheaps, and a further 25% on sites once mined for limestone and which now have dangerous subsidence problems. This 38%, which is the legacy of the product cycle of mining and quarrying, is particularly expensive to reclaim for 'hard' end uses.

The reclamation programme is also made more difficult by the fact that the Black Country grew as a series of separate towns. This brought about a complex mixture of land uses. Derelict land is scattered within the urban fabric of housing, transport routes and industries *giving a negative image to the area and creating a disincentive to investment* (BCDLS, 1992).

The Strategy works as one element in the broader policies for urban regeneration. The Black Country Development Corporation (BCDC) has been set up to encourage inward investment and attract businesses. Also, the boroughs have benefitted from other programmes such as the Urban Programme Assisted Areas. Two major aspects of the reclamation strategy, therefore, are to make sites available for businesses and to improve the conurbation image by improving environmental quality. This aims to make the area more attractive to businesses and investors.

Strategic sites

A key element of the Strategy is to identify *strategic sites,* those sites whose location, character and size

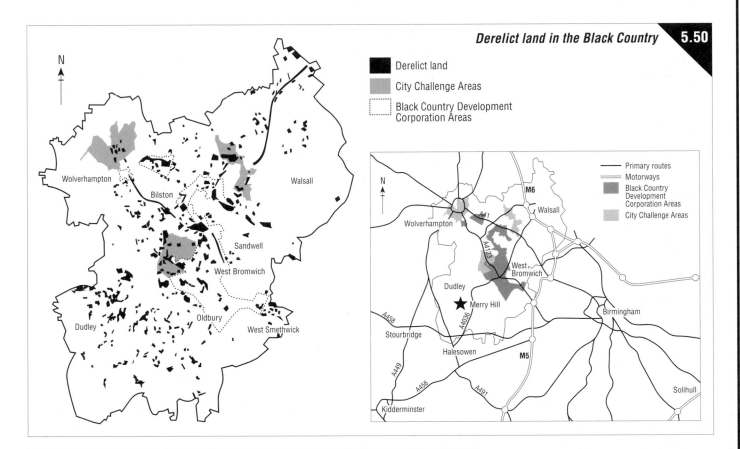

Derelict land

City Challenge Areas

Black Country Development Corporation Areas

Primary routes

Motorways

Black Country Development Corporation Areas

City Challenge Areas

GOAL
To reclaim land for housing, industry and open space and at the same time improve the image of the area by removing the visual blight of dereliction. The rolling programme is also about doing it as quickly as possible with the level of funding available, in partnership with the private sector and providing an inner city alternative to peripheral green belt development outside the conurbation.

STRATEGIC AIMS
- To increase the rate of derelict land reclamation for the benefit of the local community and to enhance the economic, social and environmental regeneration of the Black Country.
- To assign reclamation priorities to schemes that provide the maximum impetus for regeneration.
- To improve the environment of the Black Country.

OBJECTIVES/PRIORITIES
- To adopt a scheme of joint Black Country local authority working as part of a rolling programme.
- To contribute to a five-year supply of residential land.
- To contribute to the provision of commercial and industrial sites, to enable economic development and regeneration to take place.
- To provide new open space, greening, and recreational areas to improve living conditions.
- To aid regeneration by increasing the attractiveness and image of the area as a place to live, work and invest.
- To remove the danger of contaminated and derelict land, reducing the threats to health, safety and the natural environment.
- To improve the quality of the environment through the provision of open space, new greenspace and support for nature conservation and enhancing facilities for public relaxation and recreation.

mean that their reclamation will bring substantial economic and environmental benefits to the surrounding area. Priority is given to the reclamation of these sites.

- Burton Road, Dudley, for example, a 29 ha former tip was reclaimed for housing and open space in a partnership scheme with a private developer.

- The Pendeford Development Site, Wolverhampton, was a 23.8 ha former airfield reclaimed for housing and a business park.
- Sheepwash, Sandwell, was a 35 ha toxic tip reclaimed for open space and nature conservation.
- Junction 10, Bentley, Walsall, was a 2.3 ha former mining area reclaimed for a 120-room hotel alongside an M6 junction.

In 1992 a further 20 strategic sites had been identified, covering 130 ha. About half this land was privately owned. In order to speed up reclamation of these private sites, the borough councils may need to take the expensive option and obtain a compulsory purchase order and then buy the land. By the end of 1992, 177 ha on 35 sites within the BCDLS area had been acquired in this way.

Achievement

Between 1986 and 1992 the Strategy brought about the reclamation of 668 ha. During the early 1990s, it was funding projects covering about 100 ha a year, involving spending of up to £5 million, mainly from Derelict Land Grant funds from central government. The reclaimed sites provided land for 1600 new houses, 219 ha of open space and greenspace and 714 000 sq. ft of industrial and commercial floorspace on 46 sites. This represented a potential inward investment by businesses of £90 million which could create up to 1000 jobs. In addition, small-scale schemes on 230 neglected and unsightly sites covering 35 ha had been funded as part of the Black Country Facelift Programme, whose aim is to raise the image of the area by upgrading the visual environment. Separate government grants of around £10 million a year were being given to deal with the subsidence hazard from underground limestone workings. Resource 4.51 summarises the targets for 1993–96 and illustrates the balance of end uses.

The Strategy is really an *enabling* programme. It 'acquires' sites and makes them available for redevelopment, or assists private owners to reclaim their land. It then co-ordinates a combination of public sector funds and private investment for 'hard' and 'soft' end uses. While it is the 'hard' uses such as housing and industry which ultimately bring returns on the investment, the only practical way to reclaim difficult sites such as old quarries or linear rail strips, is as 'soft' uses for conservation and recreation. This has indirect economic benefits in that it enhances the environmental quality and image of the area.

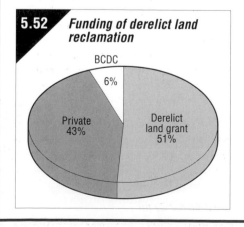

5.52 **Funding of derelict land reclamation**

BCDC 6%

Private 43%

Derelict land grant 51%

Part B: The Blackbrook Valley Project and Saltwells Wood Local Nature Reserve (LNR)

All environmental projects in the Black Country evolve through a four-phase model:

- identifying the potential.
- initiating the project.
- realisation ('making it happen').
- monitoring or evaluating.

The Blackbrook Valley Project illustrates this process and how difficult it is to achieve and maintain success.

The site

The Blackbrook Valley runs in a north-south direction through the heart of the Black Country. Originally a series of farms, it has endured almost 300 years of industrial exploitation based on the coal seams, iron bands and clay strata exposed in the valley sides. By the mid-eighteenth century, the iron industry and coal mining were booming, followed in the nineteenth century by the addition of steel. Between 1870 and 1940, fireclay was extracted from Doulton's Clay Pit, which today forms a central feature of the Nature Reserve. Two canals were built along the valley to transport the bulky raw materials and products of these industries.

By the 1970s, the mines and quarries were gone and the metalworking and steel industries were in their final decline. Amid this dereliction, patches of woodland and one farm survived. The Lodge Farm council housing estate and the Lodge Farm reservoir, developed in an old clay pit, still survived. Dudley council had responded to the growing hazards of dereliction by partially infilling Doulton's Clay Pit to reduce accidents in the lake which had flooded the deep hole. In the 1970s, another, the Yew Tree Pit, was filled in and made into a playing field. A 1977 report on open space in Dudley proposed *that any redevelopment should respect the existing open space in the valley, since it formed a valuable green wedge between industrial and residential areas.*

5.53 **BCDLS targets, 1993–96**

End use	Area (ha)
Housing	32
Industrial/commercial	110
Mixed land use schemes	55
Public open space	184
Total	381

5.54 **Key questions in the process**

- How is the project being organised?
- What types of partnership?
- Who is providing the funding – how much and for how long?
- What role does the local community have?
- Who are the key 'gatekeepers', i.e. those able to take decisions?

The plan and process

Since 1980, the Blackwood Valley Project and the Saltwells Wood LNR have evolved in parallel. The nature reserve has a separate management plan and staffing, but is the heart of the environmental element of the valley project.

The *gatekeepers* and *animateurs* can be identified in the path of Resource 5.54. 'Gatekeepers' are individuals and organisations able to take decisions, while 'animateurs' are those individuals whose commitment and enthusiasm make things happen. Although the Saltwells Wood LNR is only 70 ha in size, the energies which have created and sustained it are international, national, regional and local. For example, site identification was an outcome of an EC environmental project, but the actual selection of the site by the Council of Europe was achieved by the hard lobbying of two experts with local knowledge. The Nature Centre building, opened in 1983, was funded by an EC Urban Aid grant. At a national level, the NCC had designated Doulton's Clay Pit as a Site of Special Scientific Interest (SSSI) in 1955 and has continued to be involved in the conservation management of the reserve.

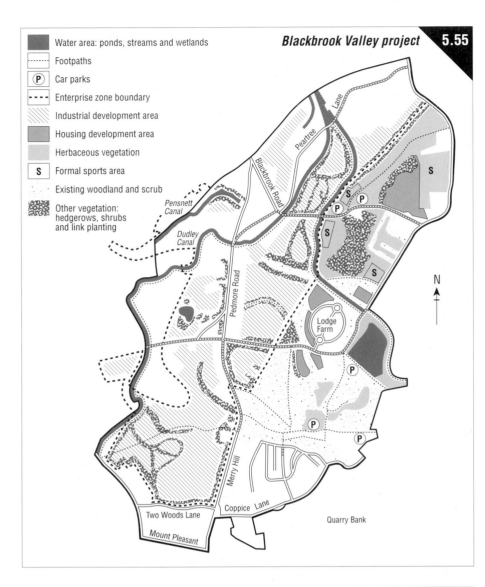

Water area: ponds, streams and wetlands

Footpaths

(P) Car parks

Enterprise zone boundary

Industrial development area

Housing development area

Herbaceous vegetation

S Formal sports area

Existing woodland and scrub

Other vegetation: hedgerows, shrubs and link planting

Peartree Lane

Blackbrook Road

Pensnett Canal

Dudley Canal

Pedmore Road

Lodge Farm

S P P

S

S

P

P

P

P

N

Two Woods Lane

Coppice Lane

Mount Pleasant

Merry Hill

Quarry Bank

1980
Nature Conservancy Council (NCC), Landscape Institute (LI), and Council for Environmental Conservation demonstration project as part of the Council of Europe Urban Renaissance Project.

> The selected site should be typical of inner city environments, with their range of problems.

1981
NCC and LI experts identify the Blackbrook Valley has having the potential for a demonstration project. Saltwells is designated as a Local Nature Reserve.

> Dudley borough initially reluctant as they wish to obtain Enterprise Zone (EZ) status.

1981
The Project is initiated by the setting up of a Steering Group to oversee the planning and implementation.

> Dudley borough accept the project as the DOE accept the whole valley as an EZ, including the 'soft' end uses for conservation and recreation. Steering committee is made up of 'interested parties': landowners, borough and county councils, NCC, LI, DOE. The committee is chaired by a Dudley Planning Officer.

1981 - 82
Feasibility Study produced for discussion.

> Attempts to involve local people and to give priority to landscape quality.

1982 - 84
Landowners apply for permission to develop opencast mining in the Saltwells LNR. Following rejection by the local planning committee, the landowners appeal. There is a public inquiry and the DOE finally refuse permission.

> a Local people came together to oppose the mining application and united in favour of the project and the reserve.

1986
A management plan is agreed for the Valley and the LNR.

> b Ecological surveys to provide evidence for the public inquiry and the DOE finally refuse permission.

1986 - 92
Implementation of the plans, i.e. the realisation phase.

> In 1989, the LNR is extended. Local groups fully involved in practical projects. Funding fluctuates as government policy changes.

5.56

Doulton's clay pit

Factors which influence the process.

The selection of the site by the Council of Europe for an Urban Renaissance demonstration project was clearly the first critical boost. The second, which also occurred in 1981, was the designation as an official Local Nature Reserve, which gave the site protection and access to funding. The third critical hurdle was the commitment of the Dudley borough council. At first the borough was reluctant to support the reserve as they were keen to have the whole Blackwood Valley designated as an Enterprise Zone (EZ). EZ status qualified an area for government funding and freedom from planning restrictions in order to stimulate economic development in declining inner city areas.

CASE STUDY 5.4 *The management of derelict land*

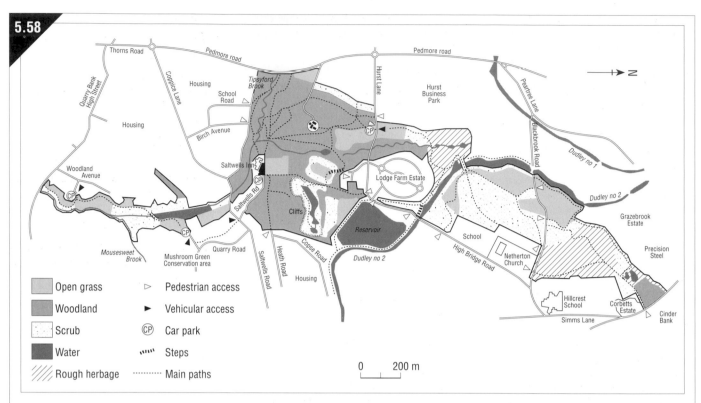

5.58

Legend:
- Open grass
- Woodland
- Scrub
- Water
- Rough herbage
- ▷ Pedestrian access
- ► Vehicular access
- CP Car park
- Steps
- Main paths

0   200 m

The aims of the Master Plan include the following:

- A landscape to serve local people should be created and managed.
- A comprehensive network of ecological should be established corridors throughout the valley.
- To enrich the wildlife of the area, only native species should be planted.
- Voluntary groups and the local community should be encouraged to play an active role in the redevelopment of the valley.

However, the government looked for plans which were dominated by industrial, transport and housing projects. Dudley council were afraid that the inclusion of a large environmental element, that is, 'soft' end uses, would reduce their chances of achieving EZ status. Only when the government agreed that derelict land grants could be used for environmental purposes such as woodland enhancement and planting inside the Saltwells Wood LNR did the council become enthusiastic supporters of the reserve as part of the Valley Project.

Another critical factor was gaining the support of the local community. At first, the local people had not been consulted. A 1989 report explains why:

The novelty of such a scheme ... might well have provoked a less than enthusiastic response from local people had they been formally consulted. Indeed, the experience of the wardens in the first few years suggested that many people strongly opposed the transformation of 'their' wasteland, where they could dump rubbish, ride motorbikes and shoot wildlife, into a nature reserve (Un. of Aston Conference, 1989).

Ironically, the catalyst which changed local attitudes was the planning application for opencast mining in 1982. Although Dudley borough own the land in the Saltwells Reserve, the original owner, the Countess of Dudley, retains the mineral rights. When the local people realised the potential environmental impacts of mining, they mounted a powerful campaign supporting the nature reserve. From that point, the wardens who run the reserve have been able to involve local groups in carrying out schemes within the reserve, for example, clearing rubbish and planting trees. Today, considerable sections of the community regard this as their 'defensible space' and maintain informal watch over how it is run and used. Schools and colleges make considerable use of the reserve for educational and voluntary work projects.

Gatekeepers

Throughout the life of the reserve there has been an ongoing battle for funds. The key gatekeepers here are the Steering Committee who seek out the sources of money and the holders of the purse-strings. The latter include the Dudley Planning, Education and Leisure Services committees, the Black Country Development Corporation (BCDC), government quangos such as English Nature and the Countryside Commission, and government schemes such as the Urban Programme. The key figure is undoubtedly the Chair of the Steering Committee of the Reserve. His great enthusiasm and powers of persuasion have been crucial in maintaining support and essential income of over £100 000 a year. On the ground, the key post is occupied by the Senior Warden, who acts as the link between the policy-makers and the users of the reserve. Even his salary is constantly under threat, and staffing levels and funding for projects fluctuate from year to year.

The outcome

It is clear, therefore, that projects such as the Saltwells Wood LNR are at the mercy of policy shifts at several levels. Despite such uncertainty, the original derelict site has been developed into a varied set of environments, which balance conservation and recreation values. The plan combines both heritage and natural resources to create this quality of environment and experience. Its aims, meanwhile, remain constant:

- To conserve and enhance the existing landscape.
- To minimise the impact of development.
- To encourage the use of the area as an educational resource.
- To increase community involvement.

Activities

1 What have been the main causes of derelict land?

2 Summarise the regional distribution of derelict land in England, and suggest reasons for the variation.

3 Why do derelict sites vary in their potential for development?

4 Outline the benefits and limitations of 'hard' and 'soft' end uses of derelict land reclamation, citing examples from the BCLDS, the Blackwood Valley Project and the Saltwells Wood LNR.

5 Analyse the development of the Saltwells Wood LNR through the five questions set out in Resource 5.51.

CHAPTER 6

Managing industrial change

Introduction

Industry is usually studied by *location*, *character* and *organisation*. Organisation in a firm refers both to the decision-making structure and the way in which the production is run, that is, the production chain in terms of methods and location. Changes in all three characteristics have accelerated over the past 30 years. For example, there has been a shift away from manufacturing industry in many developed countries, while manufacturing is growing rapidly in the devloping countries. Between 1985 and 1990, trade of manufactured products by developing countries was growing at almost 7% a year. Trade of developed countries averaged only 3.5% growth. In 1993, however, manufacturing industry in the UK employed five million people, 22% of the workforce, and contributed 20% of the nation's GDP.

Industry lies at the heart of development. A country is classified according to its industrial status:

- A developed country (DC) is industrialised.
- A newly-industrialising country (NIC) is achieving development because it is industrialising.
- A less-developed country (LDC), has yet to generate a significant industrial base.

As the geographical distribution of industry ebbs and flows across the world, so an individual region or country is forced to adjust. As developed countries move towards service-based (tertiary) economies, particularly the USA, Japan and Western Europe, so a wave of manufacturing growth surges outwards to more peripheral locations. This process has been encouraged by the increasing power and influence of huge multinational, multiplant corporations whose operations are global, for example Nissan and IBM.

The emergence of these huge corporations has been called *creeping giantism*, and is often defined in terms of the *economies of scale* and *control of the market*. It is based on the belief that large scale production using modern technology gives greater efficiency and lowers the production costs per unit. The more a company can dominate the

market for a particular range of products, the safer are its policies and its profits. The central principles are embodied in *power* and *control*.

These giant corporations organise themselves in a variety of ways, which may be related to their cultural backgrounds.

6.1 **Changes in employment in manufacturing: Great Britain, 1971–91**

Type	Employees(mill) 1971	Employees(mill) 1991	Change (%)
1 Heavy manufacturing	1.27	0.68	-46
2 Metal-using industry	3.66	2.14	-42
3 Other manufacturing	2.99	1.94	-35
Total 1-3	7.92	4.76	-40

[From: Townsend, A. *Uneven regional change in Britain*, 1993]

6.2 **Manufacture as a share of total exports, 1975–87(%)**

Group	1975	1987
Africa	5	13
S. & E. Asia	45	74
Latin America	13	31
Developed countries	73	77

[From: Nixson, F. 1993]

Manufactured exports from developing countries (%)

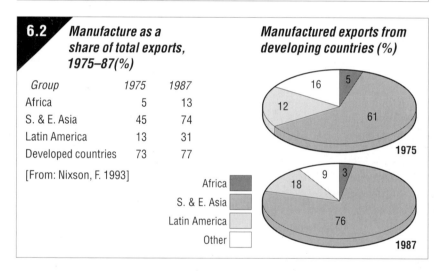

Africa
S. & E. Asia
Latin America
Other

6.3 **The process of industrial change**

I **INDUSTRIALISATION** - The increasing importance of industry in the economy of a region or country

II **DE-INDUSTRIALISATION** - The shrinking of the manufacturing base

III **RE-INDUSTRIALISATION** - The emergence of new industries to replace the old ones

IV **TERTIARISATION** - Services take up an increasing share of economic activity.

The Japanese *keiretsu,* for example, is structured differently from the typical North American corporation.

The traditional model of a capitalist corporation is of a hierarchical structure of operating units, which are controlled from a single headquarters where all decisions are made. This vertically-integrated structure has been called the *Fordist* system, after the way Henry Ford organised the mass-production of vehicles from his Dearborn, USA headquarters. Such a rigid, hierarchical structure is rare today. The new breed of company structure is more of a network of parallel components, each of which exercise a wide range of decisions independently. This flatter network structure gives greater responsibility and flexibility. The intra-firm components are responsible for production decisions and can adapt to changing conditions. This is called the post-Fordist approach. Case Study 6.3 illustrates the Fordist/post-Fordist shift.

Industrial location and regional economic conditions are increasingly determined by the organisational strategies of these corporate giants. Thus, the traditional theories of industrial location, such as those of Weber and Hoover, are less useful today. For example, transport accounts for an average of only 3% of total costs of manufacturing goods today. It is, therefore, possible to construct models based upon the way production is organised and decisions are taken. Market location remains an influential factor, but decision-making and production can become more decentralised as production and communications technology advance. As consumers become more sophisticated, marketing techniques develop and competition intensifies. Companies try to organise their production with more flexibility. Thus, global corporations shift their production facilities around the world to achieve the lowest production costs while maintaining consistent quality of product.

Traditional industries become vulnerable to these locational and organisational shifts. The case studies in this chapter illustrate the effects of such fundamental changes in industrial character and organisation. Case Study 6.1 examines the Black Country, traditionally the manufacturing heartland of the West Midlands, as it tackles the de-industrialisation and re-industrialisation process. Case Studies 6.2 and 6.3 illustrate organisational alternatives by global manufacturing corporations, and the impact upon industrial location. The Ford Corporation (Case Study 6.2) has evolved from a highly centralised firm, through a phase of autonomous, to one which is genuinely global in the way it intends to organise its production. The Nike Corporation (Case Study 6.3) is an excellent example where production flexibility and low labour costs, rather than market location have dominated the choice of organisational structure. It illustrates, too, the industrial model where corporate headquarters, finance, marketing, research and development remain in a core region, while the production takes place in peripheral regions through complex sub-contracting arrangements. This chapter is useful as a basis for evaluating the popular theories and models of industrial location.

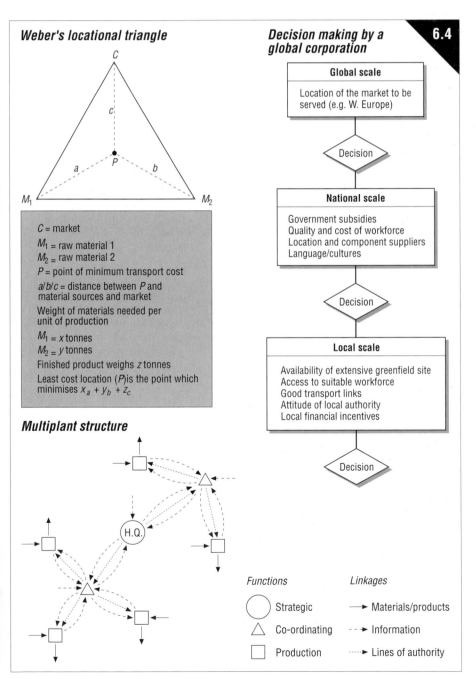

Weber's locational triangle

C = market

M_1 = raw material 1
M_2 = raw material 2
P = point of minimum transport cost
a/b/c = distance between P and material sources and market
Weight of materials needed per unit of production
M_1 = x tonnes
M_2 = y tonnes
Finished product weighs z tonnes
Least cost location (P) is the point which minimises $x_a + y_b + z_c$

Multiplant structure

Functions

◯ Strategic
△ Co-ordinating
▢ Production

Linkages

→ Materials/products
--→ Information
····→ Lines of authority

Decision making by a global corporation 6.4

Global scale

Location of the market to be served (e.g. W. Europe)

Decision

National scale

Government subsidies
Quality and cost of workforce
Location and component suppliers
Language/cultures

Decision

Local scale

Availability of extensive greenfield site
Access to suitable workforce
Good transport links
Attitude of local authority
Local financial incentives

Decision

CASE STUDY 6.1 *The challenge of industrial change*

Background

Regions which rely upon industry must learn to adapt to constantly changing conditions. Older industrial districts in the UK, such as West Yorkshire, Clydeside, South Wales and Belfast, have endured more than 25 years of de-industrialisation as their traditional industries of coal, iron and steel, heavy engineering, shipbuilding and textiles have declined. There has been a continuing battle to avoid the spiral of economic, social and environmental decline.

Until 1980, the West Midlands was a long-established industrial region which seemed to be weathering the storm relatively well. Its central location, diversity of products, skilled labour force, and mixture of large, medium and small businesses, had given it some flexibility and ability to respond to change. However, the national trend away from manufacturing (secondary) towards service (tertiary) industries, during the 1980s rendered the West Midlands vulnerable.

6.5

Derelict building in Hebden Bridge, Yorkshire

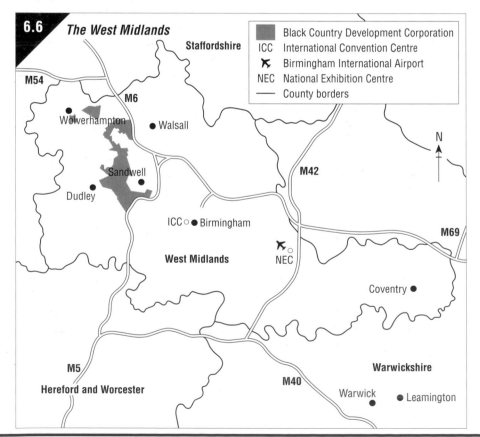

6.6 **The West Midlands**

Staffordshire

M54
M6
Wolverhampton
Walsall
Sandwell
Dudley
ICC ○ ● Birmingham
West Midlands
NEC
M42
Coventry ●
M69
M5
Hereford and Worcester
M40
Warwick ●
Warwickshire
Leamington ●

N

Key:
- ▦ Black Country Development Corporation
- ICC International Convention Centre
- ✈ Birmingham International Airport
- NEC National Exhibition Centre
- — County borders

Key understandings

♦ Older industrial districts may have outdated industrial structures and deteriorating physical environments.

♦ The Urban Development Corporation is an element of UK central government policy for assisting areas which are experiencing serious industrial decline.

♦ Industrial urban boroughs identify priority areas within their boundaries and apply to central government for UDC status. The UDC gives funding, organisational and promotional support, but does not take over the role of the borough authorities.

♦ In the West Midland region the Black Country Development Corporation is a UDC which has been facilitating economic and environmental revival in this industrial heartland since 1987.

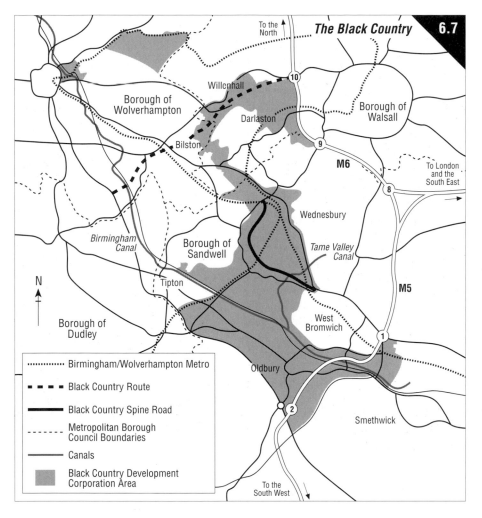

6.7 The Black Country

Map labels:
- To the North
- Willenhall
- Borough of Wolverhampton
- Darlaston
- Borough of Walsall
- Bilston
- 10
- 9
- M6
- To London and the South East
- 8
- Wednesbury
- Birmingham Canal
- Borough of Sandwell
- Tame Valley Canal
- M5
- Tipton
- N
- Borough of Dudley
- West Bromwich
- 1
- Oldbury
- 2
- Smethwick
- To the South West

Legend:
- ·········· Birmingham/Wolverhampton Metro
- ▬ ▬ ▬ Black Country Route
- ▬▬▬ Black Country Spine Road
- - - - - Metropolitan Borough Council Boundaries
- ——— Canals
- ▓ Black Country Development Corporation Area

Business closures and unemployment rates rose above the national averages.

This shift away from manufacturing severely affected the Black Country, the industrial heartland of the region and a conurbation between Birmingham and Wolverhampton. The Black Country economy has remained dependent upon the iron and steel manufacturing base which made it prosperous from the early nineteenth century. Districts within the Black Country which have been especially hard-hit, have been designated an Urban Development Area (UDA), managed by an Urban Development Corporation (UDC). This UDC programme has been one of the government's main policies for urban and economic regeneration since the early 1980s (see Case study 5.1, London's Docklands). A UDC channels funds, organisational and promotional support into its designated area. It works with but does not replace the local council. The Black Country Development Corporation (BCDC) is a particularly interesting example as it crosses the boundaries of four local authorities. It, therefore, involves considerable inter-council collaboration.

Urban Development Corporations, 1990

	Date of designation	Designated area (DA)(ha)	Population at 31 March 1990	Employment at 31 March 1990
Black Country	1987	2 598	36 050	75 054
Bristol	1988	420	1 500	14 000
Cardiff Bay	1987	1 093	N/A	N/A
Central Manchester	1988	187	500	15 000
Leeds	1988	375	N/A	37 113
London Docklands	1981	2 226	50 000	48 000
Merseyside	1981	960	7 000	36 000
Sheffield	1988	900	300	18 000
Teesside	1987	4 565	1 090	12 434
Trafford Park	1987	1 267	N/A	27 000
Tyne & Wear	1987	2 375	5 383	43 408
Laganside	1989	121	N/A	N/A
Total	–	17 087	101 823+	326 009+
N/A = not available				
Added 1992: Heartlands	1992	1 000	16 656	–

6.8 Employment growth in Urban Development Corporations

	Employment in DA at March 1990	Number of jobs transferred into DA	Number of jobs created in DA
Black Country	75 054	N/A	4 734
Bristol	14 000	N/A	N/A
Cardiff Bay	–	–	–
Central Manchester	N/A	N/A	300
Leeds	37 113	N/A	5 421
London Docklands	48 000	15 724	4 593
Merseyside	36 000	N/A	1 500
Sheffield	18 000	N/A	3 000
Teesside	12 434	N/A	3 000
Trafford Park	26 150	2 450	
Tyne & Wear	43 408	N/A	3 245

N/A = not available

T & C P November 1990, p295

CASE STUDY 6.1 *The challenge of industrial change*

Facilitating change: the BCDC

The West Midlands setting

The West Midlands region has long been famous for its range of manufacturing industries. It was hard-hit by the economic recession of the early 1980s. The economic revival in the UK during the mid- and late-1980s was fuelled by growth in the service industries. The West Midlands was left vulnerable by such a shift in industrial emphasis. Despite having shed at least one-third of its manufacturing jobs during the 1980s, 1990 saw the region's industrial structure even more dependent upon manufacturing than ten years earlier.

The recession brought about the loss of a further 20% of manufacturing jobs between 1990 and 1993. Yet unemployment figures for the region were not significantly higher than the national proportions. Adjustments in the manufacturing emphasis of the region, that is, a shift away from steel and metal goods towards vehicle components and mechanical engineering, have been energised by the continued presence in and around the region of companies such as Rover, Vauxhall and Ford. The growing demands from Japanese manufacturers, Honda, Nissan and Toyota, have also helped prevent a sudden decline. The presence of a cluster of vehicle component firms in the West Midlands was a key factor in influencing Toyota's decision to build their assembly plant at Burnaston, near Derby.

The situation and prospects as evaluated in mid-1993 are summarised in Resource 6.12, although the uncertainty of such forecasts is highlighted by the purchase of Rover by BMW in early 1994. As Honda has had a collaborative relationship with Rover for some years, the takeover has altered Honda's policy. BMW may yet change the component supply organisation for what is, in effect, its Rover division. (See Case study 6.2 for a discussion of the changes in the vehicle industry.)

6.9	West Midlands manufacturing industry, 1980–90				
	1980		1990		
Type	Location quotient	% of UK output	Location quotient	% of UK output	
All manufacturing	1.3	11.2	1.5	11.8	
Motor vehicle and parts	2.9	26.2	3.4	30.5	
Mechanical engineering	1.4	11.6	1.7	14.0	
Other metal goods	3.7	31.6	3.4	28.5	
Metal manufacture	2.3	19.0	2.2	16.7	
Non-metal manufacture	2.5	16.5	2.6	18.1	

NB: UK Location quotient = 1.0

[Source: *Financial Times*, 14 July 1993]

6.10	West Midlands unemployment, May 1993 ('000 & %)					
	M	%	F	%	Total No.	%
W. Midlands	217	14.5	66	6.2	283	11.1
UK	2239	14.0	675	5.6	2914	10.4

[Source: *Financial Times*, 14 July 1993]

Central government has introduced a variety of programmes for economic, social and environmental regeneration. For 1993–94 the West Midlands was allocated £165 million from the Department of the Environment (DoE) under these programmes. Local authorities have themselves provided further funding.

The Black Country and the BCDC

The Black Counrty Development Corporation was formed in 1987 as a joint venture by the four metropolitan boroughs of Dudley, Sandwell, Walsall, Wolverhampton. They have identified districts in each of their areas which together form a problem core covering 2630 ha. Designation as an Urban Development Corporation (UDC) attracts government funding and relaxed planning constraints. The twin goals are to sustain the existing industrial base, and to encourage inward investment and new economic activity in this area. The BCDC is an organisational and promotional agency, and works with rather than replaces the individual boroughs. This programme is one element of a broader strategy which covers all aspects of life in the Black Country.

An important task of the UDC is to monitor the current economic condition and so identify strengths and weaknesses. This information can be used as a basis for decision-making. In this way, the BCDC produced an economic profile of the designated area in July 1992. The profile vividly illustrates the character and problems of the Black Country as a whole. Note that the figures, except where stated, refer to the BCDC designated area *not* to the Black Country as a whole.

The economic history of the Black Country has left the area with a distinctive industrial structure. Unlike the country as a whole, which has seen a progressive shift towards the tertiary sector, the BCDC area remains dependent upon secondary industries, especially engineering, vehicles and metal goods. This has resulted in above average unemployment rates. The decline and structural change are highlighted in Resource 6.16. During the 1980s, Goodyear remained the largest employer, but the traditional steel industry suffered.

Step by cautious step to recovery

The region is reviving, with its industrial competitiveness enhanced by devaluation. The services sector has suffered a shake-out, but growth is expected to resume. Paul Cheeseright reports

The fundamental question about the West Midlands is not whether the regional economy will revive after recession. That revival, in erratic fashion, has started. Rather the question is whether the second recession in 15 years has pushed the economy towards atrophy.

The immediate prospects are for modest growth. In broad terms, the flow of orders began to revive in the early months of the year: business confidence has risen to the highest levels for three years in expectation that the pressures on po=rofitability will be relieved.

But at the same time, the downturn in the European econmies has blunted the thrust of recovery which, in any case, was off a low base. Three quarters of companies are working under full capacity, according to the latest calculations of forecasters at the Confederation of British Industry and Business Strategies.

Any sustained national rise in consumer and investment spending would translate fairly quickly into a flow of orders for the engineering industry of the region and hence into the wider economy. Manufacturing remains the economic staple.

This is both a strength and weakness. Although the West Midlands is traditionally the manufacturing heart of the UK manufacturing as a source of employment has declined, is declining and is likely to continue to decline. The growth of employment in the services sector, until checked by the latest recession, was slower in the West Midlands than elsewhere in the UK.

Noting that, as a traditional industrial region, the West Midlands is expected "to have above average vulnerability" to competition from within the EC, while remaining highly dependent on exports to other members of the EC, the Forum is anxious about the ability to compete. "By the year 2000, it has been estimated that 70 per cent of all European jobs will require brain rather than manual skills, yet levels of academic and skill attainment are relatively low in the West Midlands. Of particular concern is that several of the older manufacturing areas appear to lack access to the higher level skills required for the modernisation of the region's industries," the Forum says.

In fact, skills shortages never wholly disappeared – even during the recession – and there have been indications in recent surveys that skills shortages have begun to return as the economy revives. Corporate trainig budgets were frequently pruned during the recession. The training and enterprise councils which now stimulate and oversee much of the industrial training are too recent to have made a lasting impact.

There is also a social element to the question. In general, the areas which need the jobs most, because of their high unemployment, are the areas where employment opportunities have diminished.

Planning policy and official funding is directed towards refressing that balance throughout the Birmingham-Black Country conurbation. The effort is to renew tired and derelict inner city areas so that more employment opportunities will emerge and more people will be trained to take advantage of them.

Yet the pressures for development on the green belt, the steady flow of tenants into business parks on the edge of the conurbation and the movement of companies to greenfield sties, in areas such as Telford, testify to a drift of corporate activity away from the inner city areas of the region, rather than towards it.

Working through this mix of overlapping problems – inherent skilsl shortages and a lack of jobs where jobs are needed most – will be of the first importance to the development of the region into the next century.

But if their solution is at least partially dependent on the level of economic activity, there are encouraging factors.

• The competitive position of industry changed between the recessions of the 1980s and the 1990s. Generally it is now more productive, more export-oriented – at least among the large and medium-sized groups.

• There has been a widening of the economic base in two senses: an influx of overseas investment has stimulated the regional economy, not only through its demands for local goods and services, but also through its spread of diverse management techniques: and at the same time there has been growth in the services sector.

The third encouraging factor is the developing links between the universities – Aston, Birmingham, Coventry, Warwick, Wolverhampton and the rest – and industrial groups. Co-operation of this kind will stimulate the movement of companies towards higher technology and new products, bringing into play different disciplines and harnessing wider ranges of skills. here the future of the region rests.

[*Financial Times* 14.7.93]

West Midlands: Central government funding for urban regeneration, 1993–94

Programme	Allocation (£1 million)
Urban Programme	27.0
City Grant	8.8
Derelict Land Grant	20.6
City Action Team, special budget	0.4
Urban Development Corporations	72.0
City Challenge Schemes	29.6
Task Forces	2.6
Urban Partnership Fund	3.6
Coalfield Area Fund	0.8
Total	165.4

[Source: *Financial Times*, 14 July 1993]

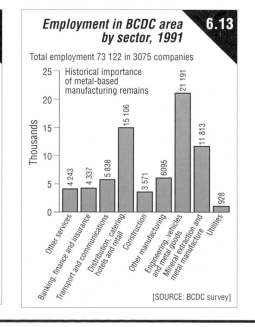

Employment in BCDC area by sector, 1991

Total employment 73 122 in 3075 companies

Historical importance of metal-based manufacturing remains

Thousands

Other services 4 243
Banking, finance and insurance 4 337
Transport and communications 5 838
Distribution, catering, hotels and retail 15 106
Construction 3 571
Other manufacturing 6095
Engineering, vehicles and metal goods 21 191
Mineral extraction and metal manufacture 11 813
Utilities 928

[SOURCE: BCDC survey]

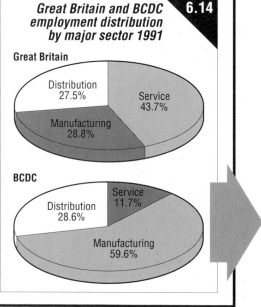

Great Britain and BCDC employment distribution by major sector 1991

Great Britain
Distribution 27.5%
Service 43.7%
Manufacturing 28.8%

BCDC
Distribution 28.6%
Service 11.7%
Manufacturing 59.6%

CASE STUDY 6.1 *The challenge of industrial change*

Bilston and Round Oak steelworks had gone, the latter site being redeveloped as the Merry Hill Shopping Centre and Retail Park. The three BSR plants too, had gone. Sizes of the enterprises had decreased. By 1989, only Goodyear employed over 2000 people. Overall these 'top ten' employed only one-half the total of ten years earlier. The large number of small firms has always been a feature of the Black Country metal industries, but today such enterprises have significant disadvantages. A further outcome of this 'metal bashing' emphasis is the low level of job opportunity for women.

It is also important to be able to forecast trends, that is, to identify those industrial and employment sectors which are likely to grow. A forecast made by the West Midlands Enterprise Board (WMEB) in 1992 made gloomy reading for the BCDC. The forecasts suggested that the BCDC policy should encourage service-sector firms in order to offset further manufacturing losses. However, the BCDC believe that they ought to retain the manufacturing base while creating quality environments which will attract service enterprises.

The difficulties the BCDC faces in deciding how to help companies is illustrated by the lists of Resource 6.20. In 1989, employers identified the key constraints as a shortage of skilled labour and appropriate premises. Thus, the BCDC could have decided to focus on providing training programmes and buildings. However, the needs perceived by employers in 1991 are quite different. The crucial constraints at that time – competition and market size – are less easily resolved or helped by the Corporation.

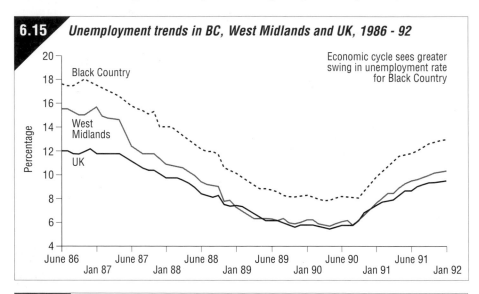

6.15 Unemployment trends in BC, West Midlands and UK, 1986 - 92

Economic cycle sees greater swing in unemployment rate for Black Country

6.16	Black Country manufacturing establishments (excluding construction)			
	1978		*1989*	
Company	*Employees*	*Company*	*Employees*
1 Goodyear	4 000 – 5 001	1 Goodyear	4 000 – 5 001
2 B S R – Stourbridge	3 000 – 4 001	2 W & T Avery (Scales)	1 500 – 2 001
3 Round Oak Steel Works	2 000 – 3 001	3 Lucas Aerospace	1 500 – 2 001
4 B S R – Warley	2 000 – 3 001	4 Crabtree Electrical	1 000 – 1 501
5 Bilston Steelworks	2 000 – 3 001	5 Mitchells & Butler	1 000 – 1 501
6 Rubery Owen	1 500 – 2 001	6 Cannon Industries (cookers)	500 – 1 001
7 W & T Avery	1 500 – 2 001	7 B I P Chemicals	500 – 1 001
8 F H Lloyd	1 500 – 2 001	8 Wednesbury Tube	500 – 1 001
9 B S R – Garrets Lane	1 500 – 2 001	9 Barrets & Baird	500 – 1 001
10 T I Accles & Pollock	1 500 – 2 001	10 Yorkshire Imperial Alloys	500 – 1 001
Total employment by Top 10	25 597	*Total employment by Top 10*	13 776

The top 10 manufacturing Black Country companies now employ half that of ten years ago.

[Source: BCDC, Economic Profile, July 1992]

6.17	Characteristics of small (<50 employees) and large(>200 employees) companies for BCDC Area (1991)
Small companies	*Large companies*
Typically involved in distribution and retail	Typically involved in metal goods and engineering
One-fifth export goods	Four-fifths export goods
39% have introduced IT	95% have introduced IT
21% working at or above three-quarter capacity	62% working at or above three-quarter capacity
Have cashflow problems	Have strong competition

[Source: BCDC Survey 1991]

6.18 Male and female employment in West Midlands, Great Britain and BCDC, 1990

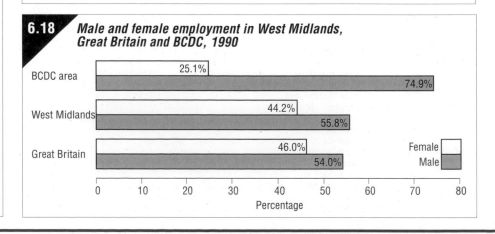

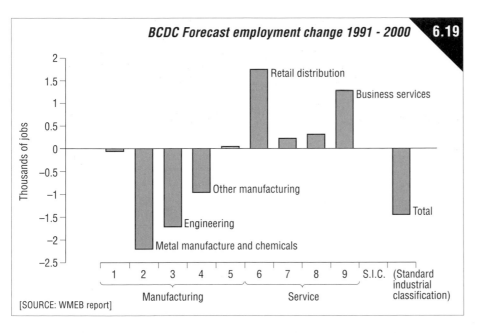

BCDC Forecast employment change 1991 - 2000 — 6.19

Thousands of jobs (y-axis, -2.5 to 2)

Bars by S.I.C. (Standard industrial classification):
- 1 (Manufacturing) – slightly negative
- 2 Metal manufacture and chemicals – approx -2.2
- 3 Engineering – approx -1.7
- 4 Other manufacturing – approx -1
- 5 – slightly positive
- 6 Retail distribution – approx +1.75
- 7 – approx +0.25
- 8 – approx +0.3
- 9 Business services – approx +1.3
- Total – approx -1.4

Manufacturing: 1–5; Service: 6–9

[SOURCE: WMEB report]

BCDC area: Perceived constraints to growth, 1989 and 1991 — 6.20

	1989		1991
Rank	Constraint	Rank	Constraint
1	Shortage of skilled labour	1	Competition
2	Premises	2	Market size
3	Competition	3	Cashflow
4	Cashflow	4	Premises
5	Investment capital	5	Shortage of skilled labour
6	Manufacturing capacity	6	Investment capital

[Source: BCDC Business Surveys]

Activities

1 Promotion is an important role of a UDC. An examination of the publicity material published by the BCDC allows us to identify the main thrusts of their strategy. Resource 6.22 shows items of the promotional literature distributed by the BCDC in 1993. Analyse this material and make a list of the benefits claimed, under the following headings:

   a Location and accessibility

   b Support and assistance

   c Site availability and environmental quality

   d Interconnectivity with markets

2 What types of economic activity are they hoping to attract?

3 One of the 'flagship' enterprise successes of the BCDC policy is the Automotive Component Park (ACP) announced in 1993. Resource 6.22 outlines this project, to be funded jointly by BCDC, other central government programmes and the local boroughs. Describe the project, what it will produce, what benefits it will bring and why the Black Country is an advantageous location.

4 Use the example of the BCDC to describe and explain the role of a UDC in the organisation and management of change in declining industrial districts.

Automotive component park to create 3,000 jobs — 6.21

Europe's first "Automotive Component Park" (ACP) is to be built on the former Patent Shaft Steelworks site in Wednesbury, creating 3,000 jobs for local people.

The 115-acre park will become home to companies manufacturing the thousands of bits and pieces which go into a modern motor car, to be ferried to car assemblers and motor manufacturers around the world.

The ACP is being acclaimed as the new "gateway to Europe" for United States component suppliers, being at the heart of the nation's motorway network which provides easy access to the whole of the UK and all major sea and airports. It is also within two hours' drive time by heavy goods vehicles of major car assembly plants operated by Rover, Peugeot, Toyota, Jaguar and Honda.

The ACP was launched simultaneously at an international automotive exhibition in Detroit, USA; in the Black Country; and in London, where a contract was signed with developer Kyle Stewart Ltd to build the first 30 acres of the ACP.

Corporation Deputy Chairman Christopher Hawkins said: "This is one of the biggest single projects in the history of the Black Country. It is also a landmark for Europe – the first substantial business park dedicated solely to the manufacture of automotive components.

Black Country in Britain's industrial future and in the future of the car industry into the 21st century," Mr Hawkins said. "It is expected to create some 3,000 jobs, many of which will be skilled, well paid manufacturing jobs, ideally suited to the particular range of skisl for which the workforce of the area is justly famous."

The ACP will feature state-of-the-art buildings designed to the precise requirements of occupiers. Shared research and development facilities, component testing facilities and a recycling and waste management transfer station also add to the attraction of the park for component manufacturers.

Wednesbury Councillor Bill Archer has also given a nod of approval for the ACP. Speaking on Radio WM he said: "This is absolutely wonderful news. These are real jobs and I'm sure that Wednesbury people will be absolutely over the moon. The sooner it's done, the better."

The ACP will be located alongside the new £93 million Black Country Spine Road which, when completed in 1995, will provide direct access to the UK motorway network via junction 1 of the M5 and Junction 9 of the M6.

[BCDC News, Spring edition, 1993]

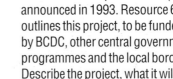

6.22

The Black Country:
They built the motor industry around us

An approach that ensures that the right quantities are purchased and made at the right time and quality and that there is no waste Voss, 1987

In the UK, the 'Just in Time' production discipline has been pioneered by the motor industry – indeed some manufacturers effectively carry no component stocks at their UK Plants.

Significantly, the Black Country – with its traditional strength in engineering – finds itself strategically placed to respond to the time-critical demand for components.

Just one hour's drive by HGV from the Black Country are car assembly plants operated by Jaguar, Peugeot, Reliant, Rolls Royce, Rover and Toyota – together (even before Toyota's new plant is operational) producing more than half a million cars per annum.

Within two hours' drive are additional plants operated by Rover and Toyota (under construction), plus Ford, General Motors and Honda, constructing a further half million vehicles.

Produce and deliver finished goods just-in-time to be sold, sub-assemblies just-in-time to be assembled into finished goods, fabricated parts just-in-time to go into the sub-assemblies and purchased materials just-in-time to be transformed into fabricated parts Schonberger, 1982

The Black Country Development Corporation's area is particularly well suited to JIT delivery schedules. With Junctions 1 and 2 of the M5, and Junctions 9 and 10 of the M6, in the area, with onward connections to the M42, M40 and M54, its access by road to the rest of the UK is exceptional.

It is no coincidence that the area is well served by hauliers, and the Parceline organisation's central distribution point is strategically located beside Junction 1 of the M5.

Many component manufacturers and suppliers are already established in the Black Country, while suppliers new to the UK frequently choose the Corporation's area above all others. The German-owned vehicle lock manufacturer HUF UK Ltd selected a base in the Black Country after exhaustive research into a number of possible UK locations.

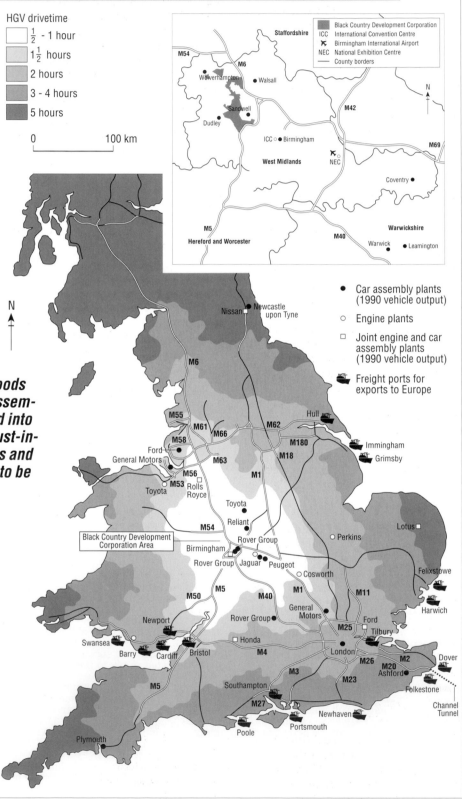

HGV drivetime
- ½ - 1 hour
- 1½ hours
- 2 hours
- 3 - 4 hours
- 5 hours

0   100 km

- ● Car assembly plants (1990 vehicle output)
- ○ Engine plants
- □ Joint engine and car assembly plants (1990 vehicle output)
- Freight ports for exports to Europe

CASE STUDY 6.2 — *The large corporation at work*

Background

The motor vehicle industry illustrates the process of *creeping giantism*. It has become dominated by a small number of global corporations, of which Ford is the second largest, after General Motors. Over the past 30 years the American control of this industry has been increasingly challenged, especially by Japan. For example, in 1955 the American 'Big Three' – General Motors, Ford and Chrysler – manufactured 70% of the world's motor vehicles. By 1990 this had fallen to 30%.

To remain competitive, car manufacturers have had to adjust their organisation, including the way decisions are made and the way the chain of production is set up. The size of the market has grown, but customers demand more choice and better quality at competitive prices. The traditional Fordist approach to mass production has been replaced by the post-Fordist strategy. Long production lines of a limited number of models has been replaced by automated, but flexible production lines. This allows smaller batch production while using a mix of standardised components.

Vehicle manufacturers switch factory locations and component suppliers in order to reduce labour costs and to gain entry to markets. For example, in the 1960s, the US car manufacturers opened assembly plants in Mexico to benefit from the low wage rates and the absence of trades unions. In the 1980s, Japanese companies established transplants in the UK in order to be within the tariff wall of the European Union. Manufacturers have adopted the less hierarchical organisational structures where all decisions do not have to be made by corporate headquarters. The individual parts of the global corporation are taking on more responsibility.

The Ford Corporation exhibits these changes well. In the 1950s the company was still hierarchical and vertically integrated. All decisions came from the corporate headquarters in Dearborn, USA and most production plants were concentrated in the traditional industrial north-east, for example, Detroit and the southern shores of the Great Lakes. By the 1960s, however, the corporation had dispersed across the world. In 1967 the organisational structure was changed to five world groupings: North America; Europe; Asia–Pacific; Latin America and the Middle East. While fitting within Ford's global strategy, each grouping has enjoyed wide-ranging freedom to control its production chain. This structure has remained in place although the company put forward an even more globally-integrated plan for discussion in 1994.

This case study illustrates the change in organisational strategy by global corporations by examining the way Ford operates in Europe.

Key understandings

◆ Transnational corporations operate through a wide range of organisational structures.

◆ Industrial location is significantly influenced by management decisions on the organisation of the production chain.

◆ Most transnationals now operate through a 'flatter' corporate structure, which gives increased decision-making power to the separate components.

◆ The primary goals of transnational corporations are power, control and flexibility and they organise themselves to achieve these goals.

Ford's model options

Which one is right for you? 6.23
• *Fiesta Mistral* • *Sapphire* • *Equipe* •

EXTERIOR FEATURES	3-door Fiesta			5-door Fiesta		
EXTERIOR APPEARANCE AND STYLING	Mistral	Sapphire	Equipe	Mistral	Sapphire	Equipe
Bodyside mouldings: Argent	●	●	●	●	●	●
Bumpers: Grey with argent insert	●	●	●	●	●	●
Paint, metallic	●		▲	●	▲	▲
Spoiler, tailgate, black	●			●		
Wheels: 4 x 13 Steel with full wheelcovers and 165/65 SR x 13 tyres	●		●	●		●
Wheels: 4 x 13 Steel with full wheelcovers and 155/70 SR x 13 tyres		●			●	
EXTERIOR FUNCTIONAL						
Safeguard immobiliser system	●	●	●	●	●	●
Door mirrors: black busing with internal manual control	●	●	●	●	●	●
Heated rear window	●	●	●	●	●	●
Fuel filler flap with locking cap	●	●	●	●	●	●
Locks: Anti-burst, high-security door locks	●	●	●	●	●	●
Locks: Childproof rear door locks				●	●	●
Locks: Central locking including torch key	*	●		*	●	
Electric option pack: Central locking with torch key; electrically operated front windows; and remote tailgate release	▲	●		▲	●	
Wipers: two speed/intermittent front with electric wash	●	●	●	●	●	●
Wipers: Tailgate wiper with electric wash	●	●	●	●	●	●
EXTERIOR LIGHTING						
Halogen headlights; rear fog light; reversing light	●	●	●	●	●	●

Ford Europe: responsible and flexible?

The company called Ford Europe was formed in 1967 by the amalgamation of the existing companies in the UK and Germany. Today Ford Europe sits alongside Ford North America and the three other groups as an equal component of the US-based parent corporation.

The basic production decision for multiplant producers like Ford is whether or not to dedicate one plant to one particular model. This method, although simple, can be inefficient as demand levels fluctuate. Also, at model change-over times the plant will be used at below capacity. Ford has adopted a mixed system of dedicated and flexible plants. While some sites produce only one model, such as Halewood and the Escort, the general pattern is to spread models over more than one site and for sites to have more than one model. The Escort, for example, is produced at Halewood, Valencia and Cologne.

The investment decision for the new Zeta engine, for example, was for all production to be based at Bridgend, South Wales. However, when the second phase of the investment programme had to be carried out, Ford Europe decided to locate this second engine factory in Cologne, thereby spreading the risk. This raised renewed fears about Ford's long-term commitment to the UK, as the company were known to be concerned about productivity levels and about the ageing plant at Dagenham. During the 1980s Ford all over the world had been in the forefront of pioneering 'lean' production methods. They used fewer workers, high technology and improved component supply to match Japanese productivity and quality levels. As a result, Ford employment in the UK fell from 75 000 to 48 000, while output increased in total. In 1993, however, the Dagenham plant employed 13 000 people to produce 240 000 vehicles, while Nissan produced 27 000 vehicles from their new Sunderland plant, with only 4600 employees.

Putting the pieces together

A car factory is an assembly plant where components made elsewhere are put together. How this component supply is organised is a vital decision. The Japanese owe much of their success to their 'just-in-time' system. This works by supplying components to the assembly plants only as they are needed on the assembly lines. Stocks of components do not have to be kept, and models and specifications can be altered with a minimum of fuss. Components arrive in small batches and are used almost immediately. The 'batch delivery' system allows flexible production but component suppliers need to be located close to the assembly plants. Locational clusters similar to Toyota City have developed around Japanese car plants in the USA. Many suppliers do not approve of this system as it makes them heavily dependent upon a

6.24	Ford production in Europe, 1990		
Location	Models		Output ('000 per year)
Dagenham	Fiesta		250
Halewood	Escort		150
Cologne	Fiesta		150
	Scorpio		150
Saarlouis	Escort		350
Ghenk	Sierra		300
Valencia	Fiesta		175
	Escort		125
	Total		1650

6.25 Productivity levels and costs in different countries		
Plant	Hours per car	Labour costs ($US/car)
a. Fiesta		
Cologne	29.9	1084
Valencia	33.3	921
Dagenham	52.2	1344
b. Escort		
Saarlouis	33.9	1070
Halewood	63.8	1481

[From: Wells & Rawlinson, 1992]

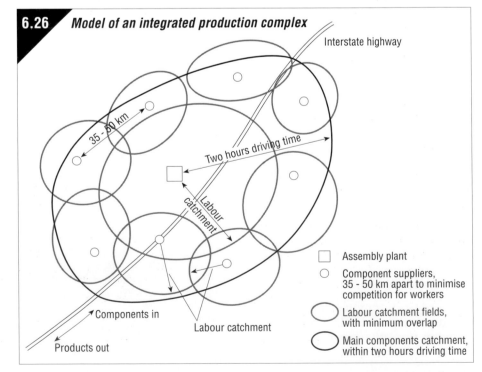

6.26 Model of an integrated production complex

Interstate highway

35 - 50 km

Two hours driving time

Labour catchment

Components in

Products out

Labour catchment

□ Assembly plant

○ Component suppliers, 35 - 50 km apart to minimise competition for workers

Labour catchment fields, with minimum overlap

Main components catchment, within two hours driving time

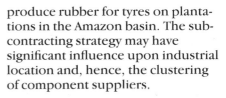

Japanese make UK the land of the rising sun

By Kevin Eason

Car component makers are set to win £1 billion worth of new sales in Europe as British firms take business from foreign competition. The British component industry has become the most efficient in the world.

A report says the revolution in the component industry is due to Japanese car manufacturers setting up plants in the UK. Their demands for the highest efficiency and quality has transformed an industry which lost thousands of jobs over the past decade.

Honda, Toyota and Nissan will spend more than £3 billion between them on components before the end of the decade, with the main share going to British companies. Toyota says British suppliers have proved so efficient that it will bring forward its target date for cars made at Burnaston, Derbyshire, to have 80 per cent local content.

The company, which will be spending £700 million a year on components within three years, has 160 suppliers: 82 in the UK, 40 in Germany and 18 in France. Of 36 raw materials suppliers, 21 are British.

Honda, expected to spend £500 million annually by 1995, has 155 suppliers, 105 from the UK. Nissan, the biggest of the Japanese companies, is spending almost 80 per cent of its annual £850 million components bill with British factories. Of 198 suppliers, 130 are British.

[*The Independent* 26.6.92]

produce rubber for tyres on plantations in the Amazon basin. The subcontracting strategy may have significant influence upon industrial location and, hence, the clustering of component suppliers.

Strategic alliances involve collaboration between otherwise independent firms to achieve specific ends. For instance, in the 1980s Honda was linked with Rover to gain improved access to the European market. Rover was keen to collaborate as it was having financial difficulties. In 1994, the takeover of Rover by BMW disrupted this relationship. Ford and Volkswagen have joint ventures in Europe. For example, a new plant in Portugal helps to share development costs and to strengthen their competitiveness against the Japanese challenge. Manufacturers may use 'badge engineering' to help fill a gap in their model range. They may also use common parts on their models. Volkswagen, for example, lacked a 4-wheel-drive light pick-up truck, so they came to an agreement with Toyota. When you buy a 'Taro' pick-up you are buying a Toyota with a VW badge.

Ford draws its component supplies from the countries with the assembly plants. The maps of Resource 6.29

single firm. Consequently, as component suppliers themselves become bigger, so they try to arrange contracts with different customers. There are signs, too, that even the Japanese vehicle makers are moving towards a more flexible system. While Nissan in Sunderland does draw over half its components from suppliers in the north-east, Honda at Swindon had not attracted a component supplier cluster. Helped by its partnership with Rover, it has drawn upon the existing components cluster in the West Midlands. Toyota is adopting a policy of drawing components from several places in Europe to its UK operations.

Two increasingly common strategies used by Ford and other major manufacturers are *subcontracting* and using *strategic alliances*. With subcontracting, a firm puts out certain aspects of its operation to specialist suppliers while continuing to engage in production itself. Vehicle manufacturers may make their own engines, but contract other companies to make and supply components such as seats. This is a move away from *vertical integration* wherein a manufacturer built up the capacity to produce all components. For example, Ford once tried to

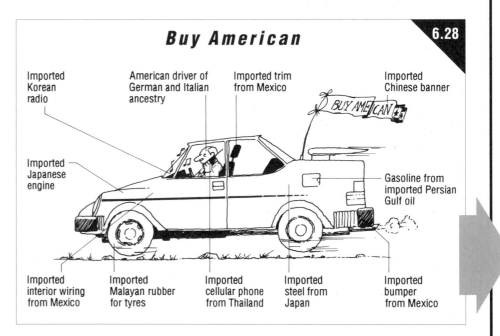

Buy American 6.28

Imported Korean radio
American driver of German and Italian ancestry
Imported trim from Mexico
Imported Chinese banner
Imported Japanese engine
BUY AMERICAN
Gasoline from imported Persian Gulf oil
Imported interior wiring from Mexico
Imported Malayan rubber for tyres
Imported cellular phone from Thailand
Imported steel from Japan
Imported bumper from Mexico

Managing industrial change 177

CASE STUDY 6.2 *The large corporation at work*

show that these suppliers are not necessarily clustered around the plants. Germany is clearly the dominant source. It supplies over half of Ford Europe's component needs, but produces only 40% of the vehicles. As part of its 'lean' production system, Ford has pioneered its 'Q1' system of assessing its component suppliers. Only suppliers who measure up to the required standards will be given contracts. This is known as the *zero defect* or *total quality* approach. Delivery, not distance, is the crucial criterion. As long as delivery is reliable and cost-efficient, it is of little consequence to Ford where the supplier is located.

Ford Europe reduced its component suppliers from 2500 to less than 800 between 1983 and 1990, and by 1995 will have only 600 suppliers. These larger, more sophisticated suppliers are increasingly likely to be multi-site and multi-national, and will serve several customers.

Each country does have component supplier clustering. For example in Germany, the Ruhr and Sauerland dominate. In the UK, the West Midlands has the principal cluster, lying midway between Ford's main assembly plants at Halewood and Dagenham. In Spain, Barcelona dominates, although there is a minor

cluster around the assembly factory at Valencia. In France, there is a scatter around Paris and along the Loire valley, which is related to the French vehicle industry rather than Ford's locational policy. In each country, the maps show both dispersal and clustering, indicating that Ford has no policy to agglomerate suppliers around assembly plants along the Japanese model. Even with relatively recent plants such as Halewood and Valencia, there is little clustering effect. Rather, the Ford plants are located outside the traditional core regions of vehicle production, but still have to use those core regions for supplies. Ford's 'Q1' strategy stresses efficiency and quality of delivery rather than the 'just-in-time' priority of proximity and frequency.

The component suppliers enjoy several advantages:

- They can stay in their traditional locations but could expand near to their main customers if necessary.
- They are less tied to one customer and, hence, have greater security and flexibility.
- They have more opportunity to grow and invest in research and development. Thus, the typical German components firm will supply all of the major German production locations and foreign plants.

It is impractical for the supplier firm to have one location to serve all these customers on a 'just-in-time' basis. Equally it is unrealistic to expect each supplier to set up an operation alongside each of its customers.

Ford claims that UK-built vehicles contain around two-thirds UK components and materials. All the major vehicle manufacturers have truly international supply and assembly production chains. This may be the result of inter-firm collaboration. For example, the new Ford plant in Portugal is a joint venture with Volkswagen, with most components coming from Germany. It becomes

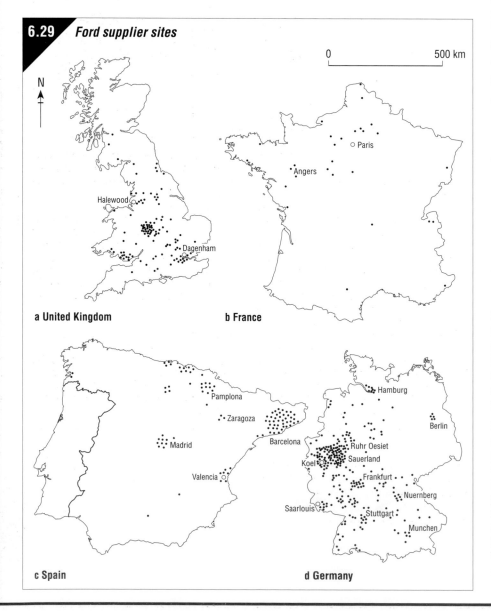

6.29 *Ford supplier sites*

0 ——————— 500 km

a United Kingdom

b France

c Spain

d Germany

'Foreign' cars are best of British

by Mark Skipworth and John Harlow

If you want to buy a British car, choose a Honda, Peugeot or Nissan. Ford and Vauxhall, traditionally favoured by patriots, are being overtaken by foreign manufacturers who produce popular models with up to 80% British parts.

But a study by the Motor Industry Research Unit (Miru), published this weekend, has exposed the myth of buying British. It analysed the British content in more than 30 best-selling models, estimating the value of the UK components as a proportion of the vehicles' costs.

Only two out of five Ford models surveyed are assembled in Britain. Although its Fiesta and Escort are almost entirely British, its new four-wheel drive Maverick is produced by Nissan in Spain. The Mondeo, with up to 15% of its components made in Europe and shipped to Asia to be put together, is finally assembled in Belgium.

Ford is not unique. Four out of five Vauxhall models are assembled abroad, including in Spain and Finland, while the final assembly of the Cavalier and Astra is shared between Britain and Germany. The heavily advertised new Corsa, with an estimated 15% UK content, has an Austrian engine in its popular 1.2LS version, a German gearbox and Spanish body.

The blurring of widely accepted images does not stop there. Motorists who want to buy a Volkswagen Polo for German reliability may be surprised to learn the vehicle is assembled in Spain. Some engines for the Audi 80 come from Mexico. Advertisements featuring the Fiat Cinquecento in an Italian setting should be re-shot in Poland, where it is assembled.

By contrast, Japanese manufactur-

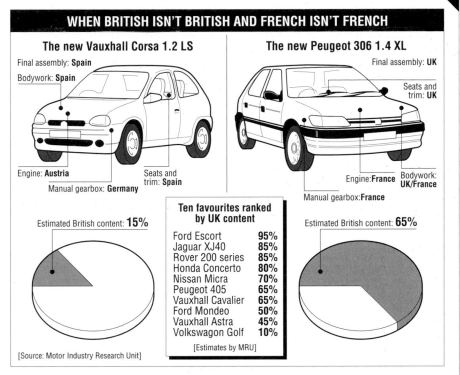

WHEN BRITISH ISN'T BRITISH AND FRENCH ISN'T FRENCH

The new Vauxhall Corsa 1.2 LS
- Final assembly: **Spain**
- Bodywork: **Spain**
- Engine: **Austria**
- Manual gearbox: **Germany**
- Seats and trim: **Spain**

Estimated British content: **15%**

The new Peugeot 306 1.4 XL
- Final assembly: **UK**
- Seats and trim: **UK**
- Engine: **France**
- Bodywork: **UK/France**
- Manual gearbox: **France**

Estimated British content: **65%**

Ten favourites ranked by UK content

Ford Escort	95%
Jaguar XJ40	85%
Rover 200 series	85%
Honda Concerto	80%
Nissan Micra	70%
Peugeot 405	65%
Vauxhall Cavalier	65%
Ford Mondeo	50%
Vauxhall Astra	45%
Volkswagon Golf	10%

[Estimates by MRU]

[Source: Motor Industry Research Unit]

ers are developing British car factories in an attempt to circumvent European import restrictions. Mazda is planning to set up in Europe and is considering Britain, which has some of the lowest labour costs among industrialised countries, as a possible location.

Krish Bhaskar, director of Miru, said most people seeking to buy British would choose either a Ford, Rover or Vauxhall. "The truth is that the British content of many Japanese cars is now equalling or surpassing other vehicles that we traditionally consider British."

Vauxhall, part of the giant American conglomerate General Motors, insisted last week it continued to use many British components. It said the average UK content of its vehicles reached 67% last year, but it admitted: "It is very difficult to define a British car. The days of

sourcing from one country have long since gone and manufacturers are casting their net not just across Europe but around the world to obtain parts."

Ford said the concept of a "world car" was attractive because it achieved global economies of scale. "To cut down on duplication of production, which involves massive investment, makes more economic sense and promotes centres of excellence."

The Miru study also finds that manufacturers are increasingly looking further afield to take advantage of low labour costs. For example, Spain's labour costs are half those of Germany, but Asian countries such as Thailand are four times cheaper than Spain.

increasingly difficult to identify a vehicle as 'British' or 'French'.

The intensity of competition in the motor vehicle industry is illustrated by the announcement that Ford is considering another fundamental organisational change. Even the five world groups are not big or efficient enough, and if the proposal becomes reality, then Ford will operate on a fully global scale.

6.31 Ford prepares for global revolution

Andrew Lorenz and Jeff Randall

Ford, the world's second-largest vehicle maker, is about to launch a huge corporate shake-up in a bid to achieve what no multinational company has yet managed: to operate on a completely global basis.

The organisational revolution, driven by Alex Trotman, Ford's British-born chairman, is the most significant in the history of the company since Henry Ford expanded from Detroit into Europe more than 60 years ago.

It has sweeping implications for the Ford of Britain organisation, for Ford's big factories at Dagenham, Halewood, Bridgend and Southampton, for Jaguar, Ford's luxury-car maker, and for Britain's leading motor component manufacturers such as GKN, Lucas, T&N and BTR.

One result of the strategy could be Jaguar's emergence as a world centre for upmarket car design and production, possibly replacing the Granada/Scorpio products in Europe. That would create the potential for huge expansion at Jaguar's West Midlands plants.

Motor industry sources say Ford intends to overturn its continental structure, under which America and Europe separately develop, make and market vehicles. Instead, Ford will aim to eliminate duplication by restructuring worldwide along product lines, with different regions designing, making and selling cars all over the world.

Ford's globalisation plan does not mean selling the same product in all markets. It means selling different products in different markets, but producing them from a co-ordinated manufacturing unit.

Under the plan, Europe could become Ford's world centre for medium-sized cars and small engines.

No other car company has attempted total globalisation. Although Japanese companies such as Toyota, Nissan and Honda make and sell similar products throughout the world, their decision-making, design and development processes remain concentrated in Japan, and marketing is organised on a continental basis. Full globalisation is being attempted by multinationals in other industries, such as Unilever and Nestlé in consumer products, but nobody has yet succeeded in bringing it off.

The Ford chief told The Sunday Times: "As automotive competition becomes more global as we get into the next century, the pressure to find scale economies will become greater and greater. If, instead of making two engines at 500,000 units each, you can make one engine at 1m units then the costs are much lower. Ultimately, there will be a handful of global players.

Ford of Europe believes Ford is losing many of the economies of scale it could achieve if organised globally. It is crazy for Ford to be investing millions in building new plants in America while Ford in Europe has plants lying idle.

Trotman and his colleagues have concluded that full globalisation is the only way to beat competitors such as the Japanese and, in Europe, Ford's archrival General Motors, which retains a cost advantage over Ford.

Ford also believes it needs globalisation to capitalise on fast-emerging markets in the Far East and Latin America.

[*The Sunday Times* 27.3.1994]

Activities

1 What are meant by *dedicated* and *flexible* factories? Illustrate their use by Ford Europe.

2 Rank the production of Ford Europe by countries in order of size of output. What factors might cause this ranking to change?

3 What is meant by the *just-in-time* system? What advantages are claimed for it?

4 JIT production leads to a clustering of component suppliers around the assembly plant. Has this happened with the Ford Europe organisation? If not, why not? What relationship does the Ford corporation have with its component suppliers?

5 In what sense can it be claimed that Ford Europe has adopted a 'post-Fordist' approach to industrial location and organisation?

6 From Resource 6.31, suggest:

a why Ford is considering changing to a global organisational structure.

b what the key features of this new structure might be.

CASE STUDY 6.3 *Nike: whose shoe is it anyway?*

Background

Large-scale manufacturing industry is said to have entered the post-Fordist stage of its evolution. The term *Fordist* is derived from Henry Ford, who introduced mass production techniques to vehicle manufacture in the 1920s. When setting up the production line for the Model T car, it is claimed that Henry Ford commented: 'You can have any colour as long as it's black.' His comment was to form the basis of mass production in large factories, in which a product is developed to the same specifications, using the economies of scale to keep unit costs down. Once a production line was set up, it operated on long runs of the same or similar products and involved rigid work practices and production technologies. The manufacturer (producer) controlled the market and the buyer (consumer) had a limited selection from a narrow range of standardised products. By the 1960s, this Fordist strategy dominated a wide range of industries throughout the world.

Over the past 30 years or so this situation has changed. The consumer has become a much more powerful force in determining a manufacturer's strategy. There is a complex two-way (symbiotic) relationship between producers and consumers:

- Markets have grown but have become more competitive.
- Consumers have become more sophisticated and are demanding greater choice.
- Manufacturers introduce new models and brands with increasing frequency to keep abreast of the competition, and to tempt the increasingly selective and demanding consumer.

The concepts of 'fashion' and 'status', promoted by vigorous marketing campaigns, have become powerful forces in consumption and in production. The dilemma for the manufacturer is to produce in mass quantities at competitive prices, yet be flexible enough to switch production quickly to new or modified products, and at the same time, to have an increased number of 'brands' or 'models' on the market. There is a need for flexible technologies and institutional structures. Companies either adopt the 'just-in-time' strategy or locate factories in regions with low labour costs, to keep production costs down.

This combination of high volume production and flexible batch production is at the heart of the post-Fordist industrial strategy. Manufacturers have responded in different ways to this need for 'flexible mass production'. This case study follows the evolution of the Nike Corporation in what is essentially a new mass industry, heavily reliant upon fashion and status, and with a very broad market spread.

Key understandings

- There is a symbiotic relationship between producers and consumers.
- Traditionally, a developed world core draws raw materials from a less developed periphery.
- A developed world core utilises the human resources of less developed peripheries as cheap labour.
- Large-scale manufacturing industries are entering the post-Fordist stage of their evolution.

Post-Fordist industrial strategy of the Nike Corporation

Nike is an American company with its headquarters in Beaverton, Oregon. In 1990, the company sold over 45 million pairs of athletic footwear in the United States, but not a single pair was made within the country. Every shoe was assembled in an independently-owned factory. The company has adopted a total subcontracting strategy. It concentrates its production in east and south-east Asia, while retaining the research, development and marketing decision-making within the United States. This is an excellent example of a major transnational corporation which has based its strategies upon two models of economic organisation and location: a revised approach to the *core-periphery* model, and the *new international division of labour* (NIDL) model.

In the traditional core-periphery model of economic development and organisation, a developed world core draws raw materials from a less developed periphery. It then uses the periphery as a market for some of the goods produced. This has also been described as *economic colonialism*. The next phase in this core-periphery concept has been for the developed core to utilise the human resources of the periphery as 'cheap labour'. Nike has located manufacturing plants in less developed countries in order to benefit from low labour costs. In the third stage of development, though, the LDC of the periphery passes through various development thresholds and becomes an NIC (newly-industrialised country). It becomes capable of raising and attracting its own investment capital and of developing its own industrial base. The periphery now has within it, its own cores and, hence, its own periphery zones. Nike has adapted to this process too.

This model can be applied to Nike's organisational progress.

CASE STUDY 6.3 *Nike: whose shoe is it anyway?*

Resource 6.33 summarises the chronology and allows us to follow the changing geography of this progress.

Apart from the experiments in America, the UK and the Irish Republic, between 1975 and 1985, Nike has never manufacturered its own products. *No athletic footwear firm now wholly owns any integrated production facilities ... it is typified by the large scale vertical disintegration of functions and a high level of subcontracting activity* (Donaghu & Barff, 1991). There is a shift away from vertical integration, a hallmark of the Fordist approach to industrial organisation. A central body does not control and is not involved in all stages of the production process, from raw materials to marketing.

In terms of the core-periphery model (Resource 6.35), Nike never operated at the Stage 1 level, where the

6.32

NIKE

ALL MEN ARE CREATED EQUAL, THEN SOME BUY NIKE.

Be the first amongst equals.
Check out the latest Nike range at your local stockist.

6.33 *Nike's progress*

1964 A small Oregon company, Blue Ribbon Sports (BRS), becomes a distributor for the Japanese manufacturer of the Tiger brand of athletic shoes.

1970 BRS ends the Tiger contract.

1971 BRS negotiates with another Japanese manufacturer to make its own brand of shoe to be known as Nike. Research and development will be in Oregon but all production will be in Japan.

1974 The Japanese production company begins to subcontract Nike shoe assembly to Taiwan and South Korea, using materials and components produced in Japan.

1975 BRS, now the Nike Company, strengthens its control over production by opening a factory in the USA, and becoming more involved in organising and managing the south-east Asian production.

1979 Nike holds 50% of the US running shoe market and has its Nike-Air cushioning system in production. A production factory is opened in the UK.

1983 Rising costs and the continued desire for production control, cause Nike to break its connection with the Japanese company. Meanwhile Nike extends its connections through south-east Asia, and opens a factory in the Irish Republic.

1985 The UK and Irish factories are sold, followed in 1986 by the closure of the US factory.

1988 Production contracts are established in Malaysia and Indonesia.

1990 Revenues exceed $2 billion, with over 400 models of footwear.

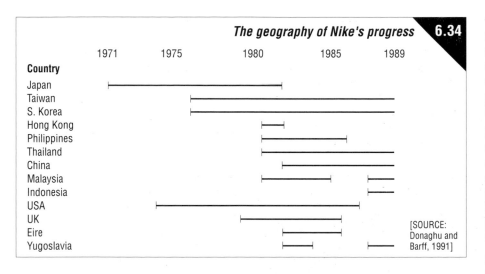

The geography of Nike's progress `6.34`

Country	1971	1975	1980	1985	1989

[SOURCE: Donaghu and Barff, 1991]

periphery was used for materials and markets. Stage 2 was more of a strategic alliance with a partner in Japan, which at that time was an NIC within the eastern Asian periphery. (A strategic alliance is one in which two or more firms form a joint venture or co-operative agreement.) All production took place in the NIC, while the BRS partner in the USA handled the distribution and marketing. Stage 3 represents the situation wherein the Japanese manufacturers were subcontracting assembly to firms in South Korea and Taiwan in the early 1970s. At this stage, Japan

becomes a 'core' which is itself using a 'periphery'. Stage 4 sees South Korea and Taiwan as production cores in their own right. These countries now have their own support industries for components for assembly. Nike has broken its direct ties with the Japanese companies and deals directly with these new cores. Japan now acts only as a source of some materials and components. Thailand and China become the active periphery.

Japan plays a very minor role in Stage 5, while South Korea and

Taiwan remain the production core. Malaysia and Indonesia have joined the active periphery. As they and the other periphery countries lack the support industries, many of the components for assembly are supplied by South Korea and Taiwan.

Nike's subcontracting system has several distinctive features. The company does not use the term 'subcontractor', but 'production partner', since the relationship between Nike and the individual production companies is one of shared responsibilities.

Resource 6.35 shows the subcontracting structure and highlights the key categories of producers in the first tier. The *developed partners* are the elite producers with whom Nike has long-term alliances and who produce exclusively for Nike. In return, Nike rarely varies the monthly orders by more than 20%, thereby guaranteeing a regular workload. These firms produce the latest, top-of-the-range 'statement products' and play a role in product development. Individual firms make 10 000–25 000 pairs of shoes a day. These firms are based in the south-east Asia core of South Korea and Taiwan, and themselves subcontract

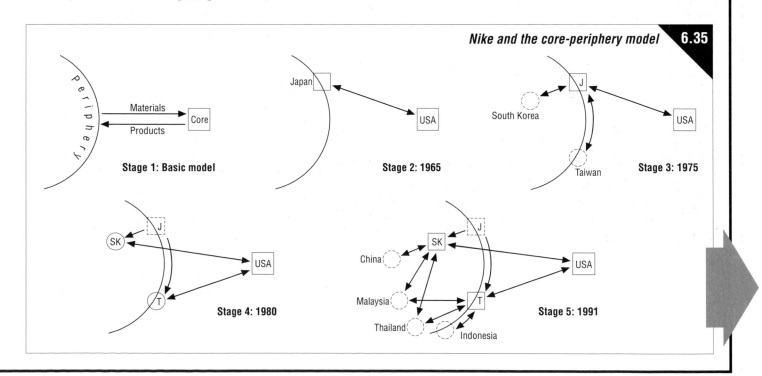

Nike and the core-periphery model `6.35`

Stage 1: Basic model

Stage 2: 1965

Stage 3: 1975

Stage 4: 1980

Stage 5: 1991

Hyperactive Asia

Colorful labels like "young tigers" and "little dragons" have made the world aware that East Asia is a hot spot for economic growth. The economies of the nine East Asian countries, excepting Japan – China, Hong Kong, South Korea, Taiwan, Malaysia, the Philippines, Singapore, Indonesia and Thailand – have strikingly outperformed those of the industrialized countries over the past several years. Since 1989, while the annual growth rate of advanced countries, as measured by the average of members of the Organization for Economic Cooperation and Development, dwindled from 3.4% to almost nothing, that of Asia's mythical beasts surged ahead at 6% to 7%.

Who is buying the products churned out by these hyperactive economies? Increasingly, the hyperactive economies themselves. The view of these countries as cottage industries catering primarily to the U.S. or Japanese or European market is outdated. Over the past 20 years, the proportion of their exports absorbed by their own neighbors has risen from 19% to 30%. At the same time, the shares of the group's total exports that go to the U.S. Japan and the European Community have declined.

These shares, however, are merely smaller slices of a bigger pie, because total exports of the nine have been growing exponentially. They amounted to $488 billion last year, well ahead of the U.S. with $441 billion and Japan with $327 billion. Exports of the nine to the U.S., the E.C. and Japan were worth $106 billion, $74 billion and $62 billion, respectively, but these impressive figures are overshadowed by the nine's $144 billion exports to one another. This reflects a degree of self-sufficieny in trade that partly shields East Asia from recession elsewhere.

[*Time*, 28.6.93]

Nike's organisational structure

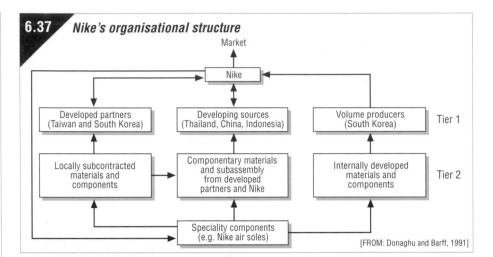

[FROM: Donaghu and Barff, 1991]

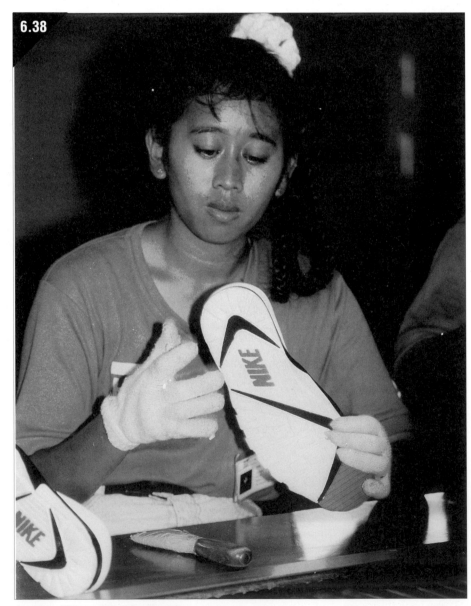

Inside a Nike production factory

Sporting Nike athletic wear

part of their assembly to periphery countries such as Malaysia and China. The essential characteristic is their flexibiity of production.

The *volume producers* manufacture 70–80 000 pairs of shoes a day. Located mainly in South Korea and Taiwan, they are not contracted exclusively to Nike and may produce for up to ten companies. They are subject to 'capacity subcontracting', having to produce the mainstream models for which there is a bulk demand. As demand may vary widely, and because Nike does not have an exclusive contract, the monthly orders may vary by up to 50%. These companies are less flexible than the developed partners and cannot switch models as quickly. They draw their components and

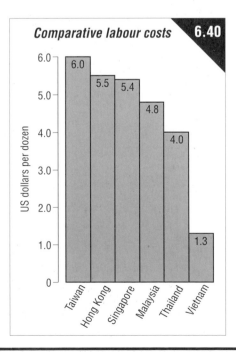

Comparative labour costs 6.40

US dollars per dozen

Taiwan 6.0
Hong Kong 5.5
Singapore 5.4
Malaysia 4.8
Thailand 4.0
Vietnam 1.3

materials from both local and more distant companies.

The NIDL (New International Division of Labour) model is a version of the core-periphery model expressed in labour market terms. *The spatial dispersal of production from the core to the periphery of the global economy and the continued concentration of research development and technologically sophisticated activities in the core* (Donaghu & Barff, 1991). Straightforward production tasks are carried out by low-cost labour in the periphery, while expensive, skill-intensive jobs are held in the headquarter establishments located in the core. This geographical disintegration of production has been accelerated by growing competition and assisted by improvements in communications and simplification of production processes. Such trends are readily applicable to the footwear industry where the production process remains essentially low-technology and labour intensive.

Labour costs have been a primary factor in Nike's locational policy. For example, as Japan's labour and production costs rose, so Nike looked increasingly to South Korea and Taiwan. In turn, as costs in these two countries rose, they, with the encouragement of Nike, have subcontracted more of their assembly to neighbouring Asian countries, even though the materials and components are still supplied from the core countries. *The average hourly wage in manufacturing in Taiwan and South Korea is [1991] about three times that of Mexico's Maquiladoras [industrial enclaves within Mexico where US companies can produce, yet avoid most import-export taxes etc] and even higher than Portugal's* (Donaghu & Barff, 1991).

The markets

A number of transnational companies locate production facilities near or within growth markets for ease of access and to avoid import quotas and tariffs. Among the best-known are the Japanese vehicle

CASE STUDY 6.3 *Nike: whose shoe is it anyway?*

manufacturers who have located inside the USA and the EU. Nike's locational decisions have not been determined by such factors. Around 50% of Nike's market is in North America, with Europe as the second largest outlet. Apart from experiments in the 1970s and early 1980s, Nike has never based production in these regions. There is no doubt that athletic footwear is a 'style statement' for the millions of fashion-conscious young people in eastern and south-eastern Asia. Nike does compete strongly in this exploding market. Market proximity has not, however, been a significant factor in the company's locational decisions.

Conclusion

Nike has developed an intricate system of production based upon a two-tier structure of subcontracting 'partners'. This production is typi-fied by vertical disintegration, flexi-bility of location and rigidity of assembly processes. The combina-tion of enforcing standardised pro-ducts with flexible subcontracting arrangements is the way Nike has responded to the increasingly com-petitive and constantly shifting market. This is an excellent example of the 'post-Fordist' approach. A flex-ible, demand-driven production system contrasts with the supply-driven, continuous flow and full capacity production.

[Source: Donaghu M.T. 'Nike just did it: International subcontracting and flexibility in athletic footwear pro-duction', *Regional Studies*, 24(6), 1991, 537–552]

Activities

1 Give brief definitions of 'Fordism' and 'post-Fordism' as organisational strategies for manufacturing industry.

2 Using the Nike example, assess the usefulness of the core-periphery model in explaining the economic development process.

3 In what ways does the NIDL model help to explain shifts in industrial location?

4 Why has the footwear industry proved to be an appropriate industry to introduce into a country relatively early in the development process?

5 On the assumption that Nike remains a successful company, construct a 'Stage 6' to the core-periphery model of Resource 6.35 as it might appear in the year 2000. (Think carefully of how the model has evolved and what is likely to happen next.)

CHAPTER 7

Energy options

Introduction

The availability of energy has a direct effect upon our quality of life. It controls switching on a light, taking a trip by car or plane, keeping drinks cool, listening to music or going to the dentist. How this energy is obtained and generated also affects us in terms of how much it costs and how many jobs it creates. It also has a direct bearing on the communities it supports or destroys as we switch from one energy source to another, and its generation and distribution have effects upon the environment. Policy decisions on which energy source to use and how energy will be made available to us influence our lives at every turn.

Where and how the world will generate its energy has become a vital issue. Every day there are more people on earth, and each individual has steadily increasing energy demands. For example, if you live in Los Angeles you consume at least ten times more energy per day than if you farm in Iowa. In turn, the Iowa farmer has ten times the daily energy consumption of a Vietnamese rice farmer. As a country passes from the less developed stage (LDC), through the newly industrialising phase (NIC) to the developed (DC) status, so the per capita energy needs increase. Forecasters now talk of the 'global energy gap', the possibility that within the next 50 years or so, there may be a shortfall between energy supply and energy demand.

There is an equally strong concern about which sources of energy to develop. Technology allows an increasing variety of

7.1

Modern energy options

energy sources to be utilised and, consequently, greater choice in how we generate our energy. Policies can include ideas of *conservation*, *sustainability*, and measures of how 'environmentally-friendly' a particular form of energy generation is. Policies which have emphasised *non-renewable* resources (coal, oil, natural gas, nuclear, geothermal) are shifting to include an increased component of *renewable* resources (solar, wind, waves, tides, hydro, wood and other biomass). The inevitable exhaustion of non-renewable sources is a major reason for this shift in policy.

The three case studies of this chapter discuss several of the key issues. The exploitation of North Sea oil and natural gas reserves (Case Study 7.1) is an excellent example of the *product cycle* of a non-renewable resource. It is cost-effective, yet already past peak production levels. It has been an important factor in the decline of the UK coal industry. Located offshore, the visual impacts of natural gas exploitation are confined to a small number of large coastal facilities. However, as with all fossil fuels, there are atmospheric emissions when the resource is consumed.

Case Study 7.2 examines the 'balance sheet' of wind power as an energy source. Classified as an unconventional source of energy, this renewable product involves low

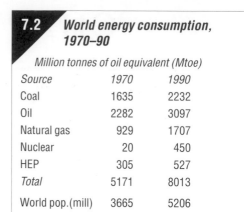

7.2 **World energy consumption, 1970–90**

Million tonnes of oil equivalent (Mtoe)

Source	1970	1990
Coal	1635	2232
Oil	2282	3097
Natural gas	929	1707
Nuclear	20	450
HEP	305	527
Total	5171	8013
World pop.(mill)	3665	5206

[From: Allen,J.E *Energy resources for a changing world 1970–1990*]

technology and is widely available. By some measures it is environmentally friendly, but also has severe impacts. The materials focus upon these environmental issues.

Case Study 7.3 examines the political and environmental aspects of HEP generation. Hydro-electric power harnesses a renewable resource and produces power at economic costs. However, as the Gabcikovo scheme on the Danube river shows, it can arouse political tensions between countries. The tensions arise in part from the environmental impacts of river diversion and because of the question of ownership.

7.3

Nuclear power station at Sellafield

CASE STUDY 7.1 *UK energy: the oil and gas option*

Background

The United Kingdom, like other industrialised countries, has undergone an energy revolution during the past 40 years. In 1950, 90% of the energy consumption came from coal. By 1973 it was down to 38% and by 1990, it was less than 20%. At its peak in 1913, the UK coal industry produced nearly 300 million tonnes a year from several hundred pits. By 1990 the output was less than 100 million tonnes from fewer than 50 pits. By the mid 1990s, there may be less than 20 pits mining barely 40 million tonnes a year. Today, Big Pit in South Wales is a piece of industrial heritage for tourists. This evolution can be attributed to a complex mix of economic, technological, scientific, political and environmental factors.

Even though hydro-electric and nuclear power have increased in proportions, the major shift has been to the use of oil and gas. During the 1950s and 1960s new oil-fired power stations were built and were fed cheap imported oil. However, the breakthrough which 'energised' the revolution was the discovery of natural gas in 1965 and oil in 1969 under the North Sea. The first UK offshore oil came ashore in 1975 and by 1984, the UK was the

Key understandings

◆ Oil and natural gas are non-renewable resources.

◆ Exploitation of oil and natural gas depends upon a combination of economic, technological, scientific, political and environmental factors.

◆ Management of such resources by commercial companies and governments must take into account national and international considerations.

◆ Because the resources are finite and non-renewable, it is important to be able to forecast future reserves and to plan for their use within the setting of alternative sources of energy.

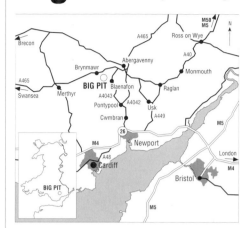

Big Pit — Unique underground tour of a coalmine

7.4

Big Pit closed as a working colliery in 1980, exactly 100 years after it first produced coal. In Blaenafon the mining of coal and ironstone on a large scale began in the 1780s and some of these older workings are connected with Big Pit. The pit is now a museum where visityors can go underground and discover how miners have worked and lived over the past 200 years.

Some of the features at Big Pit, Blaenafon

• A unique underground tour, with an ex-miner as your guide

• The original colliery buildings, including the winding engine-house, the blacksmith's shop and the pithead baths

• Exhibitions illustrating the history of South Wales coal industry and the way of life of the mining communities

• The miners' canteen, now offering a range of hot and cold snacks and meals, confectionery and ice cream

• A gift shop well stocked with souvenirs and publications

• A professional photographer to record your visit

• Ample free parking space, and a picnic area

world's fifth largest oil producer, after USSR, USA, Saudi Arabia and Mexico, respectively. Resource 7.6 charts this phenomenal history.

Like coal, oil and gas are non-renewable resources. The direct environmental impacts of the oil and gas developments are much less than those of coal because the fields are offshore. The onshore facilities may be in relatively remote locations. The reserves *will* run out,

however. This case study examines the potential for oil and gas production in the UK. Much of the material is based upon an article written by an oil company executive, and so sees the oil and gas industry in a positive light. It is important, therefore, that this material is read with regard to the broader setting of energy policy, bearing in mind the alternatives, their economics and the environmental implications.

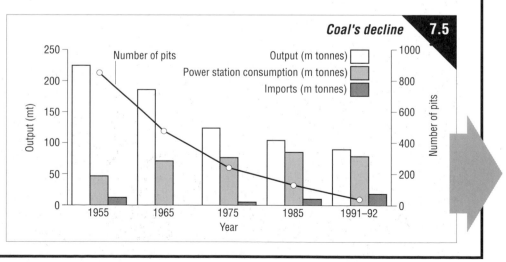

Coal's decline 7.5

CASE STUDY 7.1 *UK energy: the oil and gas option*

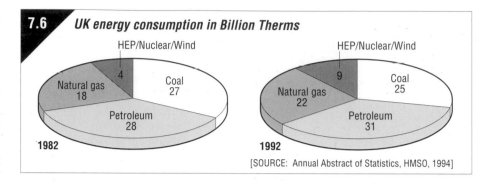

7.6 UK energy consumption in Billion Therms

1982
- HEP/Nuclear/Wind 4
- Coal 27
- Natural gas 18
- Petroleum 28

1992
- HEP/Nuclear/Wind 9
- Coal 25
- Natural gas 22
- Petroleum 31

[SOURCE: Annual Abstract of Statistics, HMSO, 1994]

7.7 The chronology of oil and gas in the UK

1930s Small oil and gas finds in Nottinghamshire, Yorkshire and south-east Scotland.

1959 Exploration interest is stimulated by discovery of the large Dutch gas field around Groningen.

1960 The world's leading oil exporting countries form OPEC and, increasingly, control world oil supplies and prices. This causes oil importing countries such as UK to explore for their own supplies.

1964 A UN convention defines national limits and rights on the continental shelf. This allows the UK government to pass the Continental Shelf Act which defines the terms of exploration licences for UK waters. Licences for 348 blocks are awarded to companies (One block equals 12' latitude by 10'longitude. Each covers 210-240 km² of sea bed.)

1965 Gas is discovered in the southern North Sea sector. The first find at 3000 m depth and 64 km off the Humber estuary, is soon producing 10 mcf (million cubic feet) a day.

1966 British Gas decides to convert all of its operations from a coal to a natural gas base as the gas fields come into production.

1969 Oil is discovered in the central North Sea sector.

1970–74 Large, rich oilfields are discovered beneath the central and northern sectors of the UK North Sea.

1973 OPEC forces a four-fold increase in oil prices because of the Arab-Israeli conflict.

1975 The first UK North Sea oil comes ashore. Onshore this triggers a construction boom of land facilities and ocean rigs.

1980 UK oil production equals home consumption.

1984 UK becomes the world's fifth largest oil producer. Annual capital investment by the oil and gas industry is £3 billion, 25% of the UK total.

1985 The peak production year is over 2.5 mb per day (million barrels per day) from 29 fields. This provides £12 billion in tax revenue for the government. Oil provides 60% of UK energy needs, and natural gas a further 20%.

The future for oil and natural gas in the generation of UK energy

Oil is mainly used in vehicle fuels and petro-chemicals. Gas is used directly for domestic purposes and, increasingly, for the generation of electricity. It is this latter role which has caused such serious problems for the coal industry in the early 1990s. The electricity generators are the main market for coal, and because of privatisation, have been able to buy gas more cheaply than coal. As purchase contracts come up for renewal, so the companies switch to natural gas, leaving coal with a reduced market. This accelerated the closure of mines during 1992–94. The outcome of the shift of policy is summarised in Resource 7.8.

The peak year for UK oil and gas production was 1985, but resource 7.9 shows that production in *existing* fields is already falling steadily. Without new fields being exploited, dependency upon these resources is seriously threatened. Resource 7.10 summarises the situation in 1990, and shows that 70% of discovered oil and 60% of discovered gas was already in production or being developed.

Estimating future production is very difficult. We need to distinguish between 'reserves' and 'production'.

7.8

Sullom Voe energy terminal complex

The power and the Tory

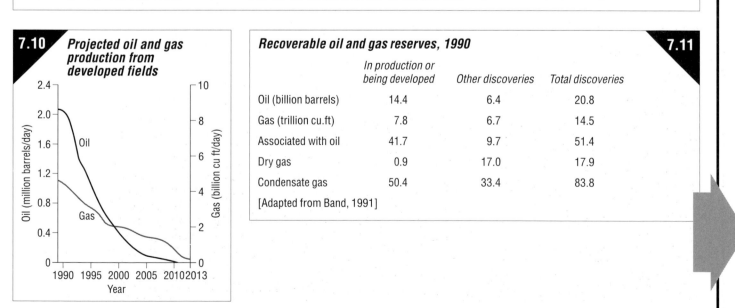

Almost unnoticed, a rash of large new power stations is being built around Britain. Their fuel is gas, pumped in from the offshore fields and being billed as the greenest fossil fuel around.

At the last count, seven gas-fired power stations were under construction in England and Wales, from Humberside down to Hertfordshire. A further seven have the official go-ahead from the Department of Energy. Sixteen more proposals, ranging in size from 50 to 1,500 mega-watts (MW) of generating capacity, are being considered by the Government.

So fast and furious is the activity, that, even if only those stations with existing approval are built, there will be an additional 9,000MW of new capacity added to the national grid by the late nineties.

If every gas station planned reached fruition, there could be more than 20,000MW of new capacity within 10 years. This represents 40 per cent of the peak winter demand for power in Britain.

A number of related factors have fuelled the "dash for gas". Firstly, the development of combined cycle gas turbine (CCGT) technology – by which the exhaust gases from a primary turbine are used to produce steam for a second – allows much more efficient use of the fuel.

At the same time, gas has become more readily available, partly because the EC dropped its ban on using gas for power generation, partly because the British Government has allowed other suppliers to compete with British Gas. The price of gas has also looked attractive compared with other fuels.

Finally, the privatisation of the electricity supply industry has allowed independent companies to compete with the two existing power station operators, PowerGen and National Power. With a short three-year construction time and much lower capital costs, CCGT stations are economically attractive.

Gas is generally seen as a clean, pollution-free fuel. Compared with coal, it is greener. Modern gas-fired power stations produce virtually no sulphur dioxide and about a fifth of a coal station's output of nitrogen oxides – both contributors to acid rain. In terms of the greenhouse effect, gas produces only 60 per cent of the carbon dioxide created by the equivalent heat output from coal. The greater efficiency of energy conversion in CCGT stations – up to 50 per cent, compared with 35 per cent for coal – improves this comparison even further.

These green credentials do not impress Friends of the Earth. If environmental considerations are uppermost, FoE argues, then energy efficiency measures and renewable energy projects must take priority. The only terms on which it can accept new gas power stations is if they operate on a combined heat and power (CHP) basis, providing both electricity and industrial or domestic heat. This could increase their efficiency rating by up to 80 per cent.

The crude result of the dash for gas, according to a new report from the Coalfield Communities Campaign (CCC), will simply be to close more coal-fired stations prematurely and accelerate the rundown of the coal industry. In the longer term, according to the CCC analysis, the Case Against Gas, such pressure would be put on the limited stocks of UK gas that prices will rise, eventually necessitating gas imports. If the gas boom continues, British reserves could be exhausted within 25 to 30 years.

The campaign portrays the exercise as a waste of one national resource (deep mined coal) to plunder another (gas) for short-term profit.

The environmental arguments against the gas power station boom are now beginning to be reflected in local opposition to new plans.

Typical of the new gas plans is the proposal for a 1,200 MW CCGT station at Avonmouth, on the outskirts of Bristol, promoted by Seabank Power, a company formed by British Gas and Midlands Electricity. Coming hard on the heels of a separate plan to import up to 10 million tonnes of foreign coal through the nearby docks, the scheme has angered environmentalists and the coal mining lobby.

One issue of immediate local concern is that, without a 100 per cent guaranteed supply of gas, the Seabank station has asked for approval to burn (more polluting) oil for up to 45 days each year.

[*The Guardian*, 31.1.92]

7.10 **Projected oil and gas production from developed fields**

Oil (million barrels/day) / Gas (billion cu ft/day) vs Year (1990–2013). Oil curve declines from about 2.05 in 1990 to near 0 by 2010. Gas curve declines from about 4.4 (1.1 on left scale) in 1990 toward 0 by 2013.

7.11 **Recoverable oil and gas reserves, 1990**

	In production or being developed	Other discoveries	Total discoveries
Oil (billion barrels)	14.4	6.4	20.8
Gas (trillion cu.ft)	7.8	6.7	14.5
Associated with oil	41.7	9.7	51.4
Dry gas	0.9	17.0	17.9
Condensate gas	50.4	33.4	83.8

[Adapted from Band, 1991]

CASE STUDY 7.1 *UK energy: the oil and gas option*

Even when we can estimate reserves with some accuracy, a number of factors affect whether they will be utilised. The following reserves need to be taken into account:

- Reserves in fields currently in production.
- Reserves in fields which are known but not yet in production.
- Reserves in predicted future discoveries.

Early in 1989, for example, total proven reserves of oil were more than 13 billion barrels, with a further 4.7 billion barrels probably available in known fields. There is a possibility of a further 6.0 billion barrels from known and developed reserves. These could be exploited if prices rise sufficiently to support the high extraction costs. The overall total of 23.5 billion barrels would last around 40 years at present levels of consumption. That would amount to 1.7 million barrels per day.

Forecasts

The oil and gas industry divides the North Sea into three 'petroleum provinces' or basins: Northern (59°–62°N), Central (55°–59°N) and Southern basins (52°–55°N). In 1991 the UK Offshore Oil Operators Association (UKOOOA) forecast likely oil discoveries for the Central and Northern basins at more than 20 years. Using the assumption that an average of 45 'wildcat' (exploration) wells would be sunk each year, the graph in Resource 7.14 shows the probability of discovery levels.

7.13 *Factors affecting future production*

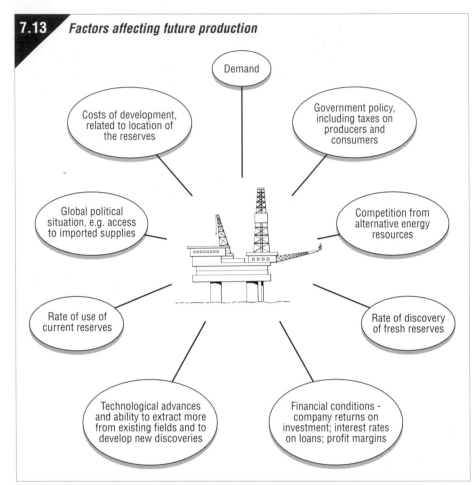

7.14 *Future discoveries: Central and northern basins*

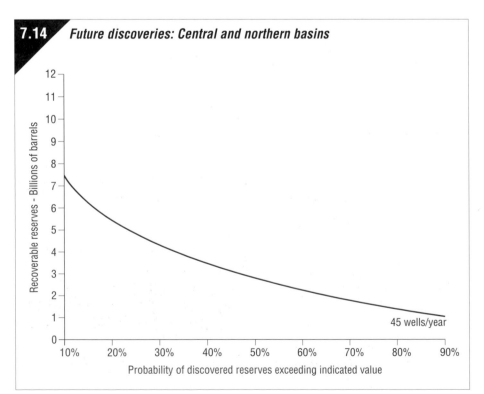

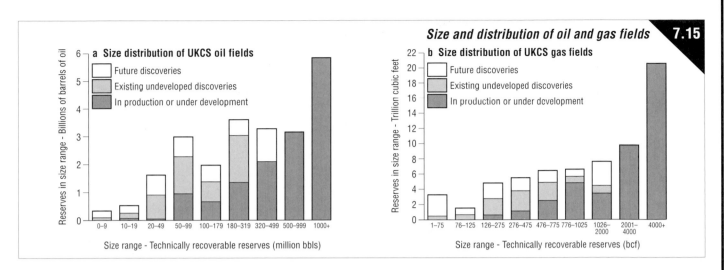

Size and distribution of oil and gas fields — 7.15

a Size distribution of UKCS oil fields

Legend:
- Future discoveries
- Existing undeveloped discoveries
- In production or under development

y-axis: Reserves in size range - Billions of barrels of oil

x-axis: Size range - Technically recoverable reserves (million bbls): 0–9, 10–19, 20–49, 50–99, 100–179, 180–319, 320–499, 500–999, 1000+

b Size distribution of UKCS gas fields

Legend:
- Future discoveries
- Existing undeveloped discoveries
- In production or under development

y-axis: Reserves in size range - Trillion cubic feet

x-axis: Size range - Technically recoverable reserves (bcf): 1–75, 76–125, 126–275, 276–475, 476–775, 776–1025, 1026–2000, 2001–4000, 4000+

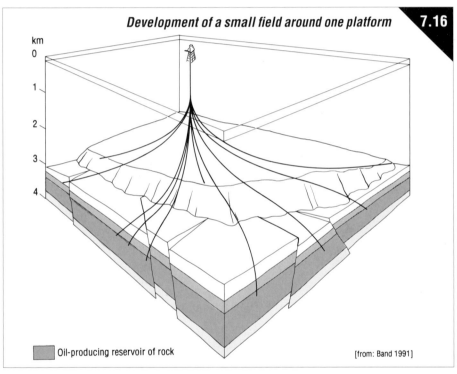

Development of a small field around one platform — 7.16

Oil-producing reservoir of rock

[from: Band 1991]

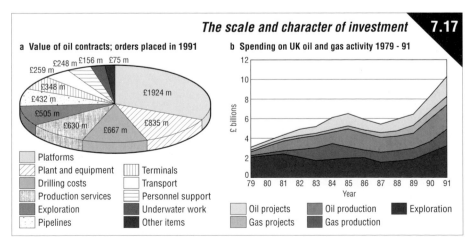

The scale and character of investment — 7.17

a Value of oil contracts; orders placed in 1991

£248 m, £156 m, £75 m, £259 m, £348 m, £432 m, £505 m, £630 m, £667 m, £835 m, £1924 m

Legend:
- Platforms
- Plant and equipment
- Drilling costs
- Production services
- Exploration
- Pipelines
- Terminals
- Transport
- Personnel support
- Underwater work
- Other items

b Spending on UK oil and gas activity 1979 - 91

y-axis: £ billions (0 to 12)
x-axis: Year: 79 80 81 82 83 84 85 86 87 88 89 90 91

Legend:
- Oil projects
- Gas projects
- Oil production
- Gas production
- Exploration

There is a 50% probability that discoveries in the Central and Northern basins would yield 3.7 billion barrels of oil and 5.0 trillion cubic feet of gas.

Another significant forecast is that over the next 20 years, discoveries and production will be, increasingly, from smaller fields. For example, there are unlikely to be any further fields with recoverable reserves greater than 500 billion barrels, or more than 2000 trillion cubic feet. Fields already known but undeveloped are only about one-sixth the size of those currently in production. Smaller fields have shorter lives and are more expensive to develop and operate. North Sea oil and gas is, therefore, a good example of an industry where the cheapest and more accessible resources are utilised first. Exploration is moving steadily into more extreme environments, such as the deeper and sterner oceans off north-west Scotland. Costs and risks will undoubtedly rise. Furthermore, the forecast totals for future discoveries are much lower than those of the earlier fields. Resource 7.16 indicates the huge investments required.

Using the 45 exploration wells a year forecast, the UKOOOA study further postulated: If three new fields were developed each year as a result of this drilling programme and from what we know of the likely size of these fields, the production levels would be as shown

CASE STUDY 7.1 *UK energy: the oil and gas option*

in Resource 7.17. The potential appears to peak around the year 2000 and then to decline steadily. Setting this potential supply alongside the yield from existing fields, the forecast is that oil supplies from the North Sea will fall from around 1.8 billion barrels a year in the mid-1990s to 1.2 billion barrels by 2013. Gas production is unlikely to decline until well into the twenty-first century .

[Based on: Band G. 'Fifty years of UK offshore oil and gas', *The Geographical Journal*, 157(2), July 1991, 179–189]

Activities

1 Briefly describe the story of North Sea oil and gas in terms of the past, the present and the future.

2 Using the North Sea oil and gas reserves as an example, explain what is meant by the *product cycle* for a non-renewable resource.

3 Why has natural gas instead of coal been increasingly preferred for the generation of electric power? Why has this affected the UK coal industry so severely?

4 Why is it becoming ever more expensive to exploit the remaining oil and gas reserves? How might this affect the competitiveness of these sources of energy?

5 At present, the UK does not have an integrated policy for power and energy supply. Use the materials of this case study to support the case for such a national policy.

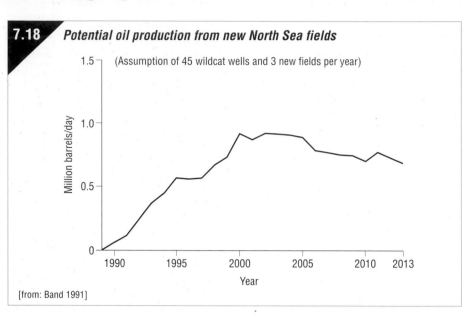

7.18 **Potential oil production from new North Sea fields**

(Assumption of 45 wildcat wells and 3 new fields per year)

[from: Band 1991]

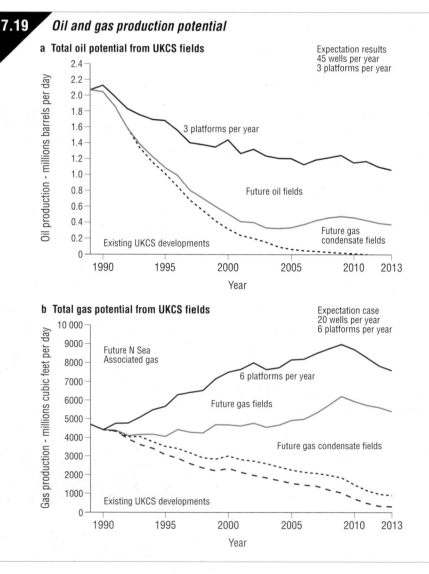

7.19 *Oil and gas production potential*

a Total oil potential from UKCS fields

Expectation results
45 wells per year
3 platforms per year

3 platforms per year

Future oil fields

Future gas condensate fields

Existing UKCS developments

b Total gas potential from UKCS fields

Expectation case
20 wells per year
6 platforms per year

Future N Sea Associated gas

6 platforms per year

Future gas fields

Future gas condensate fields

Existing UKCS developments

CASE STUDY 7.2 — *The environmental impacts of wind power*

Background

Using wind as an energy source is nothing new. The surge of interest in generating electricity by harnessing wind energy, is. Wind is freely available, is entirely renewable, leaves no waste or pollution and requires simple technology. An article published in 1993 stated that *Wind power is one of the world's more advanced renewable energy technologies, and can be economically competitive with most other traditional fuel sources and, more recently, with nuclear power* (Coles & Taylor, 1993).

How to generate sufficient power from windfarms to satisfy the enormous demands of urbanised, industrialised societies, is a problem. The generative capacity of a power station run on coal, oil, gas, water power or nuclear fuel on a single site helps to explain the continued reliance upon these mainstream sources. In 1992 the worldwide capacity of windfarms was only 2000 megawatts, over 80% of which was in the USA. The forecast is that by the year 2000, this capacity will have risen to 10 000 megawatts. Several European governments have set wind power targets in their national energy plans. By the year 2000, Denmark hopes to generate 10% of its electricity from wind energy. In the UK, public opinion seems to be in favour of wind power. Studies conducted by the Countryside Commission of those communities which are affected by wind turbines, have found that the local population is generally in favour of wind power.

A traditional windmill, Marlborough, Wiltshire

National wind energy targets for European countries (MW) — 7.21

Country	Target	By year
Denmark	1200	2005
Germany	200	1995
Greece	400	2000
Italy	600	2000
Netherlands	1000	2000
Portugal	12	1993
Spain	90	1993

Shelter from the storm — 7.22

Crispin Aubrey

This week yet another study confirmed that, despite the recent spate of adverse publicity, electricity generating wind farms are popular with people who live nearby. The latest survey was conducted for the Countryside Council for Wales, whose attitude towards the technology is extremely wary. It shows that between 74–83 per cent of people living near three Welsh wind farms find them acceptable developments. The sites include Europe's largest wind farm at Llandinam in Powys, and source of much recent controversy. By contrast, only 47 per cent of those surveyed at a control site without a wind farm, also in Wales, found the prospect acceptable.

Fieldwork for the CCW survey was conducted over a year ago by Bangor University. Its broad conclusions have only just been released, and full details are published today. Its findings fall firmly in line with more recent surveys, confirming a low level of opposition once a wind farm is up and running.

This February, market research consultants Robertson Bell questioned 255 people living near a development of 20 turbines at Taff Ely in South Wales. It had then been operating for six months. The results show that only 2 per cent strongly opposed the development of wind farms in the area; only 3 per cent said they could hear any noise from their homes.

Similar findings were obtained by the company at Kirkby Moor, a prominent cluster of 12 turbines on the edge of the Lake District. There, out of 264 people questioned, just 4 per cent strongly opposed the development, with 5 per cent very concerned about noise. At both sites there was equally strong support for the environmental advantages of wind power, such as its lack of pollution and use of a natural energy source.

Other surveys have tried to discover the feelings of local people in advance of wind farms being built. Despite angry opposition around some proposed sites, such as Flaight Hill near Hebden Bridge in Yorkshire, these also reveal a tolerant attitude towards a relatively new feature in the countryside.

At Bryn Titli in mid-Wales, where a development of 22 turbines is under construction, Robertson Bell found 72 per cent of local people supported the idea. Only 14 per cent were opposed. Even on the south coast, where the population is more concentrated and NIMBYism could be expected to blow strong, wind farms seem welcome. Door to door questioning by the local Friends of the Earth group of 1,000 residents round Selsey in West Sussex, where 10 turbines are planned, showed 83 per cent in favour.

One of the most detailed studies of attitudes towards wind power was conducted for the Department of Trade and Industry by Exeter University both before and after the building of Britain's first wind farm at Delabole in Cornwall. The authors concluded that "many of the worries local residents had about the wind turbines before the structures were built have proved unfounded after they were up and functioning."

[*The Guardian* 8.4.94]

CASE STUDY 7.2 *The environmental impacts of wind power*

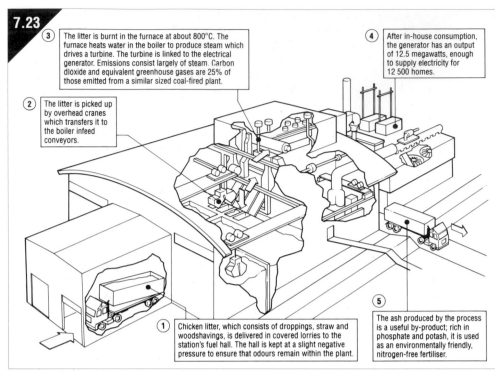

7.23

③ The litter is burnt in the furnace at about 800°C. The furnace heats water in the boiler to produce steam which drives a turbine. The turbine is linked to the electrical generator. Emissions consist largely of steam. Carbon dioxide and equivalent greenhouse gases are 25% of those emitted from a similar sized coal-fired plant.

④ After in-house consumption, the generator has an output of 12.5 megawatts, enough to supply electricity for 12 500 homes.

② The litter is picked up by overhead cranes which transfers it to the boiler infeed conveyors.

① Chicken litter, which consists of droppings, straw and woodshavings, is delivered in covered lorries to the station's fuel hall. The hall is kept at a slight negative pressure to ensure that odours remain within the plant.

⑤ The ash produced by the process is a useful by-product; rich in phosphate and potash, it is used as an environmentally friendly, nitrogen-free fertiliser.

Farming batteries

The world's first commercial power station fuelled by litter from broiler poultry farms was commissioned in July last year, on a disused second world war airfield near Eye, in northeast Suffolk. This month. Fibropower, the British company which built and runs the plant at Eye, is opening its second poultry-powered power station, on Humberside. The company is seeking a site for a third station.

Both the first and the second Fibropower plant have been built with financial aid from the government, as part of its declared commitment to encouraging the development of renewable energy sources.

Fifty trucks arrive every day, each carrying 25 tons of litter from about 200 local intensive chicken and turkey farms. The litter, a mix of wood shavings, straw and droppings, makes a good fuel for power generation.

[Source: *The Times Magazine*, 21.8.93]

In 1992, the UK was generating only eight megawatts and had no national policy or target for wind power. The Electricity Act of 1989 requires the 12 regional electricity companies in England and Wales to ensure that some of the power generated does come from sources other than fossil fuels. Most of this, around 100 000 MW, will come from nuclear power stations. The act does permit government support funding for the development of renewable energy technology. This support is called the Non Fossil Fuel Obligation (NFFO). By the end of 1991, 56 schemes had received NFFO support. The support contracts are a form of subsidy while the windfarm developers become established. They expire in 1998, by which time the schemes must be commercially self-supporting. Most wind farms are fairly small, holding fewer than 20. The largest, at Penrhyddian-Llidiartywaun in Wales, has 103 turbines. Not all are to connect into the national grid, but are for specific uses. The Chelker Reservoir scheme near Skipton, Yorkshire has four turbines to power a pumping station.

The developers and the UK Department of Energy hope that EU (European Union) funds will be made available to extend this period of support. A longer support period would allow development in less windy and less conspicuous sites. This is important as one of the main constraints upon windfarm development is their environmental impact, especially in small, densely-populated countries such as the UK. This case study examines the impact issue by identifying the locational requirements of windfarms and the current planning criteria responses by decision-making organisations.

Key understandings

◆ Wind power can be a cost-effective, environmentally-friendly form of generating energy.

◆ Windfarms require consistently windy sites, are space-consuming, and have a negative effect on environment.

◆ Careful siting can minimise environmental impact, hence planning criteria for location need to be clearly identified and applied.

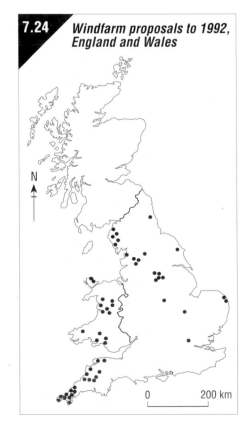

7.24 **Windfarm proposals to 1992, England and Wales**

Managing windfarm impacts in the UK

Resource requirements and constraints

The most obvious locational requirement for a successful windfarm is a windy site. Resource 7.26 shows that such sites are mainly along the coastline or across the uplands of the north and west. Many of the best wind sites are also in areas of high scenic and conservation value, which have been designated to give them protection from obtrusive development pressures. This includes areas such as National Parks, Areas of Outstanding Natural Beauty and Heritage Coasts. Other potential sites are too near settlements or Green Belts.

Planners estimate that approximately 6000 km² are environmentally suitable for the development of wind power. If all of this were used, it would accommodate enough turbines to generate approximately 20% of the UK's electricity needs. At least 70% of this suitable area lies in Scotland, which is not included in the NFFO programme. Scientists claim that *with the best wind energy resource in Europe Scotland would soon become the wind energy centre of the UK. With its high wind speeds and vast areas of rugged landscape it is possible that windfarms could be much better absorbed into the landscape and become more profitable* (Coles & Taylor, 1993). Resource 7.27 shows the environmentally suitable areas in England and Wales.

The mechanics of windpower

Wind power devices are known as *wind turbines* or *wind energy conversion systems (WECS)*. The several types of machine can be classified into two categories:

- Traditional multi-bladed machines give high mechanical power (torque) from blades rotated by frictional drag at tip speeds below that of the wind.

- Other machines obtain rotational energy by aerodynamic lift (as in aircraft propellors), and have higher tip speed velocity ratios.

Only the more efficient turbines or WECS are capable of generating electricity.

The basic equation on which wind turbines are based is:

$$Pw = 1/2pAV^2$$

Pw = Power of the wind

p = Density of the air

A = Area swept by the blades

V = Wind speed

The power obtained increases in proportion to the square of the blade radius and the square of the wind speed. WECS in operation today are not able to extract more than 40% of this power although 60% is theoretically possible. Turbines may use a horizontal axis rotor mounted at the top of a tower or a vertical axis with the gearing system at ground level. The most common are horizontal axis WECS,

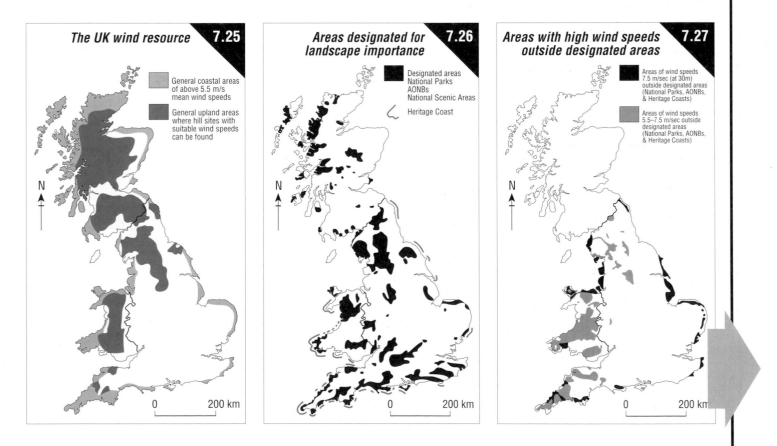

The UK wind resource `7.25`

General coastal areas of above 5.5 m/s mean wind speeds

General upland areas where hill sites with suitable wind speeds can be found

N

0   200 km

Areas designated for landscape importance `7.26`

Designated areas
National Parks
AONBs
National Scenic Areas

Heritage Coast

N

0   200 km

Areas with high wind speeds outside designated areas `7.27`

Areas of wind speeds 7.5 m/sec (at 30m) outside designated areas (National Parks, AONBs, & Heritage Coasts)

Areas of wind speeds 5.5–7.5 m/sec outside designated areas (National Parks, AONBs, & Heritage Coasts)

N

0   200 km

CASE STUDY 7.2 *The environmental impacts of wind power*

7.28 *Types of wind turbines*

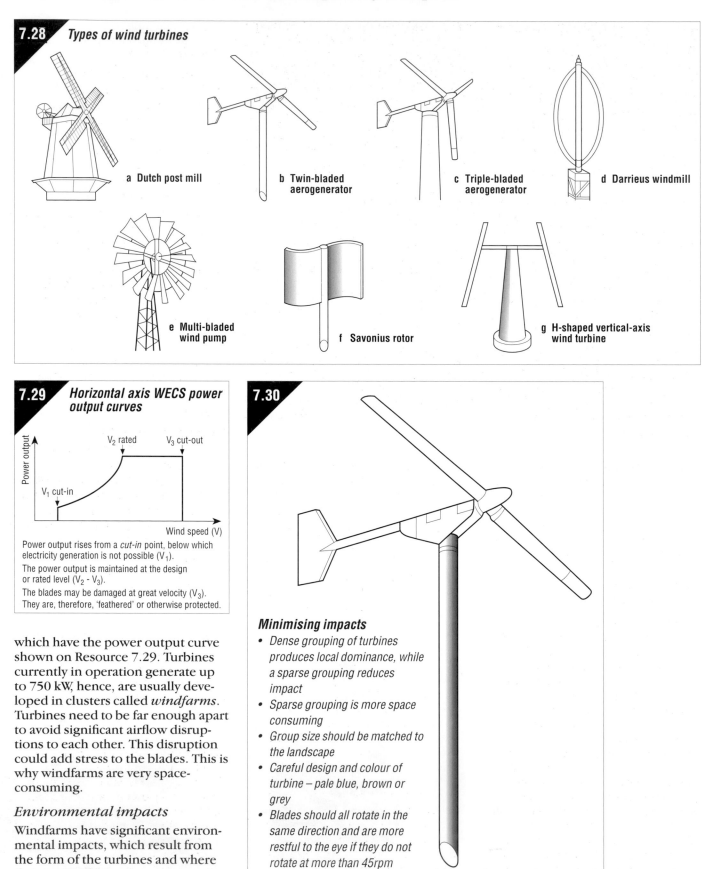

a Dutch post mill

b Twin-bladed aerogenerator

c Triple-bladed aerogenerator

d Darrieus windmill

e Multi-bladed wind pump

f Savonius rotor

g H-shaped vertical-axis wind turbine

7.29 *Horizontal axis WECS power output curves*

Power output rises from a *cut-in* point, below which electricity generation is not possible (V_1).

The power output is maintained at the design or rated level ($V_2 - V_3$).

The blades may be damaged at great velocity (V_3). They are, therefore, 'feathered' or otherwise protected.

7.30

which have the power output curve shown on Resource 7.29. Turbines currently in operation generate up to 750 kW, hence, are usually developed in clusters called *windfarms*. Turbines need to be far enough apart to avoid significant airflow disruptions to each other. This disruption could add stress to the blades. This is why windfarms are very space-consuming.

Environmental impacts

Windfarms have significant environmental impacts, which result from the form of the turbines and where they are sited.

Minimising impacts

- Dense grouping of turbines produces local dominance, while a sparse grouping reduces impact
- Sparse grouping is more space consuming
- Group size should be matched to the landscape
- Careful design and colour of turbine – pale blue, brown or grey
- Blades should all rotate in the same direction and are more restful to the eye if they do not rotate at more than 45rpm

7.31

Wind turbines

Visual impacts are strongest. Turbines can be up to 80 m tall. Most turbines in the UK are 20–30 m high with a blade diameter of 25–30 m. Designs vary but research suggests that people prefer farms with fewer but slightly larger turbines of consistent design and colour. As the Green Party have stated: *a well-designed windmill is beautiful.*

Other environmental factors to consider are noise and safety. Turbines are getting quieter as technology advances, but there is usually a hum and whirr sound around a windfarm. In the Netherlands planning law requires that *new installations should not add to the existing noise level at the nearest dwelling.* If rotor blades break they can be thrown considerable distances, especially in severe weather conditions. The 300–400 m buffer zones regarded as satisfactory for noise and visual purposes are adequate for safety also. Turbine clusters do affect the electromagnetic transmissions of radio, television and radar, by block-ing or scattering the signals. This is another factor which should be considered when locating a windfarm.

Organisations such as the RSPB (Royal Society for the Protection of Birds) are concerned about the dangers to birdlife: that birds will collide with the turbines, and that windfarms will affect migratory paths and local bird habitats. Research shows, however, that birds react quickly and that the danger is minimal.

Policies for windfarms

If the initially favourable attitudes of people towards wind power are to be maintained, then sensitive siting is essential. Guidelines by central government are very general but several organisations and local authorities have established their own criteria for making planning decisions. Resource 7.32 gives three such sets of criteria. The numbers of planning applications have increased steadily since 1990. The Countryside Commission

7.32

Criteria to consider when locating windfarms

Countryside Commission, 1991
- *Should not be permitted within National Parks, AONBs and Heritage Coasts.*
- *Should be a presumption against windfarms near designated areas such as NPs, where their visual appearance would be intrusive.*
- *Should be a presumption against windfarms where their scale, siting or cumulative effect would have a significant adverse impact on the landscape quality and recreational enjoyment thereof.*

Cornwall County Council, 1991
- *Should not significantly affect the visual amenity of a landscape that makes an important contribution to the local environment.*
- *Should not lead to a significant increase in nuisance or risk to the public.*
- *Should not lead to noise levels which would affect the occupiers of nearby properties.*

West Devon Council, 1991
- *Relationship of the proposal to the County Structure Plan.*
- *The appropriateness of the scheme in terms of the scale and nature of the local landscape and conservation areas.*
- *Proximity to inhabited buildings and the likely effect of noise on people and wildlife.*
- *Possible effect on road safety as a result of visual disturbance.*
- *Landscaping proposals to mitigate visual disturbance.*
- *Potential of local economic benefits from the scheme.*
- *The imposition of conditions for the reinstatement of the environment, e.g. trees, should the windfarm cease to operate.*

concentrates on landscape issues and the firm exclusion of wind-farms from designated areas such as national parks. In areas of great landscape value a proposal would only be allowed if it did not *significantly detract from the amenity, landscape, scientific or historic character of these areas.*

7.33 Wind farm plan 'a blot on literary landscape'

The 2,002ft Black Hill, made famous by book and film and visible from five countries, has been suggested as a possible wind farm site where giant rotor-driven turbines could generate electricity for the National Grid.

But the idea has failed to spark any enthusiasm in the Black Mountains communities which lie in the hill's shadow, and its ancient grazing rights are seen as a way of fighting off an unwanted addition to residents' way of life.

The possibility of wind farming on the Black Hill emerged in a letter written by John Williams, who owns the freehold to part of the region in the parish of Llanveynoe.

Copies were sent to the "Graziers" a group of 25 to 30 people who farm on land adjoining the hill and enjoy its grazing rights.

Within the letter are proposals by pioneering wind-farming company Micon to lease land for an initial 15 120ft-high electricity-generation windmills on the Black Hill and a service road running from the Olchon Valley.

Mr Williams wrote that the development plan, to be submitted to the Department of the Environment, would occupy a space of about 450 square yards, which, out of a total of some 2,000 acres, he says would not make a "significant difference" to the amount of grazing available.

A proposal to construct a wind farm on the 200ft high ridge would, it is feared, blight an area loved with equal passion by Britain's literati, local people, and city dwellers searching for peace.

Dismay at the prospect of 15 120ft masts topped with huge propellers invading the hill is unconfined. The 30 graziers who exercise ancient rights to raise sheep and ponies on the Black Hill are slow to anger. But now they're up in arms.

The Power family has worked Black Hill farm for almost a century.

"There's a site of special scientific interest up there," says Neville Powell. "It's one of the most wonderful places in the world. A wind farm would ruin the area."

At her cottage in the hamlet of Craswall, Christine Cleaton concurs: "The thought of huge windmills dominating such a famous skyline is quite absurd."

[*The Guardian* 7.2.94]
[*Hereford Times*, 3.2.94]

Wind power – subsidy is temptation for developers

The turbines proposed for the Black Hill would roughly equal the height of Hereford Cathedral's tower (167 ft).

The problem with wind power, as it is implemented at present, is that private developers are offered a tempting guaranteed subsidy and can try for planning permission for any site, regardless of its position, designation, etc., suitably high wind speed being the paramount consideration.

Many of these industrial developments are proposed for isolated or remote land which has changed over the centuries only through minimal use by man. These areas are the closest thing to wilderness that we have in this country, the Black Hill being a prime local example.

Can we justify all these green field sites (and there will have to be a great many to even approach the 10 per cent generating capacity figure that government is looking at) and the loss of our landscape heritage for the generation of what will, of necessity, be a tiny percentage of our electricity needs?

Twenty turbines, it has been estimated, could provide about 0.0052 per cent of the nation's current needs.

Christine Cleaton
Fir Tree Cottage, Craswall.
[*Hereford Times*, 9.6.94]

Blow to hopes for wind farms

Simon Beavis
Industrial Editor

The Government is expected to curb the number of wind farms in the face of protests that they mar the countryside, and evidence of a big increase in the number of projects being submitted for funding.

The Department of Trade and Industry's latest renewable-energy round – under which subsidies are set to go to 300–400 megawatts of power from alternative sources – is thought to have attracted up to 20 times the number of wind-farm proposals allowed for.

Tim Eggar, the Energy Minister, is alarmed at the number of objections to proposed wind farms by groups who claim that their turbines impose noise and visual blight on the landscape. The DTI has been inundated with protests as part of a campaign at local and national level orchestrated primarily by a group called the Country Guardians.

Mr Eggar said he proposed to select renewable projects from six bands to be considered for development helped by special subsidies under the Non-Fossil Fuel Obligation, the NFFO.

Apart from wind, the bands included waste incineration, hydro-electric schemes and landfill gas. Mr Eggar stressed his interest in other renewable forms, particularly coppicing – harvesting quick-growing trees for use in power stations.

The NFFO obliges the 12 regional electricity companies to buy a proportion of their power from costlier non-fossil sources.

[*The Guardian*, 9.3.94]

Reality of wind power noise

I would like to explain what it is like to live near a wind power station. I understand that there are several planned for Herefordshire or the Borders. I have no axe to grind and am not a NIMBY

I, like many of our neighbours, supported the application for the site at Llandinam, in Mid-Wales, feeling that it would be good for the environment, being a keen environmentalist. I felt that the visual impact was a price worth paying, for the supply of infinite, clean, power. We were also assured that the site would not be audible to nearby dwellings.

That was the myth; the reality is totally different. The noise has at times been unbearable, so much so, that at times we can hear it indoors with double glazing. We cannot open windows at night for fear of disturbed sleep. It would appear that the noise theory, regarding windfarms, is based on flat ground coming from Denmark. It relies on masking of turbine noise, which works when up on the site, but in the valleys surrounding the site, there is no wind and therefore no masking.

The developers have been monitoring now for almost a year and despite assurances that the problem can be solved, nothing has changed. This is a story repeated at many other sites around the country. First the initial promise that noise would not be a problem, then when it is, the assurance that it will be resolved and then nothing and still the noise.

Our site is clearly audible up to 2.5 miles away. The DTI is also taking a keen interest in this, through the Energy Technical Support Unit (ETSU), to try and understand the problem better, but admits that there is no way to predict noise levels accurately.

C.D. Lord-Smith
Y Craig,
Llidiart-y-Waun,
Llanidloes,
Powys
[*Hereford Times*, 24.2.94]

Windfarms are a controversial issue

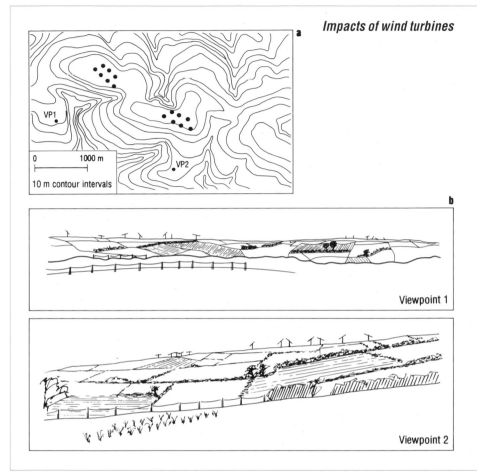

Impacts of wind turbines

a

b

Viewpoint 1

Viewpoint 2

VP1

VP2

0   1000 m

10 m contour intervals

The plan shows the two clusters of turbines (a) and the sketches impressions from selected viewpoints about 1 km distance (b). The key points are:

* closer spacing of turbines allows them to be arranged in two groups which are sufficiently far apart to be viewed as separate entities;
* there is less area domination as a result of the degree of clear space between the groups;
* the smaller number of turbines in each groups results in less clutter;
* it should be possible to relate the more manageable number of turbines in each group to the existing structure of the landscape;
* the distance between the groups is critical - if it is too little, the impact will increase;
* the technique could be applicable to larger wind farms.

The technique appears to be useful both for assessing the theoretical impact and for testing various options to ensure the best landscape fit. The technique would be expected to form part of the overall visual analysis to be supplememnted by photomontages.

[Source: LUP 1993]

Criteria used in an EIA and EIS

Visual impacts
Noise
Electromagnetic interference
Flora and fauna
Archaeology
Shadow flicker (produced as blades rotate)
Safety
Mitigation proposals (suggestions for reducing impact)
Agriculture
Site selection, including evaluation of alternatives
Wind resources – direction, strength, consistency
Landscape survey to establish character and quality
Roads – visual impacts from roads especially
Policy framework (relationship to planning policy)
Benefits (environmental and developer)

Conducting an environmental survey

CASE STUDY 7.2 *The environmental impacts of wind power*

Despite the evidence from surveys, even outside such designated areas, the possible arrival of a windfarm generates considerable opposition.

Since 1988 major planning applications are required to submit an accompanying Environmental Impact Statement (EIS) based upon an Environmental Impact Assessment (EIA). As yet, windfarm applications are not required to have an EIS but many do submit them. Resource 7.34 lists the principal aspects covered in an EIA survey which may be carried out by independent consultants employed by the developers.

A central feature of assessing the level of impact is the estimation of the *zone of influence*, or the area to be affected by the windfarm. This will vary according to the number and distribution of the turbines, the character of the environment and the required landscape modification to reduce impact. For safety needs, a zone of 400 m radius is standard, a distance used also for shadow flicker. The noise zone may extend up to two kilometres. Strong visual impacts are common up to two kilometres although large clusters may be intrusive for up to six. For large clusters on exposed sites such as the Penrhyddlan-Llidiartywaun scheme, the EIA used a 20 km zone. The figures emphasise the need for careful siting.

[Based on: Coles R.W. and Taylor J. 'Wind power and planning', *Land use policy*, 10(3), July 1993, 205–226]

Activities

The oblique aerial photograph (Resource 7.37) and the OS map extract (Resource 7.38) cover approximately the same area in eastern Wales. The small settlement is Whitton and the broad valley that of the upper R. Lugg. The summit of the distant ridge is Hawthorne Hill (407mOD). The National Trail (long distance footpath) of Offa's Dyke runs along the slopes of the ridge.

1 Study the photo and map carefully, and write a description of the landscape.

7.37

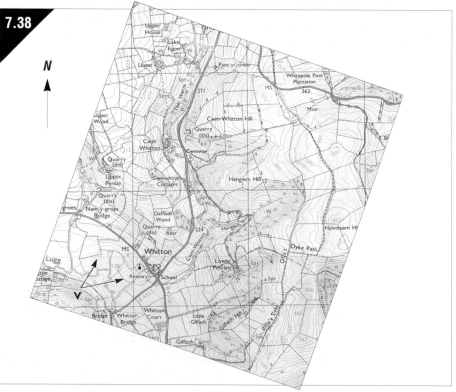

7.38

2 Using the criteria identified in the Case Study, select a location for a windfarm of 10–15 turbines.

3 Produce a brief report supporting your selected location.

CASE STUDY 7.3 *Is HEP generation a good thing?*

Background

Hydro-electric power schemes are sustainable in that they use a renewable, free resource which creates minimal pollution and which generates 'clean' energy at economic prices. However, they have great environmental impact because of their massive structures and large reservoirs, often sited in areas of outstanding environmental quality. Whether the artificial lakes enhance or detract from the beauty is debatable. A reservoir may drown an ecosystem or a farming landscape, for example, but has beauty and recreational potential. Social and political dimensions are likely to affect the issue when the river passes through or provides a boundary between several different countries.

One such complex controversy has simmered and periodically erupted for more than 40 years along the middle Danube river, where it forms the boundary between Slovakia and Hungary. The controversy centres upon the Gabcikovo-Nagymaros scheme, an important element of a series which is progressively turning the Danube into a fully-controlled system. Despite the inevitable

political and economic arguments, the governments of Hungary and Czechoslovakia signed an agreement for the project in 1977, after more than 20 years of discussion and dispute. Even then, political and environmental campaigns continued to delay the project, which was further held up by the political upheavals in central and eastern Europe during the late 1980s and early 1990s. The break-up of the Communist system and of Czechoslovakia, which became the separate nations of Slovakia and the Czech Republic in 1993, added to the tensions. It was not until 1993 that the first energy was produced from the project.

This case study highlights the issues arising from the choice of generation system selected and the social and environmental implications of this choice. It is an excellent example of the differences between natural channel-floodplain interactions and human-made hydrological systems. It illustrates that a river basin functions as an open system: changes in the input-throughput and output balance in one section, affect sections downstream.

The Gabcikovo-Nagymaros scheme of the middle Danube Basin

The setting

In 1977, Hungary and Czechoslovakia signed an agreement to build two HEP stations on the middle Danube, one at Gabcikovo and the other, downstream at Nagymaros. Political, social, ecological and hydrological issues have

---

Key understandings

◆ Middle and lower sections of river basins may create problems for HEP generation which requires high energy discharge.

◆ Diversion channel HEP schemes increase available water energy but can severely disrupt river basin hydrology. Environmental Impact Assessments are essential at an early stage.

◆ Where rivers act as international boundaries, water management schemes may cause conflicts and need careful negotiation at all stages of the development.

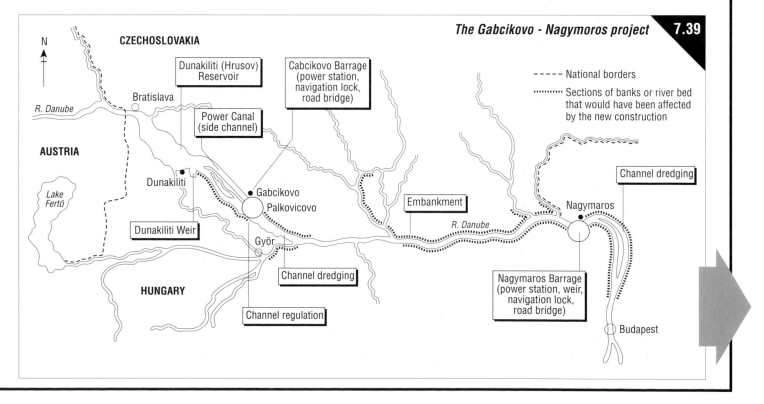

The Gabcikovo - Nagymaros project   7.39

- - - - National borders

·········· Sections of banks or river bed that would have been affected by the new construction

CASE STUDY 7.3 *Is HEP generation a good thing?*

centred around the Gabcikovo project, because it is sited in the stretch where the river is the shared boundary. The Nagymaros project, on the other hand, lies within the Hungarian borders.

The demand for electricity by the neighbouring countries is not in doubt. HEP generation requires reliable high-energy water flows. In mountainous regions of upper drainage basins these qualities may be available naturally, and can be readily enhanced by dams and reservoirs in the steep-sided valleys and gorges. The twin principles of dams and their reservoirs are to raise the 'head' of water, so creating higher-velocity discharge through the turbines, and to provide a store of water so that discharge can be matched to the level of energy demand.

In the middle and lower reaches of a river basin, the topography and flow may offer more complicated opportunities. For example, when the upper Danube passes through Austria, it falls 50 m for each 100 km distance downstream. In its middle section, where the river forms the Hungary-Slovak border, the 50 m fall covers 417 km. Furthermore, the river is flowing mainly in a broad floodplain, making the tall dam and reservoir solution impractical. Resource 7.38 illustrates the basic options for increasing the available energy:

- to straighten and so shorten the river course.
- to raise the water level, while ensuring a store of water.

The project
The Gabcikovo-Nagymaros project has adopted these principles by using the model of Resource 7.38. It has used a diversionary or side channel to straighten and shorten the river course and a barrage or weir to raise the water level and create a controlled store. The side channel, with its ovoid shape and asphalt bed and banks is much smoother than the original bed. Less energy is utilised in overcoming

frictional drag, thereby increasing the velocity.

Resource 7.40 shows the details of the project. Water is diverted at Hrusov into a 17 km channel with a design capacity of 4000 cumecs. At the Gabcikovo power station the head of water, that is, the height above the turbines, varies from 16 to 21.5 m, depending upon the discharge volume. The side channel,

however, is unable to cope with fluctuations in demand. Daily peaks occur in the morning and late afternoon, and drop markedly during the night. In order to control the releases through the side channel to match demand fluctuations, a broad barrage or weir has been built at Hrusov. This raises the water level and creates Dunakiliti Reservoir, which is shallow but broad.

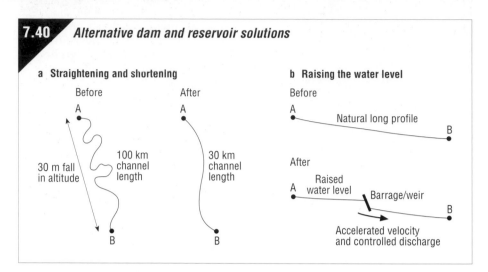

7.40 *Alternative dam and reservoir solutions*

a Straightening and shortening

Before — A, 30 m fall in altitude, 100 km channel length, B

After — A, 30 km channel length, B

b Raising the water level

Before — A, Natural long profile, B

After — A, Raised water level, Barrage/weir, Accelerated velocity and controlled discharge, B

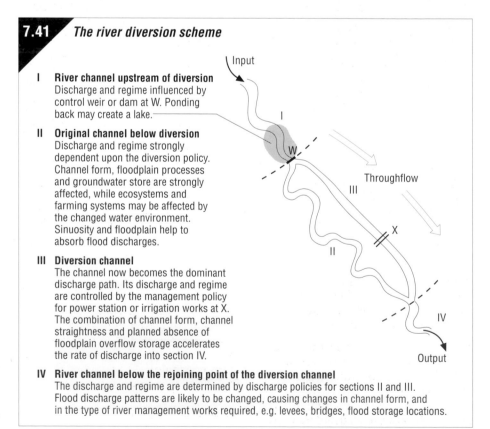

7.41 *The river diversion scheme*

Input

I River channel upstream of diversion
Discharge and regime influenced by control weir or dam at W. Ponding back may create a lake.

II Original channel below diversion
Discharge and regime strongly dependent upon the diversion policy. Channel form, floodplain processes and groundwater store are strongly affected, while ecosystems and farming systems may be affected by the changed water environment. Sinuosity and floodplain help to absorb flood discharges.

III Diversion channel
The channel now becomes the dominant discharge path. Its discharge and regime are controlled by the management policy for power station or irrigation works at X. The combination of channel form, channel straightness and planned absence of floodplain overflow storage accelerates the rate of discharge into section IV.

IV River channel below the rejoining point of the diversion channel
The discharge and regime are determined by discharge policies for sections II and III. Flood discharge patterns are likely to be changed, causing changes in channel form, and in the type of river management works required, e.g. levees, bridges, flood storage locations.

Throughflow

Output

7.42

Gabcikovo dam and power station on the Danube

7.43

The River Danube, Esztergom, Hungary

It has a capacity of almost 200 million cubic metres. The barrage also controls the release into the original Danube channel.

The Danube is an important route for freight and pleasure boats. Lock systems need to be built to bypass the power stations and barrages, and water levels must be maintained in all stretches of the channel to allow safe navigation. Even when there is no demand for power from the Gabcikovo turbines, the side channel discharge, through which all boats will pass, must be maintained. Similarly, the water level must be sustained in the 115 km stretch between Medvedov and Nagymaros. This is facilitated by the barrage control at Nagymaros.

Swelling chorus of Danube blues

7.44

Vera Rich

Tension is rising in Hungary as the deadline looms for Slovakia to divert the River Danube to feed the controversial Gabcikovo dam. A test run of one of the dam's turbines brought renewed protest from Hungarian greens, who fear their government will end its opposition to the scheme.

Gabcikovo and a dam at Nagymaros in Hungary were conceived as examples of socialist cooperation between Czechoslovakia and Hungary. But hostility to the scheme was a key issue for the Hungarian opposition movements of the 1980s. In 1990, when Jozsef Antall came to power, he cancelled work at Nagymaros and lobbied the Czechoslovaks to cancel Gabcikovo.

[*New Scientist*, 26.9.92]

The issues

The Nagymaros scheme has created little political controversy because the Danube does not form an international boundary in this stretch. It lies entirely within the borders of Hungary. In the Hrusov-Gabcikovo stretch, on the other hand, the river is the boundary between Slovakia and Hungary. The main concern of the Hungarians throughout the long controversy has been that Hungary loses while Slovakia gains. The side channel diversion lies entirely within Slovak territory, even though the power generated at Gabcikovo is shared. The Danube has been part of Hungarian culture for centuries. In losing contact with it, the Hungarians feel dispossessed. Many are upset to witness the great river reduced to a 'canal'.

The hydrological and environmental effects of the diversion has also aroused concern. Up to 4000 cumecs could be diverted via the Gabcikovo power station. In October 1992 (the period of lowest discharge) the Slovak authorities began to divert the water flow into the side channel so that engineering

CASE STUDY 7.3 *Is HEP generation a good thing?*

works associated with the change could take place. During 1993 the first power was generated at Gabcikovo.

A computer modelling programme has been carried out to simulate the changes at five gauging stations, A–E on Resource 7.43. Resource 7.44 summarises the results.

At Hrusov (B), the mean annual flow was 2045 cumecs, but once the diversion and power generation is in full production, the mean annual flow down the original channel will be only 82 cumecs. This is reflected in the 'before' and 'after' data at station C, lower down the original channel. The mean annual flow at the Gabcikovo power station (D) will be 1845 cumecs. When the waters are returned to the original Danube channel below Gabcikovo, the flow at Medvedov gauging station (E) will be 1927 cumecs. The loss from station B (2045 cumecs) is accounted for by infiltration, agricultural take-off and evaporation. These and the other figures in the table show that:

- the flow through the original channel will be severely reduced.
- substantial flow through this original channel will be restricted to high-flow season only.

The effects of the difference in channel form and river behaviour between the old, sinuous river channel and the new diversion channel is illustrated in Resource 7.45. The figures given here are computer model estimates of the peak discharge patterns during a 100-year flood, that is, a flood volume which is likely to recur once every 100 years. The four rows of the table (i)–(iv) are differentiated by the water diversion policies adopted by the managers. Column D shows the volumes being diverted and passing through the Gabcikovo power plant. Thus, under scenario (i), the maximum permitted discharge of 4000 cumecs is being routed along the diversion channel. This volume is progressively reduced through scenarios (ii)–(iv).

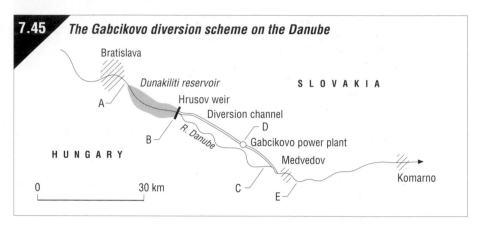

7.45 The Gabcikovo diversion scheme on the Danube

7.46 Changes in mean discharge (m³/sec)

Site	B Before	B After	C Before	C After	D After	E After
Annual	2045	82	2045	82	1845	1927
June (high flow)	2840	130	2828	129	2478	2578
November (low flow)	1460	53	1456	53	1289	1342
Daily max.	5330	1392	5065	1257	3891	5148
Daily min.	887	50	887	50	748	798

[from: Szolgay, Vienna 1991]

7.47 Peak discharges during a 100 year flood (m³/sec)

Site	A	B	C	B – C	D	E
i	10600	10078	5492	6078	4000	9492
ii	10600	10078	6430	7078	3000	9430
iii	10600	10078	7369	8078	2000	9369
iv	10600	10078	8311	9078	1000	9311

[from: Scoboda, Vienna 1991]

The input at sites A and B remain the same. The variations occur downstream from B. Thus, if we follow situation (i), of the 10 078 cumecs passing the barrage at Hrusov (site B), 4000 cumecs are diverted into the new channel, leaving 6078 cumecs to enter the old river channel (columns B–C). By the time this flow has reached site C, however, it has been reduced to 5492 cumecs. This can be attributed to the infiltration from bank seepage (water infiltrating into the groundwater from the channel bed and banks), and from water spilled out over the floodplain. Almost 500 cumecs are lost to the river by this process before site C is reached.

In contrast, there is little loss along the constructed diversion channel, which is asphalt-lined and embanked to prevent flooding. Finally, 9492 cumecs arrive at Medvedov (site E) and flow on downstream.

It is column E of the table which reveals the key understanding: that use of the diversion channel increases the likelihood of flooding in the stretch of the River Danube below Medvedov.

Under natural conditions, bank recharge and periodic flooding have sustained a high water table beneath the floodplain. This has facilitated water supply for villages and farms, and has also supported important wetlands and forests of high conservation value. The transfer of water into the asphalt-lined diversion channel will reduce these groundwater recharge mechanisms. The water table will fall, causing desiccation of the wetlands and woodlands, making water supply more difficult.

Activities

1 Explain why the diversion channel technique for HEP generation has been selected along the middle Danube.

2 What hydrological changes does the Gabcikovo-Nagymaros scheme cause?

3 Outline the economic, social and environmental benefits and costs of the scheme.

4 Why are the Hungarians particularly angered by the scheme?

5 How could the hydrological impacts upon the floodplain be modified?

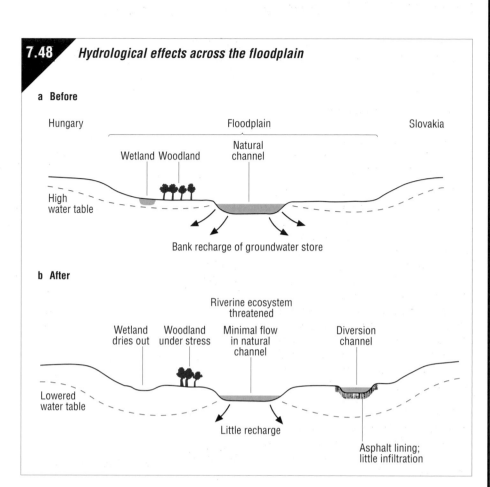

7.48 *Hydrological effects across the floodplain*

a **Before**

Hungary — Floodplain — Slovakia

Wetland Woodland

Natural channel

High water table

Bank recharge of groundwater store

b **After**

Riverine ecosystem threatened

Wetland dries out

Woodland under stress

Minimal flow in natural channel

Diversion channel

Lowered water table

Little recharge

Asphalt lining; little infiltration

CHAPTER 8

Management in quality environments

Introduction

World population is approaching five billion and each person has growing demands and expectations. Competition for global resources intensifies. Development pressures push farther across land masses and into the oceans, leaving few places unaffected. As the impacts of human activities spread, we are increasingly aware of the beauty and value of many threatened environments. Deciding how to protect and restore such precious landscapes while gaining use from them is a central issue for resource managers.

- The remaining areas where substantial natural or near-natural ecosystems survive should be protected for their own sake. This view claims that all living species have an equal right to continued existence, and that humans as ecological dominants, must act as their stewards and guardians.

- We must retain such ecosystems in order to maintain the biodiversity of the planet and so protect the long-term future.

- It is our duty to apply technological expertise to optimise the use of global resources. Only in this way can we ensure an acceptable quality of life for the expanding billions of people.

Who has the right to make decisions concerning priorities for their conservation and development? The issues of ownership and rights dominate this discussion. For example, Antarctica is the only continent which does not have a history of human settlement. It is not subdivided into parcels which are 'owned' by individual countries. Seven countries, including Britain, have territorial claims, but there is no international recognition of ownership. Environmentalists battle to have the whole continent declared a 'World Park'. Scientists campaign for it to become a global laboratory, dedicated to scientific research. Individual governments and multinational corporations see Antarctica as a set of resources to be developed. Meanwhile, in 1993, over 6500 tourists paid an average of £5000 each to visit the fringes of Antarctica, and there are already signs of ecological stress on plants

The Grand Tetons

and breeding colonies of penguins and seals.

Few areas seem likely to be assured of a long-term future based on their 'existence values' alone. Realistic strategies are based on sustainability, where conservation and development priorities are balanced. Use and yield are achieved without substantially degrading the environment and resource base over time. Governments and communities need to be persuaded that it is worth their while to protect and conserve natural resources and traditional cultural environments. The rights of indigenous peoples whose economy and cultures depend upon such resources must be respected. The skill in planning and management of such resources is to balance conservation, economic benefit and cultural values.

The issues raised in the case studies of this chapter allow us to consider the concepts of *ownership, control, values, priorities* and *power* in decision-making and management. These are all central to the issues raised in Case Study 8.1, which discusses the planning application to develop a huge quarry in a beautiful part of the Outer Hebrides, Scotland. The materials illustrate that environmental controversies can have distinctive perspectives at local, regional and national scales. Case Study 8.2, from Tasmania, illustrates how a region given the highest conservation status as a World Conservation Area can be managed to achieve conservation goals while allowing recreational use and economic return. The final three case studies, 8.3 to 8.5, make up a set which examine separate aspects of the resource development of Alaska. Case Study 8.3 concerns the introduction of a sustainable management strategy for the fish resources of Prince William Sound in western Alaska. In the light of the over-fishing of so many of the world's oceans, this has a particular urgency. Case Study 8.4 focuses upon ownership, control and political power. The indigenous peoples of Alaska have for centuries based their cultures and economies upon the use of natural resources. Today these rights and their way of life are under threat. Priorities, values and power as factors influencing resource management are highlighted in case Study 8.5. The conservation of wildlife and ecosystems comes into direct conflict with the exploitation of oil resources along the North Slope of Alaska, in the Arctic National Wildlife Reserve.

CASE STUDY 8.1 *Do 14 lanes of the M25 = a hole in the Hebrides?*

Background

Proposals to extend road networks, build new settlements, shopping centres and business parks arouse frequent protests and campaigns against their environmental impacts. The Twyford Down campaign against the M3 extension rumbled on from the late 1980s until 1993. These large-scale projects often make enormous resource demands on space and raw materials, such as mineral aggregates. For example, one mile of motorway consumes 200 000 tonnes of rock. Throughout Britain, some of the toughest environmental campaigns have been and are being fought over hard rock, sand and gravel resources for the construction industry. These include limestone quarrying in the Peak District National Park, and planning applications for extensions to sand and gravel working in the Thames Valley. Once a construction project starts and the source of raw materials is

agreed, the heavy lorry traffic generated by linking supply and demand, that is, the quarry to the site, generates considerable environmental impact.

In 1976, a government report called *Aggregates: The Way Ahead* examined future needs and alternatives for meeting this demand. This report, known as the Verney Report, stated that development pressures were greatest in south-east England, but that by the early 1990s this

---

8.2 Resource attributes of construction raw materials

- Sporadic not ubiquitous, i.e. scattered not universal in location
- Bulky, making heavy transport demands
- Finite
- Non-renewable
- Involve extraction methods which have great impact
- Vary in character according to use

---

region would have used up most of its own resources. The report identified the environmental costs of drawing supplies from a dispersed pattern of quarries and transporting the raw materials by road, especially in already crowded regions. Two key recommendations were that a national mineral aggregates strategy should be drawn up, and that an increasing proportion of mineral supply should be obtained from a small number of coastal superquarries, allowing bulk transportation by sea. In 1994, the issue was still not resolved.

A *superquarry* is defined as a coastal development capable of producing between one and ten million tonnes a year, with associated docking and loading facilities for bulk carrier vessels to transport all of the mineral output. The proven reserves must be at least 20 million tonnes, and the site should have a production life of at least 60 years. (The construction

---

8.3 *Digging for Britain*

The Mendip Hills are being carved into canyons and the heart of the countryside is being ripped out. Merehead quarry, run by Foster Yeoman, covers 400 acres (250 football pitches) and is one of Europe's biggest holes in the ground. One million tonnes of stone wait in a corner to be used on approach roads to the new Severn bridge.

Most big aggregate companies operate from the Mendips, now the most heavily quarried area in Europe. ARC, Wimpey, ECC and Foster Yeoman together produce 10 million tonnes of stone each year. There are rail links, but quarrying here generates up to 4,000 lorry movements a day.

The Department of the Environment believes the annual demand for "primary aggregates" (including crushed stone, sand and gravel) could more than double in the next 20 years, rising to as much as 440 million tonnes a year by 2011. A quarter of this will go to build new roads. One estimate is that the £23-billion National Roads Programme will consume the output of 110 average-sized quarries.

Further fuel to the debate will come with the imminent publication of revised government guidelines on aggregates extraction, known as MPG6. These will set quarrying production targets for different regions of the country, as well as environmental "constraints".

In the Mendips, the issue is as much about survival as sustainability. So much rock has been excavated that quarry workings have reached well below the water table, affecting the aquifer that supplies drinking water to nearby towns. Even the flow to Bath's famous spa is said to be under threat.

"There are already nearly 40 years' supply of rock in the pipeline from current permissions in the Mendips," says Friends of the Earth's Richard Dixon. "We want Somerset County Council to set a date for a cessation of quarrying, an end to blowing up the countryside."

While accepting that there is "quite a large land bank of existing permissions", council officials argue that these don't necessarily fit well with modern environmental constraints. But the council, as Minerals Planning Authority, also has its hands tied. under MPG6 it is likely to receive a demand for a massive 50 per cent increase in its contribution of construction aggregates, from 20 to 30 million tonnes each year.

One suggested solution to the crisis, supported by the government though not by all sections of the industry, is to shift the problem overseas. This means Spain, Norway – and Scotland.

An analysis of the draft MPG6 suggests that there could be up to six "super-quarries" around the Scottish coastline –

massive excavations destroying whole hillsides to supply the hungry south-east of England and other markets. Only one has been built so far. But already the markers are out on the island of South Harris, where a public inquiry is now due, and at several other sites, including one near Glencoe.

"Nobody wants a quarry in their backyard in England," says Kevin Dunion of Friends of the Earth Scotland. "But Scotland is expected to produce up to four times its own demand to keep the English happy."

A broad consensus of environmental and conservation groups argues that aggregate quarrying must be curtailed at source. One way would be to severely limit the way projected demand for aggregates is used to "land bank" permissions for years ahead.

Limiting supply would also have an important economic effect, increasing the cost of aggregates and forcing more careful use. At present, about 10 per cent of construction materials are wasted on site.

Another approach is to increase use of secondary or recycled materials, exploiting the millions of tonnes of stockpiled china clay, coal mining and slate quarry wastes.

[*The Guardian*, 25.2.94]

industry favours sites with potential life-spans as low as 25 years.) Superquarries are massive, environmentally-powerful developments, which inevitably arouse violently opposed views.

This case study examines the issues surrounding a superquarry proposal on the Isle of Harris, Outer Hebrides, Scotland. The issues bring into sharp focus the clash of economic, cultural and environmental values and priorities. Harris is one of the most beautiful environments in Britain, with firmly-held cultural traditions, yet is facing severe economic problems. The case study is fairly long, but the issue is complex. Study the prososal itself first, then absorb the issues and viewpoints, before attempting an assessment.

Key understandings

◆ Demand for mineral aggregates will continue to be greatest in central and southern England, where supply is most limited.

◆ Scotland has considerable potential for coastal superquarries.

◆ The main supply alternatives are either many dispersed inland quarries which generate heavy road traffic, or a small number of coastal superquarries with bulk transport by sea.

◆ In a small and beautiful environment such as the Isle of Harris, the Lingerbay superquarry would cause severe economic, social, cultural and environmental impacts, both benefits and costs.

◆ Local opinion is widely divided over the benefits and costs.

◆ The local community feels they should be more involved in the decision-making, especially concerning the economic benefits and the issue of Sunday observance, which is a deeply held element of the Hebridean culture.

◆ There is no single 'right' answer to the issue which has local, Scottish and British dimensions.

The superquarry dilemma on the Isle of Harris, Outer Hebrides

Context

In 1991, Redland Aggregates submitted a planning application to the Western Isles Islands Council for mineral extraction at Lingerbay, on the Isle of Harris. The project would involve the extraction of 600 million tonnes of anorthosite, a hard, ancient igneous rock with excellent properties for construction aggregate.

In 1980, a government-sponsored report highlighted Scotland as possessing Britain's greatest potential for coastal superquarries yielding hardrock minerals. Of 25 sites identified, the only Grade 1 (highest grade) site was at Lingerbay. Since 1986, Scotland has had a superquarry at Glensanda on the Morvern Peninsula, which is extracting over five million tonnes a year and shipping it by fairly small bulk carrier vessels. It employs between 130 and 150 people. In the early 1990s, of the approximately 60 million tonnes of crushed rock consumed by south-east England, almost two million tonnes came from Scotland. A government forecast suggests that by the year 2006, this will need to rise to seven million tonne a year to help supply a regional demand of 77 million tonnes.

In 1992, two government documents identified:

- the inevitably growing demands.
- the increasing inability of England to supply the needs.
- the potential sites in north-west Europe, including Scotland.

Once on board a bulk carrier, the crushed rock can be shipped to many markets economically.

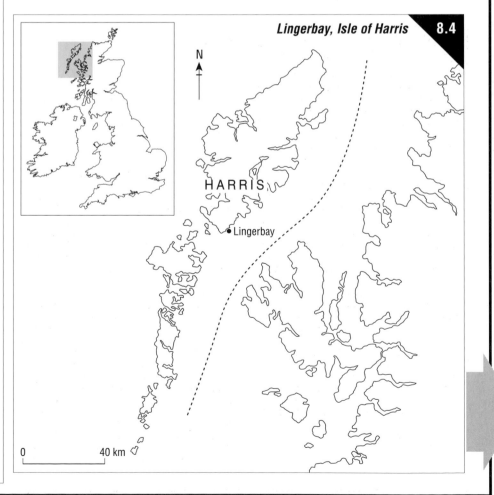

Lingerbay, Isle of Harris 8.4

HARRIS

● Lingerbay

N

0   40 km

CASE STUDY 8.1 *Do 14 lanes of the M25 = a hole in the Hebrides?*

The Glensanda Quarry

Quarry site

Many transnational construction companies are subsequently showing strong interest in Scotland's hardrock resources.

There are some existing small quarries on the Lingerbay site, dating back to planning permissions granted in 1966, 1974, 1976 and 1981. In planning decisions 'precedent' and 'existing use' are powerful arguments, but the 1991 proposal is a project on quite a different scale.

The plan

The Redland plan is to extract 600 million tonnes of anorthosite over a period of 60 years from the southeast flank of Beinn na h Aire hill. During the first ten years production will build up to the planned maximum of ten million tonnes per year. The rock will be crushed and graded on site and loaded from purpose-built jetties into bulk carrier ships. The progressive environmental changes are summarised on the four maps of Resources 8.7 to 8.10. Throughout, the impacts are of three types:

* the ever-growing hole in the hill.
* the buildings, infrastructure and material heaps.
* the land and sea traffic generated.

The Redland application sets out how the company claims it will reduce disturbance and pollution to a minimum, for example, all crushing to be enclosed to reduce dust pollution; noise levels to be carefully monitored; water to be recycled or treated before release; ship movements and waste discharging to be strictly controlled.

The public debate

During 1992, the Redlands company and the planning committee held a series of public meetings and exhibitions to present the plan and to allow public discussion. The primary concerns focused on:

1 the lack of detail in some elements of the plan.
2 the small amount of money offered by the company as a Trust Fund for the community as compensation for the development.

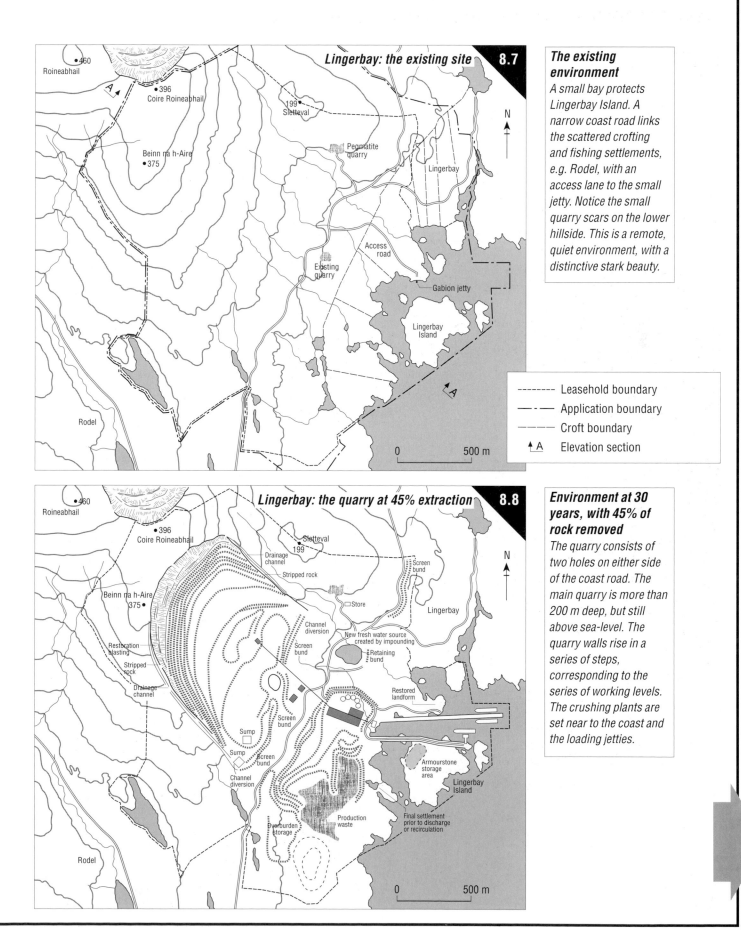

Lingerbay: the existing site 8.7

Roineabhail •460

•396
Coire Roineabhail

199• Sletteval

Beinn na h-Aire •375

Pegmatite quarry

Lingerbay

Access road

Existing quarry

Gabion jetty

Lingerbay Island

Rodel

N

A

— — — — — Leasehold boundary

— · — · — Application boundary

— - — - — Croft boundary

▲ A Elevation section

0   500 m

The existing environment

A small bay protects Lingerbay Island. A narrow coast road links the scattered crofting and fishing settlements, e.g. Rodel, with an access lane to the small jetty. Notice the small quarry scars on the lower hillside. This is a remote, quiet environment, with a distinctive stark beauty.

Lingerbay: the quarry at 45% extraction 8.8

Roineabhail •460

•396
Coire Roineabhail

Sletteval 199

Drainage channel

Stripped rock

Screen bund

Store

Lingerbay

Beinn na h-Aire 375 •

Restoration blasting

Stripped rock

Drainage channel

Channel diversion

New fresh water source created by impounding

Retaining bund

Screen bund

Screen bund

Sump

Sump

Screen bund

Channel diversion

Screen bund

Restored landform

Overburden storage

Production waste

Final settlement prior to discharge or recirculation

Armourstone storage area

Lingerbay Island

Rodel

N

0   500 m

Environment at 30 years, with 45% of rock removed

The quarry consists of two holes on either side of the coast road. The main quarry is more than 200 m deep, but still above sea-level. The quarry walls rise in a series of steps, corresponding to the series of working levels. The crushing plants are set near to the coast and the loading jetties.

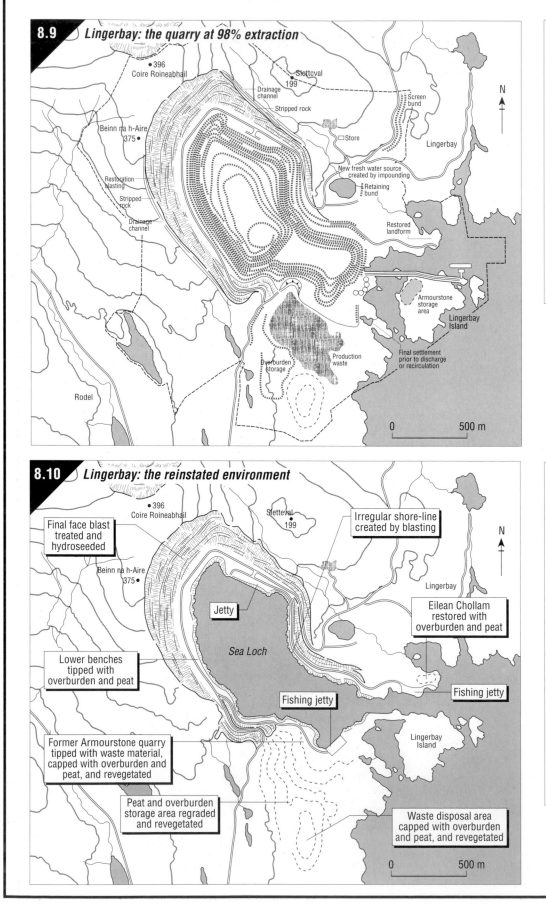

8.9 *Lingerbay: the quarry at 98% extraction*

- 396 Coire Roineabhail
- Slotteval 199
- Beinn na h-Aire 375
- Drainage channel
- Stripped rock
- Screen bund
- Store
- Lingerbay
- Restoration blasting
- Stripped rock
- Drainage channel
- New fresh water source created by impounding
- Retaining bund
- Restored landform
- Rodel
- Overburden storage
- Production waste
- Final settlement prior to discharge or recirculation
- Armourstone storage area
- Lingerbay Island
- 0   500 m
- N

The full quarry impact, with 98% of the rock removed

One 'super-hole', descends 145 m below sea-level, and cut back to the summit of Beinn na h Aire, giving a vertical section of 515 m. Notice the intended environmental restoration, e.g. along the quarry headwall; coastal landforms; one jetty removed. The coast road is diverted around the quarry flanks.

8.10 *Lingerbay: the reinstated environment*

- 396 Coire Roineabhail
- Slotteval 199
- Irregular shore-line created by blasting
- Final face blast treated and hydroseeded
- Beinn na h-Aire 375
- Jetty
- Lingerbay
- Eilean Chollam restored with overburden and peat
- Sea Loch
- Lower benches tipped with overburden and peat
- Fishing jetty
- Fishing jetty
- Former Armourstone quarry tipped with waste material, capped with overburden and peat, and revegetated
- Lingerbay Island
- Peat and overburden storage area regraded and revegetated
- Waste disposal area capped with overburden and peat, and revegetated
- 0   500 m
- N

Environment after restoration, at least 60 years ahead

A spectacular sea-loch is created by blasting a gap to allow seawater to flood the quarry. Landscaping and restoration works aim to give a 'natural' look of the area. This is a good example of the requirement that all major extractive projects must include in their initial planning proposals a fully detailed plan of how the environment will be reinstated and restored after production ceases.

(There is the Shetlands precedent wherein the islanders have amassed a substantial trust fund from the oil companies in return for the location of massive onshore facilities in connection with the North Sea oilfields.)

3 the number of jobs which would go to local people and the amount of income generated.
4 the environmental disturbance.
5 the unwillingness of the company to guarantee no Sunday working and so respect the Sabbath.

In June 1993 the Western Isles Council agreed to support the planning application, providing that additional conditions were met by the company. The Council's decision was influenced by the prospect of economic benefits of jobs, income, infrastructure and trust fund. Local opinion remained divided especially as Redlands were reluctant to give further clarification or guarantees, because of the massive capital investment and the need to retain as much freedom of operation as possible. In consequence, in January 1994, the Minister of the Environment for Scotland agreed to hold a public inquiry, chaired by an inspector who would then present a recommendation to the minister for his final decision. This enquiry opened on Harris in October 1994.

Conclusions of the Western Isles Council, June 1993

23.1 There is no such thing as the 'perfect' development proposal: Any development will bring with it certain advantages and certain disadvantages and ultimately, it can only be a matter of judgement as to what factors weigh more heavily than others.

23.2 This proposal is no exception. The principal advantages in this case lie in economic aspects, and arise from both the direct employment of the quarry and the 'spin-offs'. That, in turn, is seen as leading to a reversal of the present pattern of population decline, bringing with it more social stability. A further advantage, in the long term, is the development potential which can be created at the conclusion of quarry operations and final restoration.

23.3 Ranged against this are various 'environmental' factors. Although the main thrust of the Report is to seek relevant controls on the various environmental factors, a view could be take that, despite these efforts, the changes which will come about were the quarry to be developed would, nonetheless, be undesirable.

23.4 A view of this nature would find practical expression in a decision to refuse planning permisson. A refusal could be founded on a number of amenity and environmental groups including:

• the detriment to the landscape caused by the proposed development, based on the specific circumstances of this locality, or a general policy that developments of this scale and nature should not take place within 'National Scenic Areas'.
• that, becuase of the uncertainties over the ballst water issue, there are possible adverse effects upon the marine environment.
• the (existing) failure to reach agreement on the noise isssue, with the implication that the levels envisaged by the applicant company would be excessive.
• the potential damge to St Clement's Church, Rodel, a Category 'A' Listed Building, Guardianship Ancient Monument, and also to the Coastguard Mast and Rodel.
• the increase in traffic along the C79 and the amenity and traffic engineering implications which stem from this.

23.5 However, the Officers' view is that, in this instance, the benefits outweigh the disadvantages, and that where disadvantages are identified, there are sufficient standards and controls proposed to contain these adverse effects within acceptable limits.

Work needed for Harris, not tourism and nostalgia

Preservationists, conservationists, environmentalists, Friends of the Earth and many other bodies have had their say in opposing the quarry. Yet, a little over ten years ago many of their objections could have been applied to another industry started without protest in the Western Isles and West of Scotland. The industry concerned is doing incalculable damage to the environment. It has now begun to make an adverse effect on a lucrative visitor, the angler.

Conservationists, environmentalists, etc. seem to enthuse over their self importance, even though it must be admitted that they have done good in some places. But, where there is chance of real long term employment for people to get a decent wage then conservation, etc. must take a step back. Folly of the future and the people that matter are the young. Without people there can be no heritage, conservation and so on.

However, it seems to me that many of the aforementioned objectors would like time to stand still or go backward. How sad it would be for the people of Harris and other islands to be degraded like the Maoris of New Zealand, Indians of North America and other tribes who live in reserves like animals in a wildlife park, to be stared at and photographed by the tourist, all in the aid of conservation.

Provided the terms of contract are acceptable and all conditions can be met, surely it is for the people of Harris to decide whether they want the quarry or not. Interference from outside bodies and people with no islands connections should not be entertained.

Yours etc.,
IVOR HORTON,
Isle of Harris
[*Stornoway Gazette* 16.5.92]

CASE STUDY 8.1 *Do 14 lanes of the M25 = a hole in the Hebrides?*

8.13 Public enquiry announced

PRESS RELEASE: Scottish Office, Edinburgh, 6 January 1994

The Rt Hon Ian Lang MP, Secretary of State for Scotland, announced today that he has decided to hold a public local inquiry into the proposed development of a coastal superquarry near Rodel in South Harris.

Commenting on the decision, Mr Allan Stewart MP, Minister for Local Government and Planning at the Scottish Office, said: 'We felt that the planning application raised a number of issues which deserved to be considered at a national level. A public inquiry is the proper way of doing this. Those with an interest in the superquarry proposal will now be able to present their arguments.'

Economic issues

The Harris economy is based mainly on the traditional occupations of small-scale farming (mostly crofting), fishing and the weaving of Harris tweed with, more recently, the addition of tourism. Structural changes in agriculture, commercial fishing and the fashion industry have marginalised the three traditional activities. Tourism has not been able to make up the losses. The result is that the population is in decline, unemployment is well above the Scottish average, and mean earnings are only 70% of the Scottish average. Of an economically active population of 900 in February 1993, 150 were unemployed. Young people, in particular, are leaving, and one in eight houses are 'second homes' and 'holiday cottages'.

Resource 8.14 summarises the jobs and income potential, and demonstrates the 'multiplier effect', that is, local spending of earnings by local people. In his 1993 report on the planning application, the Western Isles Director of Economic Development and Planning concluded:

If the development does NOT go ahead ... then the future for a viable, sustainable economy in Harris, with long-term job opportunities, is bleak. It is worth examining where, within Harris the minimum of 200-300 jobs that the quarry may create could otherwise be created (Director of Planning report, 1993).

Few people or organisations deny the potential of the quarry for jobs and income, but many are concerned that other economic activities will suffer. For example, although commercial fishing has been in decline, it is still a significant source of income and part of the community way of life. Local fishermen are concerned for their future. In 1990 the income from tourism to the Western Isles (including Harris) was £13 million. Harris alone attracts at least 17 000 staying visitors a year, while many more travel around the island. A 1987 visitor survey showed that they mainly visit for a quiet escape, for the scenery, or for the remoteness. The responses in Resource 8.16 express the concern that a superquarry would damage tourism significantly, although Redland maintain that it *could* be marketed as a tourist attraction. Redland's claim is certainly that in the long term, the created sea loch would enhance the attractions of the locality.

Social and cultural issues

The proposed trust fund for the community is as much a social as an economic issue, since it will be used to improve the quality of life of the Harris people. It could make available more funds for leisure facilities, for example. The community are united in their feeling that the Redland offer of £5000 a year at first, rising to £25 000 when the quarry is in full production, is far too little.

Strict observance of the Sabbath is deeply embedded in Harris culture, however, and Redland's refusal to guarantee that there will be no operations at the quarry on Sundays has raised strong reactions. Redlands have stated that they would prefer a seven day operation, but have agreed to restrict Sunday operations to maintenance and ship loading. Islanders are suspicious that unless they get a guarantee of no operations, the company will gradually increase Sunday activity. Many people are concerned that such activities would be the general weakening of Sunday observance.

8.14 Economic forecast

Phase	Years	Jobs in quarry (i)	Amounts: local wages & salaries (ii)	Local income and jobs/yr (multiplier) (iii)		Mineral output (mill tonnes/yr)
				Jobs	Local money	
1	0-5	177	£750 000	30	£300 000	<1
2	6-10	165	£750 000	80	£800 000	5
3	11+	150	£900 000	140	£1 400 000	>10

(i) The quarry jobs fall into two categories: construction and quarrying.

(ii) The calculation assumes that 20% of all the money spent locally, does actually remain local. e.g. In Phase 1, the total local spending is £1.5 million; 20% of this - £300 000 - remains locally.

(iii) The figures shown are the wages and salaries of local employees. In Phase 1, 50% of jobs go to locals; in Phases 2 and 3, 75% are local. Thus, in Phase 1, the total wage bill is £1.5 million; as 50% is earned by locals, £750 000 remains on Harris.

Letter from Mr Calum Morrison, 5 Dunmore Crescent, Leverburgh, (and also on behalf of Mr Neil Morrison, 18 Lingerbay, Harris:)

"Being a local fisherman and fishing from Lingerbay for the past 3½ years, I am extremely concerned of the effects such a development will have on both my fishing activities and also the fishing grounds and catches.

I object on the grounds that my livelihood will be affected by such a development and that Redlands haven't given my concerns much serious consideration".

Annexed to this letter of objection is a series of points which Mr Morrison states he had put to the applicants, covering the following matters:

The proposed causeway to Lingerbay Island will thwart the present ability to take the sheltered route out of the loch towards Rodel – a route always taken in the event of strong south westerly winds, and will also prevent storage of shellfish in the only suitable place in the loch. This is a particular concern as, from July to December, lobsters are stored in this area.

The building on the piers would take away the majority of the shoreline within the loch, thus depriving the use of the shoreline for crab and lobster fishing.

The pier at Eilean Cholum would also make the passage to and from the Morrisons' anchorage more difficult, as the pier closes most of the entrance to it.

By effectively causing the Morrisons to move to other fishing grounds, they would have to "start again" in terms of the acquisition of local knowledge as to the best fishing grounds.

The navigational requirements to and from the proposed harbour imply that the area could not be used for the positioning of shellfish cages, on the present anchorage, and that neither would it be possible to work drift nets for herring and mackerel.

Noise and pollution would be detrimental to marine life and in particular, would prevent shoals of fish coming sufficiently inshore to be caught locally, and would also drive away most of the shellfish from the shoreline.

The safety of the boat and of the gear would be at risk from the movements of large shipping in the area.

In short, the implementation of these proposals would render it impossible for the Morrisons to continue fishing from Lingerbay, with the results that they would have to go to new fishing grounds, at greater expense, and with less certain prospects of economic success.

(c) Tourism potential

The fact that a major international company will be creating at Lingerbay what will be a development of European importance, and may well attract large numbers of business people and others who will want to come and view the quarry developing and in production. This will create an additional type of visitor to Harris, one that will require a high standard of accommodation and will generate significant spending power.

While some tourists and potential tourists may be put off by the quarry, others will wish to see the operation and the quarry could become a major tourist attraction, similar to other industrial processes. There will be a public road through the site, and it would be sensible for Redland to recognise this demand and make provision for it at an early stage, so that people can view it and be informed about it. There is potential here to develop interpretation facilities for the quarry process and the geology of the area which in itself is interesting.

(a) (Signature Indecipherable), 22 Ecole de Ludes, 92200 neuilly
Farncine Du, 6 Rue de Pont de Jodi, 75005 Paris
(Signature Indecipherable), 10 Rue St Pierre, 27000 Evreux
C Michon, 43 Rue de Turique, 5400 Nancy

"I have recently heard about a very important, and hardly believable project: a quarry in the Isle of Harris, in Rodel more exactly, which would damage the whole area, including the hills around, and would involve the building of an artificial field and moving of crofters from Lingerbay, etc.

As a French admirer and lover of the Scottish Western Isles, and most particularly of Harris, allow me to tell you I consider it would be a real disaster for the Island. how could such a plan be put to execution in the most beautiful area of the Scottish Islands, which, moreover, is a National Scenic Area and, as such, should be protected? And what would become of the birds and animals living in this area without speaking of all the protected plants and vegetation? Do the Islanders realise the damage which would be caused, and the fact that all outsiders from Great Britain or foreign countries and all true lovers of nature would desert their isle?

(b) By tour operator

The development will in all probability be highly damaging to the industry in which I am involved, namely tourism.

According to the Annual Report of the Western Isles Tourism Development Programme 1990 (p2) the annual turnover from tourism in the Western Isles is estimated at £13 million and the industry supports over 700 jobs. The basis of the tourist industry is the natural environment of the islands. This is a resource of far greater economic value to the Western Isles and their people than the mineral which Redland wish to exploit, the main financial benefit of which, by far, will accrue outside the local authority area.

The proposed development would have a major adverse effect upon the scenery and environment of South Harris generally and profound but less easily foreseeable social effects. The environmental effects would obviously be most seriously felt in the immediate locality, but I would remind you that:

(a) This locality contains the principal tourist attraction in South Harris, namely Rodel church;

(b) The site of the development is immediately adjacent to the highest mountain in South Harris, which again is an extremely popular destination;

(c) The majority of tourists in my experience like to make the circular route around the island. The proposed development allowed to proceed, would make this route extremely unattractive and would result, I believe, in the "cutting off" to a large extent of the many tweed weavers operating in the remoter areas of the east side;

(d) A very large proportion (perhaps the majority) of visitors to the island arrive via the ferry routes between Uig, Lochmaddy and Tarbert. If the Application is approved, all visitors arriving via these routes (but in particular those coming from Lochmaddy) will have as their introduction to South Harris an undisguiseable view of one of the largest industrial developments in the British Isles. Such an introduction could only have one effect – that of making people wish to avoid the area.

The effect upon existing tourism operators in the vicinity could clearly be disastrous, and as such an operator I therefore insist that the likely effect upon the tourism industry in South Harris be fully and professionally investigated prior to any decision on the Application being taken.

CASE STUDY 8.1 *Do 14 lanes of the M25 = a hole in the Hebrides?*

8.17

No to superquarry offer, meeting says

Sunday loading of ships at Redland's proposed superquarry at Lingerbay and their 'derisory' £5 000 per annum donation to the community have been rejected out of hand by a packed public meeting in Leverburgh.

Two-hundred people filled the Leverburgh School gym on Tuesday night and voted unanimously that the Harris Quarry Working group should stand firm on the Sunday working issue.

An equally strong mandate was given to the Working Group on the community trust fund. Redland have offered £5 000 per annum in the initial stages of production rising to £25 000 at full production of ten million tonnes per annum.

But this was condemned as 'insulting', and the meeting felt a percentage of the sales price of the anthrosite extracted was a more realistic offer. The very least acceptable would be one per cent of the profits, at current prices, around £100 000 per year.

[*The Stornoway Gazette* 25.4.92]

8.18 *The Sunday observance issue*

PROPOSED SOLUTION

The solution to the problem is seen as being a separate Agreement between Redland Aggregates Ltd and the planning authority (Council) which will provide for the safeguarding of Sunday. The Company has agreed to enter into such an agreement as a willing party. The terms of the Agreement are set out in a separate document circulated with this Report. The fundamental element of the Agreement is that Redland Aggregates Ltd will not carry out any work at the quarry or berth ships or load ships on Sunday except in an emergency or for the carrying out of essential maintenance which is defined as being:

- **any maintenance which is necessary to the operation of the quarry and without which the quarry will be unable to operate on the first normal shift on the Monday next following or on any occasion where life or property are threatened. (Except as hereinbefore provided). No maintenance work which can be carried out during weekdays shall be carried out on Sundays.**

This is the wording which has been agreed between the Company and representatives of the Churches in South Harris.

Environmental issues

Resources 8.7 to 8.10 demonstrate the inevitable impact of this project. The landscape of this part of Harris will be changed forever. The area lies within a National Scenic Area, Scotland's equivalent of national park status. There should be, therefore, a presumption *against* a project which would create such severe impact. Some long-term residents of Harris claim that the strongest protests are heard from middle-class 'incomers' from England and other parts of Scotland.

In June 1993, Scottish National Heritage declared its opposition:

Inappropriately sited superquarries could gravely damage Scotland's outstanding coastal and marine environments. If the growing commercial interest in such developments is to bring real benefits to Scotland they must be guided to sites where the economic gains will be achieved at least cost to the natural heritage. SNH sees it as vital that the Lingerbay proposal should be assessed in a national context. The site lies within one of Scotland's

8.19 *The Hebridean National scenic area*

National scenic areas

0 ——— 40 km

N

ATLANTIC OCEAN
HARRIS
NORTH UIST
SOUTH UIST
SKYE

---

finest landscapes – the South Lewis, Harris and North Uist National Scenic Area (NSA) – and raises complex issues in relation to the marine environment … A national strategy is essential, especially when natural heritage assets of national value are at stake. This is certainly the case at Lingerbay, and that, together with Redlands' failure to reassure us over the possible impacts on the marine environment, is why SNH is objecting to this application (Press release, 23 June 1993, SNH, NW Region, Stornoway).

In addition to the visual and aesthetic impacts, there are threats of noise, dust, air and water pollution. While there may be dispute over the extent of such pollution, in an area designated as possessing outstanding environmental quality, the inevitable impacts would favour the rejection of the superquarry. This could be countered only if the long term prospect of the 'sea loch' and its environmental and recreational potential are valued highly enough.

The answer

The Lingerbay superquarry is a classic example of an issue to which there is no one 'correct' answer. At the local scale, if economic factors are given priority, then accepting the quarry would be appropriate. On the other hand, if cultural and environmental factors are given priority, then there is a strong case for rejection. The balance may shift, however, when the issue is placed into a national context. That the UK needs hardstone aggregates, is the indisputable reality. It needs to be decided, though, whether it would be preferable to concentrate supply on a few coastal superquarries and move the materials in bulk by ship, or to rely on inland quarries dispersed through more populated regions and generating much heavy road traffic.

Activities

1 Define what is meant by a *superquarry*.

2 Describe the Lingerbay project and its environmental impact on the local environment.

3 Analyse the Lingerbay superquarry in terms of the matrix below:

	benefits	costs
economic		
social/cultural		
environmental		

4 Why do people in the small communities of Harris feel so strongly about observing the Sabbath?

5 On the national scale, what are the key issues of environmental management raised by this case study?

CASE STUDY 8.2 *Managing the world's wild places*

Background

The preservation of wilderness is one of the more sensitive issues facing governments and environmental managers. A 'wilderness' can be defined as a place where the natural environment remains undisturbed by human impact. More people are seeking 'the wilderness experience', and these areas are being valued increasingly for recreation as well as conservation. At the same time there are intensifying demands for other uses of these resources, for mining, logging, power generation, roads, settlement and agriculture. Because of the competition for space and use, conservation and recreation managers have realised that they can benefit by working together.

Outdoor recreationists rely on the same resources that conservationists want to protect. It is in their mutual interest to develop sustainable management strategies which balance conservation with recreational use and, hence, economic return from the resources. Conservationists recognise that environments vary in their

conservation value and the amount of use they can withstand. Recreationists, on the other hand, vary in the activities and experiences they enjoy. The key challenge is to match conservation values with recreation demands.

This case study illustrates one of the most popular methods of achieving balanced sustainable management – the use of *zoning*. Zoning matches the environmental quality and

character with an appropriate type of recreational activity or experience. The designated area is divided into zones, each of which is managed to provide opportunities for a certain type of activity and experience. When put together, the zones provide a range of opportunities, known as the *recreational opportunities spectrum*. The materials of the case study examine the 1992 Management Plan for the Tasmanian

Key understandings

◆ Truly wild and natural places are becoming increasingly rare but are also becoming increasingly attractive to people seeking 'the wilderness experience'.

◆ If wild and natural environments are to survive then they must be given special protection while accepting some degree of human use.

◆ Effective management for natural and semi-natural environments involves the balancing of conservation, economic and amenity values.

◆ One method of achieving sustainability while pursuing both conservation and recreational objectives is through zoning – matching environmental character with recreational experience.

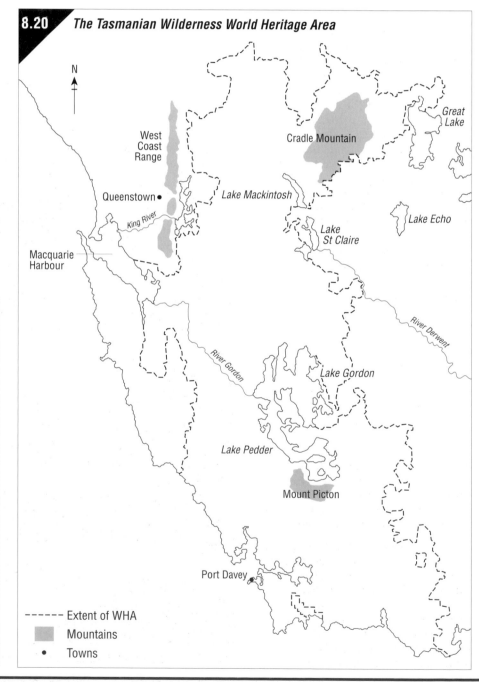

8.20 The Tasmanian Wilderness World Heritage Area

- - - - - Extent of WHA

Mountains

• Towns

Wilderness World Heritage Area, which focuses on management for wilderness values. The plan uses the zoning principle to provide a broad spectrum of recreational opportunities.

Providing for the wilderness experience in Tasmania

Setting

The Tasmanian Wilderness World Heritage Area (TWWHA) has been formed by the assimilation of a number of pre-existing national and state parks and reserves into a single management unit of over 1.38 million hectares, about 20% of the area of Tasmania. All but approximately 300 ha are owned by the state of Tasmania, under the control of the state department of Parks, Wildlife and Heritage. The various parks and reserves which now make up the TWWHA have, since their original designations gradually since 1908, been known as 'conservation reserves'. They have also experienced increasing recreational and tourist pressures, which made the production of an overall management plan increasingly urgent.

The TWWHA exists within a three-tier political and decision-making environment. Australia is run as a federation of states known as the Commonwealth of Australia. While the Tasmania government has considerable autonomy over land and water within the state, the Commonwealth government, also has rights and responsibilities. This can create tensions. For example, the Tasmania government is less opposed to mining and mineral exploration inside the TWWHA than is the Commonwealth government.

Designation as a World Heritage Area (WHA) in 1982 by the International Union for the Conservation of Nature (IUCN) gives the area the highest conservation status. It provides recognition as *a wilderness area of outstanding world value* (Management Plan, 1992) and of *immense importance to native*

8.21 *The three tier management system*

Australian Commonwealth

↕

Tasmania Government

↕

TWWHA Managers

8.22

The wild and beautiful landscape of the Tasmanian wilderness

Management inputs to control visitor movement and experience

species as an undisturbed natural ecosystem where biological, ecological and evolutionary processes can occur largely free from interference by humans (MP, 1992). Although there are more than 300 WHAs world-wide, the TWWHA is one of only three temperate wilderness areas in the southern hemisphere. Any management strategy must take this global significance into account.

Environmental quality

Resources 8.23 and 8.24 give some indication of the character of this wilderness. The designated area contains spectacular glaciated mountain scenery, karst landscapes with some of the best cave systems in Australia, hundreds of lakes in a mountain and forest setting, extensive coastal types, one quarter of all Tasmania's primary temperate rainforests and two-thirds of all the state's higher plant species. It is a stronghold for many endangered plant and animal species. There are also remains of Aboriginal cultures, such as rock paintings, which are evidence of continuous occupation over 30 000 years.

Since the settlement of Europeans in Tasmania over the past 200 years, people have made extensive use of the region in mining, logging and sheep farming. Along with recreation, the principal resource use is for water catchment. There are several dams and reservoirs fringing the TWWHA and the gorges have enormous HEP potential. Water resource management is a key issue. A proposal to dam the gorge of the Franklin River within the TWWHA in the early 1980s triggered a highly publicised, world-wide campaign by environmentalists. The campaigners won and the dam has never been built.

The environmental character of the TWWHA offers outstanding opportunities for self-reliant wilderness recreation, including walking, fishing, camping, rafting and remote sightseeing. The wilderness is seen *as a place for reflection, a source of inspiration and a symbol of the ideal of untouched nature* (MP, 1992).

Gordon Dam, one of many in Tasmania

8.25	Visitor days in Australian World Heritage areas, 1990	
WHA		Visitor days ('000)
Great Barrier Reef		2500
Kakadu		857
Uluru		450
Tasmania Wilderness		597

Visitors to Cradle and Lake St Clair — 8.27

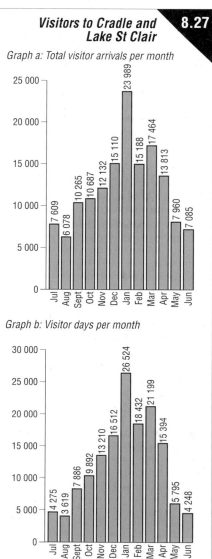

Graph a: Total visitor arrivals per month

Jul 7 609, Aug 6 078, Sept 10 265, Oct 10 687, Nov 12 132, Dec 15 110, Jan 23 989, Feb 15 188, Mar 17 464, Apr 13 813, May 7 960, Jun 7 085

Graph b: Visitor days per month

Jul 4 275, Aug 3 619, Sept 7 886, Oct 9 892, Nov 13 210, Dec 16 512, Jan 26 524, Feb 18 432, Mar 21 199, Apr 15 394, May 5 795, Jun 4 248

Need for a management plan

The number of tourists and recreation visitors are measured in thousands rather than the millions often facing National Parks. The Lake District and Peak District National Parks in the UK receive at least 20 million visitor days a year. By the mid-1980s it was clear that greater control on usage was required. Wherever roads or tracks accessible by 4-WD vehicles enhanced accessibility to the TWWHA, there were signs that visitor numbers were growing and that carrying capacities were being threatened. Recreational carrying capacity has several dimensions, making management policy complex.

The key problems facing the managers by the mid-1980s were that:

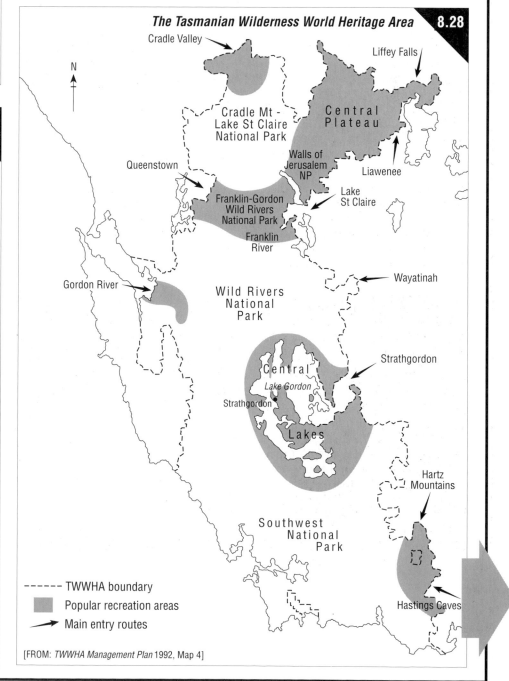

The Tasmanian Wilderness World Heritage Area — 8.28

----- TWWHA boundary
▨ Popular recreation areas
→ Main entry routes

[FROM: TWWHA Management Plan 1992, Map 4]

CASE STUDY 8.2 *Managing the world's wild places*

8.29 *The dimensions of recreational carrying capacity*

PHYSICAL or DESIGN CAPACITY *The numbers of users a site or area is designed and managed to accommodate at one time.*

ECOLOGICAL CAPACITY *The amount of use an environment can absorb over a specific time period without suffering an unacceptable degree of environmental deterioration.*

PERCEPTUAL CAPACITY *The numbers of visitors present on a site or in an area before those visitors begin to feel that the quality of their experience is suffering, e.g. they begin to feel 'crowded'.*

ECONOMIC CAPACITY *The volume of use a site or resource can absorb before the costs of maintenance/management exceed the income received by admitting additional visitors.*

- each Park and Reserve within the unified TWWHA was working to its own 'plan'.
- the recreational use was unevenly distributed and weakly controlled.
- many of the attractive reources, e.g. caves, lakes, rivers, are ecologically fragile. They have low ecological carrying capacities.
- the overall level of recreational use, by Tasmanians and tourists, was increasing steadily.
- the remoteness and naturalness so many visitors came to seek, were being threatened in the more popular areas by the growth in numbers. For many, the perceptual capacity of those areas was being exceeded.

It is in this context that the TWWHA managers have constructed their Management Plan.

The plan framework

The primary goal of the managers has been to match the character and qualities of the resources with the desired demand for recreational opportunities and experiences. The principal management objective, taken directly from the World Heritage Convention, is *to protect, conserve, present and, where necessary, rehabilitate the natural heritage* (MP, 1992). The Tasmanian dimension is seen particularly in the state government policy to promote tourism as a major vehicle for economic development, using the TWWHA as the prime attractive resource.

In an effort to accommodate the assortment of values and priorities, the plan has been based on a *zoning scheme*. The principles of this scheme have been to establish *appropriate levels and forms of recreation, associated facilities and management requirements for different parts of the TWWHA that are in keeping with maintaining or enhancing wilderness quality and environmental values* (MP, 1992, p23). In making their decisions about the character and distribution of these zones, the planners have taken the following factors into account:

- wilderness quality
- water catchments
- sensitive environments
- resources especially attractive to visitors
- existing patterns of use
- access
- pre-existing authorised uses

A four-zone system has been selected, with a set of specialised subzones. The main zone names reflect the appropriate level and type of management input (Resource 8.29).

The zones provide a diversity of recreational opportunity in appropriate settings and at an appropriate level of facility development. This strategy is an illustration of a well-established planning and management methodology known as the *recreational opportunities spectrum*, or ROS. It is based on the idea that the demand for outdoor recreational experiences ranges across a spectrum. At one extreme are those who want facilities, ease, comfort and safety. The 'car-and-stroller' visitor who wants cafes, gift shops, visitor centres, viewpoints and surfaced roads would fit into this category. At the other extreme are those who seek 'the wilderness', with its isolation, naturalness, and absence of other humans and built facilities. This demand-supply spectrum extends from the developed 'honeypot' to the natural wilderness. Zoning systems based

8.30 *The Recreation Opportunities Spectrum (ROS) for the TWWHA*

1 *Wilderness Zone* *Where natural processes will continue to operate with minimal interference, and so to retain a challenging unmodified natural setting for wilderness experiences and scientific research.*
Very low density – no regimentation

2 *Self-reliant Recreation Zone* *Where a challenging and relatively unmodified natural setting will be maintained that suitably experienced and equipped people can use for appropriate recreation purposes.*
Low density – minimal regimentation

3 *Recreation Zone* *Where management will be for relatively intensive use for a wide range of active day and overnight recreation experiences, including opportunities for the less experienced visitor.*
Medium density – significant regimentation

4 *Visitor Services Zone or Site* *Where appropriate facilities are to be strategically located to enhance access to and use of the TWWHA, while minimising the environmental and social impacts of the facilities and the visitor use.*
High density – formal regimentation

on ROS separate the different demand segments according to types of visitor.

The Wilderness Zone has been given highest priority with more than 70% of total area, showing the conservation emphasis in the TWWHA. The wilderness must be managed for very low usage levels, that is, for a small number of people spread over a large area. The zones designated for more intense development reflect access and accessibility, existing patterns of use and the quality and ecological carrying capacity of the environment. For example, the central lakes region around Lake Gordon is both accessible by road and already has a wide range of facilities. The Central Plateau area in the north-east, where there has been increasing concern about poorly-controlled use, also boasts a number of facilities. The plan will maintain use levels but control its distribution more effectively. The Visitor Service Zones tend to be located at the 'gateways' or along the fringes of zones. The other key locational feature is the establishment of 'corridors' along roads and some rivers, that is, along popular and accessible routes. The plan is organised spatially around the principles of zones, nodes and corridors.

The management of wilderness

'Wilderness' is all about isolation, naturalness, and the belief that some places on earth should be kept for natural processes to continue undisturbed by human activity. The concept of 'the wilderness experience' has risen from this idea. Increasing numbers of people seek this experience for the challenge, self-reliance, solitude, or simply the need to be close to nature. North American studies have found that the people with such motivations are sensitive to 'crowds'. If they encounter more than two or three other groups in the wilderness per day, they begin to feel 'crowded'. The quality of the experience declines. The recreation manager

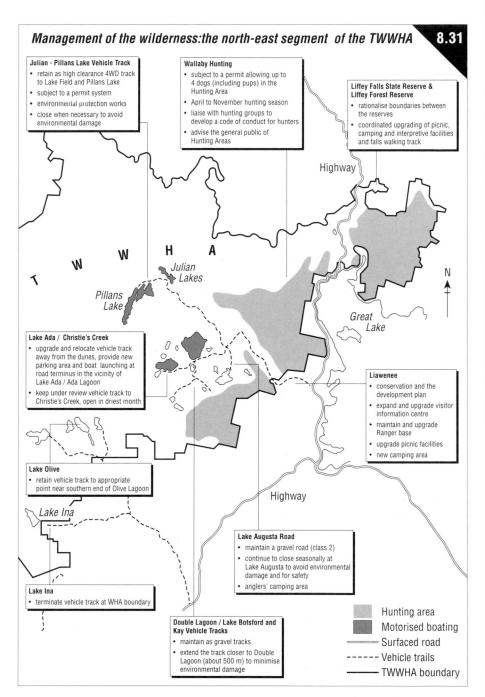

Management of the wilderness: the north-east segment of the TWWHA — 8.31

Julian - Pillans Lake Vehicle Track
- retain as high clearance 4WD track to Lake Field and Pillans Lake
- subject to a permit system
- environmental protection works
- close when necessary to avoid environmental damage

Wallaby Hunting
- subject to a permit allowing up to 4 dogs (including pups) in the Hunting Area
- April to November hunting season
- liaise with hunting groups to develop a code of conduct for hunters
- advise the general public of Hunting Areas

Liffey Falls State Reserve & Liffey Forest Reserve
- rationalise boundaries between the reserves
- coordinated upgrading of picnic, camping and interpretive facilities and falls walking track

Lake Ada / Christie's Creek
- upgrade and relocate vehicle track away from the dunes, provide new parking area and boat launching at road terminus in the vicinity of Lake Ada / Ada Lagoon
- keep under review vehicle track to Christie's Creek, open in driest month

Liawenee
- conservation and the development plan
- expand and upgrade visitor information centre
- maintain and upgrade Ranger base
- upgrade picnic facilities
- new camping area

Lake Olive
- retain vehicle track to appropriate point near southern end of Olive Lagoon

Lake Augusta Road
- maintain a gravel road (class 2)
- continue to close seasonally at Lake Augusta to avoid environmental damage and for safety
- anglers' camping area

Lake Ina
- terminate vehicle track at WHA boundary

Double Lagoon / Lake Botsford and Kay Vehicle Tracks
- maintain as gravel tracks
- extend the track closer to Double Lagoon (about 500 m) to minimise environmental damage

Legend:
- Hunting area
- Motorised boating
- Surfaced road
- Vehicle trails
- TWWHA boundary

should, therefore, plan to retain very low user-density levels. At current usage levels, the TWWHA Plan does not 'ration' access via an entry permit system, as used in many North American national parks. However, the managers will monitor usage levels and are prepared to bring in a permit system if necessary, should ecological or perceptual carrying capacities be exceeded.

When deciding on areas for designation as 'wilderness' in the plan, the TWWHA managers decided that it should be *land remote from access by mechanised vehicles and from within which there is little or no consciousness of the environmental disturbance of contem porary people* (MP, 1992). 'Remoteness' and 'naturalness' can be quantified. Remoteness is

CASE STUDY 8.2 *Managing the world's wild places*

measured as the walking time from the nearest access point for mechanised vehicles. For example, the walking speed through treeless terrain is two kilometres per hour; through forested country is one kilometre per hour. No wilderness value is derived until a distance gained by four hours walking from the nearest access point is reached. Half the wilderness value is attained after eight hours, and maximum after 48 hours walking.

Thus, wherever possible, for an area to qualify for wilderness designation on the 'remoteness' criterion, it should be at least one day's walk from a road access point.

The concept of 'naturalness' is measured through the degree of onsite and viewfield disturbance, that is, the field of view from a site or trail. For example, any visible disturbance or sign of human activity within five kilometres will negate wilderness quality. Dams, roads, quarries and settlements are especially damaging. Resource 8.32 shows that some wilderness boundaries have been drawn much closer to access points and roads.

Once designated as a Wilderness Zone, the area is managed by permitting no visitor facility development. Except for basic paths and huts, no formal trails, campsites, signposts, interpretation boards are allowed. Should such developments ultimately occur, despite the protection given within the TWWHA, then the Wilderness Zone designation would be withdrawn. Conversely, within the Wilderness Zone a number of existing roads and unsurfaced tracks are being closed to restrict access. Resource 8.34 illustrates ways in which the Wilderness Zone is protected by upgrading opportunities within the Recreation Zone of the popular Central Lakes area.

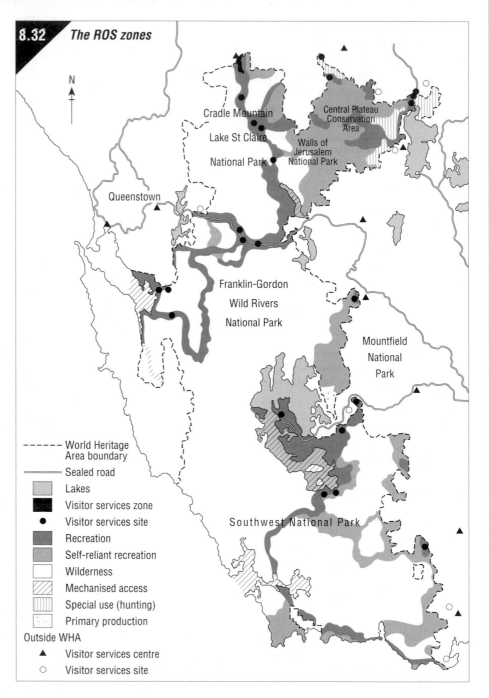

8.32 *The ROS zones*

N

Cradle Mountain

Lake St Claire

National Park

Central Plateau Conservation Area

Walls of Jerusalem National Park

Queenstown

Franklin-Gordon Wild Rivers National Park

Mountfield National Park

Southwest National Park

- - - - - World Heritage Area boundary
——— Sealed road
Lakes
Visitor services zone
• Visitor services site
Recreation
Self-reliant recreation
Wilderness
Mechanised access
Special use (hunting)
Primary production

Outside WHA
▲ Visitor services centre
○ Visitor services site

Activities

1 What is meant by *wilderness* and *the wilderness experience*? Illustrate your answers with examples from the TWWHA.

2 Define the term *recreational carrying capacity* and outline its role in environmental management.

3 Why has combining a number of parks and reserves into the single TWWHA made better management possible?

4 What is meant by the *Recreation Opportunities Spectrum* (ROS), and how has it been applied in the management of the TWWHA?

5 How does the management of an area as 'wilderness' help to balance conservation and recreation values?

CASE STUDY 8.3

Balancing economic, cultural and conservation values

The next three case studies make up a set which focuses attention upon the huge state of Alaska, USA. Each examines a separate issue, but in order to avoid repetition, a general introduction to Alaska and the basis of its resource management follows.

The planning and management framework

The word 'Alaska' probably conjures up images of a rugged wilderness, and for many Americans, the state of Alaska is their 'last frontier'. Alaska became an independent state only in 1959. It is remote, being detached from the rest of the USA. It is a vast tract of 378.2 million acres with a tiny population, only 534 400 in 1990. Almost half the population lives in and around the main city of Anchorage. Approximately 50% of the land and water area is covered by some form of protected designation, either as a national park, wildlife refuge or national forest.

Alaska is rich in resources and is undergoing an explosive phase of development. This is raising a number of high-profile environmental management issues on oil, timber, minerals, space, beauty, abundant wildlife and the claims and rights of indigenous peoples. The increasing accessibility and awareness of the land highlights the constant clashes in different value systems: economic development, conservation, traditional lifestyles and recreation and tourism. Alaska is an example of the range of crucial issues about the way in which we manage and use natural resources.

The Alaska National Interest Lands Conservation Act, passed by the federal government in 1980, is the framework within which Alaska is managed today. Also known as ANILCA or the Alaska Lands Act, its aim has been to settle disputes over land and resource utilisation rights and to allocate land to the different agencies, communities and individuals.

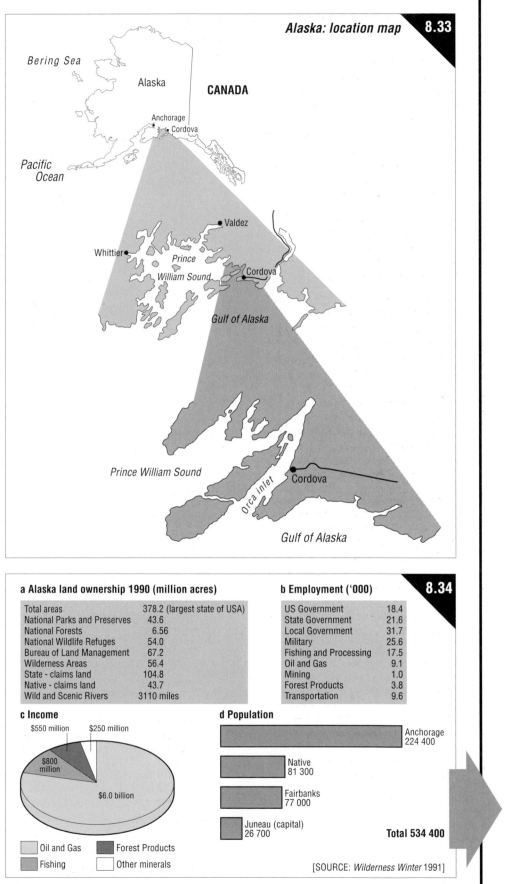

Alaska: location map 8.33

8.34

a Alaska land ownership 1990 (million acres)

Total areas	378.2 (largest state of USA)
National Parks and Preserves	43.6
National Forests	6.56
National Wildlife Refuges	54.0
Bureau of Land Management	67.2
Wilderness Areas	56.4
State - claims land	104.8
Native - claims land	43.7
Wild and Scenic Rivers	3110 miles

b Employment ('000)

US Government	18.4
State Government	21.6
Local Government	31.7
Military	25.6
Fishing and Processing	17.5
Oil and Gas	9.1
Mining	1.0
Forest Products	3.8
Transportation	9.6

c Income

- $550 million
- $250 million
- $800 million
- $6.0 billion

- Oil and Gas
- Fishing
- Forest Products
- Other minerals

d Population

- Anchorage 224 400
- Native 81 300
- Fairbanks 77 000
- Juneau (capital) 26 700
- **Total 534 400**

[SOURCE: *Wilderness Winter* 1991]

CASE STUDY 8.3 *Balancing economic, cultural and conservation values*

8.35

Matanuska Glacier, Alaska, a precious wilderness resource

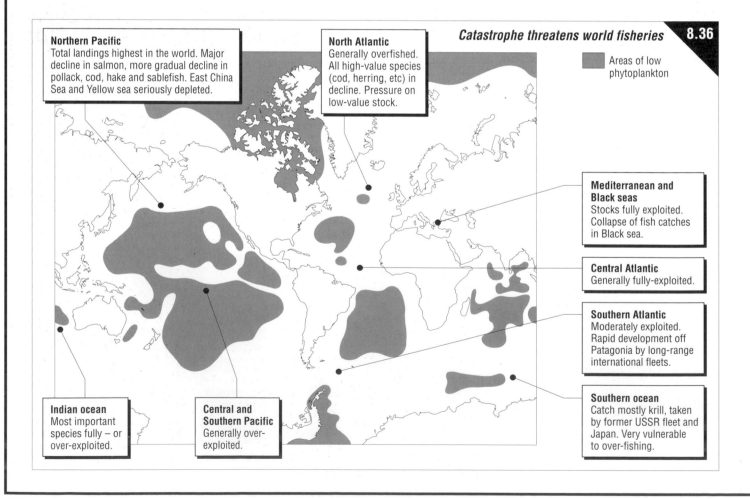

Catastrophe threatens world fisheries 8.36

Northern Pacific
Total landings highest in the world. Major decline in salmon, more gradual decline in pollack, cod, hake and sablefish. East China Sea and Yellow sea seriously depleted.

North Atlantic
Generally overfished. All high-value species (cod, herring, etc) in decline. Pressure on low-value stock.

Areas of low phytoplankton

Mediterranean and Black seas
Stocks fully exploited. Collapse of fish catches in Black sea.

Central Atlantic
Generally fully-exploited.

Southern Atlantic
Moderately exploited. Rapid development off Patagonia by long-range international fleets.

Southern ocean
Catch mostly krill, taken by former USSR fleet and Japan. Very vulnerable to over-fishing.

Indian ocean
Most important species fully – or over-exploited.

Central and Southern Pacific
Generally over-exploited.

The outcome is the intricate pattern shown in Resource 8.36, and is the basis upon which all major decisions can be made. The Act is the result of a 20-year battle between commercial interests, politicians, conservationists and Alaska Natives.

The United States is a federation of states with its central government based in Washington DC. Each state has considerable independent power, with its own constitution and state government. 'States rights' is a powerful and emotive issue throughout the US. Public land is held and managed by federal agencies such as the National Parks Service (NPS), the US Forest Service (USFS), the Bureau of Land Management (BLM) and the state of Alaska. The pattern is further complicated by the important claims made by the Alaska Natives, the indigenous peoples who hold and operate those lands and resources under a separate set of laws. The Native Lands category has been created to help protect and sustain their cultures which focus on subsistence practices.

Key understandings

◆ A natural resource community is one whose way of life is integrated with and dependent upon a set of natural resources.

◆ Fish are a renewable natural resource with a finite and quantifiable productive capacity.

◆ Management of marine resources for sustainability must balance levels of exploitation with reproductive capacity.

◆ Natural resources and the communities dependent upon them are vulnerable to natural and technological disasters.

◆ The value systems of the resource owners and managers will influence whether or not resource utilisation will be based upon exploitative or sustainable principles.

Managing natural resources for sustainability

Background

A *natural resource community* (NRC) is one whose economic and cultural way of life is dependent upon a set of natural resources:

A population of individuals living within a bounded area whose primary cultural existence is based upon a utilisation of natural resources (Dyer et al, 1992, p106).

The indigenous peoples of Alaska are organised as NRCs. They depend upon natural resources for their survival and mould their cultural rhythms, rituals and beliefs on these resources. Such societies are often held up as examples of how to live 'in harmony with nature', and to manage their environmental resources on a sustainable basis. They are contrasted with 'modern' commercial societies whose approach to finite natural resources has been essentially exploitative, exhausting the resource for maximum profit. The alarming depletion of global marine resources is a vivid example.

8.37

Alaska's abundant natural resources

Commercial NRCs realise the value of controlling their 'harvest'. Renewable resources are managed on a sustainable basis. Modern NRCs exhibit strong social and cultural interaction with their resource environment.

This case study examines Cordova, an NRC located on the eastern edge of Prince William Sound, and dependent upon commercial fishing. It illustrates how a community adapts its economic, social and cultural rhythms to environmental patterns, and how resource management policies arc working to ensure sustainability of the fish resource base. It also records the response of the community to an extreme event – the Exxon Valdez oil spill of 1989. Note that most Cordovans are not indigenous Native Alaskans, yet they balance commercial profit and traditional sustainable values.

Cordova, Alaska – The life and rhythms of a natural resource community

Setting

Cordova is situated at the head of Orca Inlet, one of many fjord-like bays around the rim of Prince William Sound. In 1990 its population was 2110, over 10% being the Eyak people, who have occupied the locality for several hundred years. During the summer fishing season the population of the town swells to around 3500. Cordova has passed through several 'boom-and-bust' cycles, starting as an ice-free port for the gold rush of 1898 and followed by the shipment of copper from the Wrangell Mountains to the north. When the copper mines closed in 1939, the town survived as a small fishing port of around 1000 people. The expansion of the Prince William Sound commercial fisheries in the 1970s based on salmon, herring and lobster, caused the population to double. A gravel road connected Cordova with Valdez and Anchorage until it was destroyed by the great Alaska earthquake of 1964. Today the town can be reached only by ferry boat or plane, although it is likely that a new road will be built by the late 1990s. This is causing considerable controversy among Cordovans (Resource 8.41).

Rhythm of the salmon

Cordova is the base for the largest fishing fleet on Prince William Sound, with over 400 boats and 55% of all commercial fishing licences. The main catch is salmon, and then herring. Salmon spend much of their lives out in the North Pacific ocean, but from June to September each year, huge numbers return to the rivers of southern and western Alaska to spawn, and then die. (A salmon always returns to the stream of its birth.) While some of the finest sport fishing in the world takes place along these streams as the salmon migrate, commercial fishing is

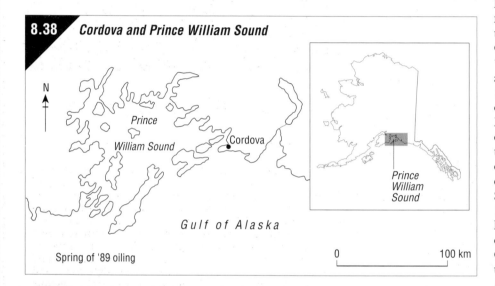

8.38 *Cordova and Prince William Sound*

Prince William Sound

Cordova

Gulf of Alaska

Spring of '89 oiling

Prince William Sound

0   100 km

8.39

Cordova town: Main street Cordova. The town sits between the mountains and the sea. It has one main commercial street. The comminity uses the street for parties in the summer, like the 'Salmonbake' to welcome some Russian fishing boats.

concentrated offshore, taking the catch as the 'run' heads for the spawning grounds.

There are five sub-species of salmon – pink, king, chum, sockeye, coho – each with its own pattern of arrival.

Cordova airport

8.40

Cordova
CITY AIRPORT

Cordova: the new road issue
8.41

Cordova road elicits strong emotions

FOR: Margy Johnson

Looking at the road from a dispassionate viewpoint, access through the wilderness would actually help save the environment. Hikers and campers can take advantage of nature's bounty. State and federal officials will have easier access to the area. Scholars and researchers could better study the eco-systems because previously remote areas could be reached more quickly. With the road we can see what we have.

Perhaps the most important point to bring up is that every delay in building the road is costing all of us in Cordova dollars out of our pockets.

Cordova is not a speck of civilization in a sea of trees. Cordova is a portion of the social and economic fabric of Alaska. Costs are high in Cordova because everything from toothpicks to oranges has to come in by air or water.

We are paying for the road not being completed and it is a price many of us can ill afford.

If you don't like the cost of groceries in Cordova, you should be in favour of a road. If you worry about medical costs because you can't afford to go to Anchorage or Fairbanks, build the road now while you are not desperate for access to a hospital.

If you don't like the high unemployment in Cordova, build the road so everyone can see the pristine beauty of our forests rather than just the privileged rich few who can afford the time and money to visit the remotve regions of the Copper River watershed.

If you worry that the trees will disappear, build the road so that state and federal inspectors can make sure they don't disappear.

Margy Johnson is a Cordova businesswoman and president of the State Chamber of Commerce. Opinions expressed in Taking a Stand do not necessarily reflect the editorial position of The Anchorage Times.
[The Anchorage Times, 22.3.92]

AGAINST: Karl Becker

According to a 1986 DOT* study, if the Copper River highway is built along the cheaper of the three selected routes, the year-round maintenance costs could run as high as $2.3 million and those maintenance dollars come out of state coffers, not the federal government's.

If the DOT is really interested in helping Cordova and the rest of Prince William Sound's communities, it could use federal funds to build a new ferry for the Sound as well as docking facilities at Chenega and Tatitlek. With a road to Whittier, which could be maintained year-round at a reasonable cost, all communities in the Sound could be within an hour's drive of Anchorage.

To equate tourism potential with highways is just sloppy arithmetic. Scenic beauty and wildlife would be better measures of the attractiveness of an area to tourists. Cordova has plenty of each and we want to protect them, especially fish, since we are, after all, a fishing community. That explains why the fishermen's union in Cordova voted by a four to one margin to oppose construction of the Copper River highway.

We're not opposed to visitors, but we don't want to be overrun a la Kenai Peninsula every summer. A little diversity never hurt anyone, especially Alaskans. Come to us on our own terms and we'll show you a great place and a great time.

Karl Becker is a fisherman and 15-year resident of Cordova.

* Alaska Department of Transportation

[Anchorage Daily News 15.8.91]

Copper River Highway

Environmental Studies

PUBLIC MEETINGS & OPEN HOUSE

The Alaska Department of Transportation and Public Facilities will be hosting several Open Houses for the COPPER RIVER HIGHWAY project. The walk-in format of an open house ensures that everyone who comes receives individual attention.

In introducing the proposed project we hope to accomplish three things: First, to provide you with an understanding of the purpose and need for the project and the design standards that will be followed; second, to get a sense of public opinion about the proposed project and specific issues and concerns you might have; and thirdly, to present the schedule and project staff so you may continue to be involved in the proposed project.

Everyone is welcome. We especially invite those who might be directly impacted by the corridor. Your relationship with the area can give us a unique perspective on the issues and concerns. Identifying problems early in the process allows us to develop and incorporate solutions as the project is developed. Some of the issues we feel may be considered include the following: engineering design criteria, project costs, socio-economic impacts, subsistence use, wildlife and habitat values, scenic and recreational resources, wetlands and floodplains impacts, water quality, historical and archeological resources, right-of-way and hazardous waste.

[Cordova Times, 8.4.92]

Native corporation sues over Copper River road

By Wesley Loy
Daily news reporter

The Ahtna regional Native corporation filed suit Wednesday against the Alaska Department of Transportation, claiming the agency is trespassing and trampling cultural sites while building the Copper River Highway.

The suit says that, in addition to damage by machinery, the state failed to consider how erosion will affect Native cultural sites, along with travelers "who would either loot or carelessly damage or destroy irreplaceable sites and artifacts."

[Anchorage Daily News 9.5.92]

CASE STUDY 8.3 *Balancing economic, cultural and conservation values*

This spreads the fishing season through the summer months. Once the young fish have returned to the sea in the spring, they remain out in the ocean for up to four years before returning to spawn.

Management for sustainability

In all major fisheries of the world there is intensifying concern over the volume of the fish stock, its reproductive capacity and the appropriate size of the 'harvest'. For example, during 1992–93, the British fishing industry was in bitter dispute with the EU over fishing quotas imposed in the North Sea, because of overfishing in the past. In the winter of 1993–94, thousands of dead seabirds were washed up along Britain's west coasts. They appeared to have died of starvation, caused, many scientists believe, by the reduction of their food supply. In Alaska's Prince William Sound, the

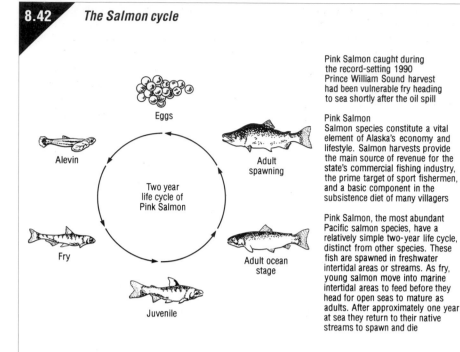

8.42 The Salmon cycle

Eggs

Alevin

Fry

Juvenile

Adult ocean stage

Adult spawning

Two year life cycle of Pink Salmon

Pink Salmon caught during the record-setting 1990 Prince William Sound harvest had been vulnerable fry heading to sea shortly after the oil spill

Pink Salmon
Salmon species constitute a vital element of Alaska's economy and lifestyle. Salmon harvests provide the main source of revenue for the state's commercial fishing industry, the prime target of sport fishermen, and a basic component in the subsistence diet of many villagers

Pink Salmon, the most abundant Pacific salmon species, have a relatively simple two-year life cycle, distinct from other species. These fish are spawned in freshwater intertidal areas or streams. As fry, young salmon move into marine intertidal areas to feed before they head for open seas to mature as adults. After approximately one year at sea they return to their native streams to spawn and die

---

8.43

Like a scene in a Hitchcock riddle

Death toll soars to 75,000 as Britain faces worst disaster of century

by James Grylls

Britain faces its worst seabird tragedy this century. Tens of thousands are taking part in a ferocious search for food.

Estimates of deaths have been put at 75,000 and rising, with 100 dead birds washed up for every kilometre of the Scottish east coast.

The figure may rise even higher after a count of beached birds along UK and European coasts next weekend. In the 1983 seabird disaster, around 30,000 died.

Carcases examined show birds that have starved to death. They have not eaten in several days and not fed properly for weeks, if not months. Their body fat is down to virtually nil.

'More birds are coming ashore on every high tide. It is already the biggest death toll among the seabird population this century.'

The bulk of the birds have died in Scottish waters but the Scottish Office, the Government's arm in the north, says it has no evidence that poor fishery management – a favourite theory – is causing the disaster. The Norwegian and Danish fleets fish in the North Sea for sprats and tiny sand eels, the seabirds' food. These go to make feed for pigs and poultry.

'It's silly to blame the UK Government because it is a European matter and we simply apply EU rules as best we can,' said a Scottish Office official. 'Any claim of overfishing has to be regarded as pure speculation.'

The Government says there is no evidence that overfishing, if any, is causing the catastrophe. Some of its experts believe the number of dead birds found may be due to an unusually persistent easterly wind, blowing to the land carcases that would nor-

mally sink out at sea.

Other bird experts, however, note how the population of puffins and other birds in the northern Scottish islands has appeared to rise and fall according to restrictions put on sand eel fishing.

But they are not convinced. 'It is all conjecture, speculation and informed guessing,' admitted David Mitchell.

'But if you do take out vast quantities of fish from the sea, it does have a knock-on effect.

'It is tempting to say birds are dying for the same reasons that fishing boats are tied up at the quayside – not enough fish. But there are lots of cycles, with either a scarcity of fish or a glut of them. Until management is improved, things won't get any better.'

[*Daily Mail* 24.2.94]

crucial issue is how many salmon should be allowed to 'escape' into their spawning streams in order to sustain the fish resource over time.

Until the 1970s, this was not a significant issue as the scale of fishing was relatively small. Since then the demand-supply equation has changed:

- World demand for salmon has grown.
- Transport and marketing techniques have improved.
- Fishing and processing technology has advanced.
- As other fishing grounds have been overfished, so more 'foreign' boats are moving into the North Pacific.

Fishing fleets based in Cordova and the other Prince William Sound harbours have, subsequently, doubled and more canneries have been established. Large 'factory' ships now enable the fishing vessels to unload their catch at sea and then continue fishing. The factory ships

may be based in Seattle or Japan. In the early 1990s Norwegian vessels moved to the Sound because of the reduction in the North Atlantic catch. In consequence, there is growing concern that harvest levels in the North Pacific are pushing against the reproductive capacity of the salmon resource.

The management response has been firm, and even the fiercely independent fishing community of Cordova today operates in a strictly-controlled environment. The management policy is directed by the Alaska Department of Fish and Game (ADFG), a State government agency, working in co-ordination with the Alaska Department of Environmental Conservation (ADEC). The five main elements in this policy are:

1 A research and monitoring programme to check the size, location and health of the salmon resource, both at sea and in the rivers, bearing in mind the two-, three- and four- year return cycles

of the sub-species.
2 All vessels must be registered and licensed. These licences are limited in number and are expensive. For example, in 1991 a full commercial licence cost $85 000.
3 The waters and inlets of Prince William Sound are divided into 11 districts. Using radar, surface sonar and counting stations on the streams, the ADFG can identify the location, size and direction of salmon 'runs'. Only when the ADFG are satisfied that there is sufficient fish in a district, will they allow boats to fish. This is known as 'declaring an opener' and is illustrated in Resource 8.45. It is the basis of the summer rhythm of life for the Cordova community. The determining factor for the ADFG is the numbers of salmon or 'escapement quota' which should be reaching their spawning grounds.
4 Mesh sizes of the nets are strictly controlled to prevent immature fish from being caught.

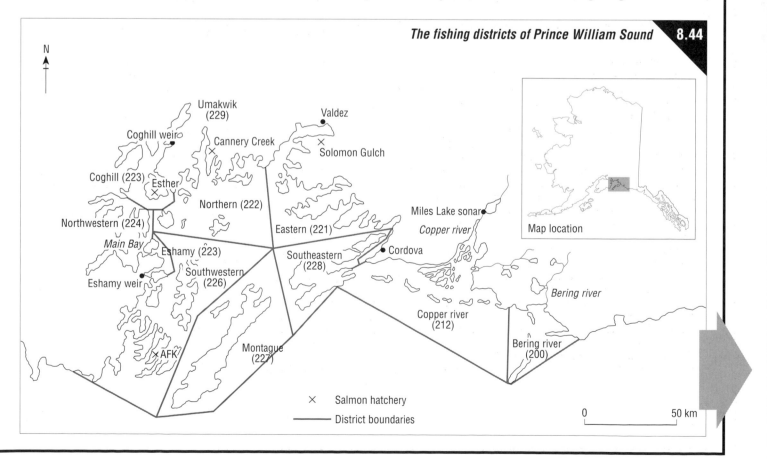

The fishing districts of Prince William Sound 8.44

Umakwik (229)
Valdez
Coghill weir
Cannery Creek
Solomon Gulch
Coghill (223)
Esther
Northern (222)
Northwestern (224)
Miles Lake sonar
Copper river
Main Bay
Eastern (221)
Eshamy (223)
Cordova
Southeastern (228)
Eshamy weir
Southwestern (226)
Bering river
Copper river (212)
Bering river (200)
AFK
Montague (227)

Map location

× Salmon hatchery
── District boundaries

0   50 km

8.45 Announcement – State of Alaska

Department of Fish and Game – Commercial Fisheries
P.O. Box 669, Cordova, Alaska 99574 Office: (907) 424-3212 Fax: (907) 424-3235

PRINCE WILLIAM SOUND SALMON ANNOUNCEMENT #119
4:00 p.m. Tuesday, August 13, 1991

Pink Salmon Returns The harvest from the 12-hour commercial fishing period on Monday August 12, is approximately 3,500,000 salmon. The cumulative common property harvest of PWSAC hatchery and wild stock pinks is approximately 6.8 million fish. As of Monday PWSAC has harvested 2,488,643 pinks.

The next commercial fishery will occur on Wednesday August 14. This fishing period will be 12 hours in duration. This period will be a clock opening and will commence at 8:00 a.m. ADT and close at 8:00 p.m. ADT.

Waters open to commercial salmon fishing will be;

1) All waters of the Esther Subdistrict as described in 5 AAC 24.200 (f)(1), inlcuding all waters of Lake and Quillion Bays. Waters within 50 feet of the barrier seine in Lake Bay will be closed to commercial fishing.

2) All waters of Unakwik Inlet (Northern District) north of a line from a point located on the east shore at 60° 54.4' N. latitude to a point on the west shore at 60° 54.1' north latitude, and south of a line from a point on the east shore at 61° 01.0' N. lat., 147° 33.0' W, longitude to a point on the west shore at 60° 57.5' N Latitude, 147° 36.5 W. longitude. Waters within 50 feet of the Cannery Creek Hatchery barrier seine will be closed to commercial fishing.

3) All waters of the port San Juan Subdistrict and Elrington Subdistrict including the waters of Sawmill Bay except that commercial fishing will be closed within 50 feet of the hatchery broodstock barrier seine. This area will be marked by a line of buoys.

Fishermen are reminded that there is limited processing capacity available for Wednesday's opener and not all processing companies will be represented on the grounds.

When stocks are threatened, mesh sizes may be decreased or increased for a while. (*Gill netting* relies on fish being able to pass part-way through a net before the gills become snagged in the mesh. The mesh size may be decreased to prevent the smaller fish from pushing into the mesh and so being trapped. *Purse seine netting* gathers up the fish within the net. If mesh size is increased, immature fish can pass through it.)

5 Four fish hatcheries have been set up around Prince William Sound to increase the size of the fish stocks and the harvest capacity. These are run by a non-profit organisation called the Prince William Sound Aquaculture Corporation (PWSAC), which is funded by the fishing and processing industry and limited state funds. As with 'wild' salmon, the fish return to spawn where they were born, at the hatchery,

unless eggs are released into spawning streams.

The objectives of this sustainable management policy are, therefore, *the achievement of desired escapement goals for major species while at the same time allowing for the orderly harvest of all fish surplus*

to spawning requirements ... *To manage fisheries to assist non-profit hatcheries in achieving cost recovery [getting their running costs back] and broad stock objectives* (ADFG, Regional Information Report, 1989).

Salmon fishing in the 1980s and the Exxon Valdez spill

The graphs of Resource 8.46 show four important characteristics of the Prince William Sound industry:

- the large scale of the salmon catch.
- the overall upward trend.
- the variability of the catch from year to year and hence the high risk nature of the enterprise.
- the dominance of the 'pink' sub-species.

In 1989 the 24.4 million catch was worth $41.3 million, harvested by a fishing fleet of 715 boats, which sailed out of four main ports, including Cordova.

On 24 March 1989 the tanker *Exxon Valdez* ran aground and spilt 11 million gallons of North Slope crude oil into Prince William Sound. At first glance, the spill appeared to have had little effect. However, three of the western districts were closed and the catch was unusually dependent on hatchery fish which made up 33% of the total. This was especially important as the wild 'pink' runs were alarmingly low.

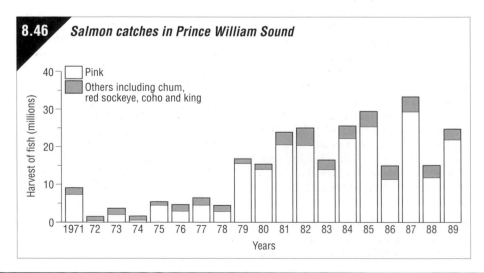

8.46 *Salmon catches in Prince William Sound*

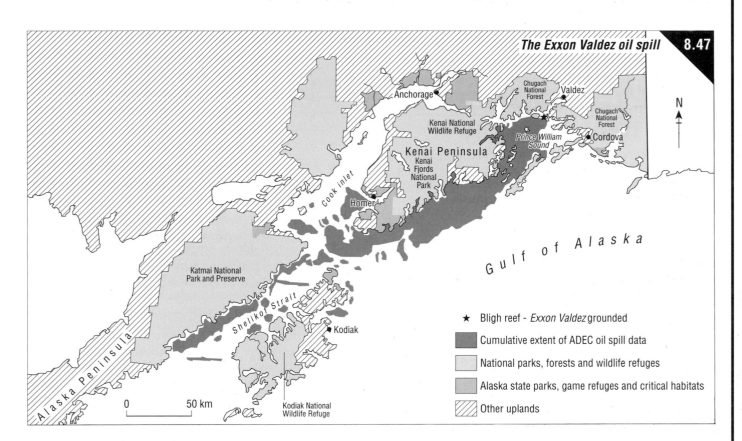

Bligh reef - *Exxon Valdez* grounded

Cumulative extent of ADEC oil spill data

National parks, forests and wildlife refuges

Alaska state parks, game refuges and critical habitats

Other uplands

Because of the life cycle of salmon, it will be several years before the ecological effects of the oil spill can be assessed. Although the 1990 and 1991 catches were high, the arrival dates were erratic and the hatchery fish continued to make up large proportions of the total harvest. The demand also collapsed and affected the price for Alaska salmon. Between 1989 and 1992 the prices offered by processing plants and canneries fell by more than half. Many boat owners decided that it was not worth their while to fish, which reduced the catch. By the summer of 1992, three of the four salmon canneries of Cordova were facing bankruptcy. The slump in demand was blamed in part upon the 'image' of Alaskan salmon as a result of the oil spill, despite vigorous efforts by the ADFG and ADEC to prevent marketing of any contaminated fish. The diary of Resource 8.51 shows how thorough the management response had been.

Fortunately for Cordova, its nearest fishing grounds were not affected by the spill, and although 15% of boats

Glut of returns finds no takers   8.48

By Hal Bernton
Daily News business reporter

Several million pink salmon may rot unharvested in the dead-end bays of Prince William Sound hatcheries as weak markets, a shortage of processors, and weird fish behavior create a chaotic climax to the 1991 salmon season.

"The fish will stay around in the bays until they roll over and die," said John McMullen, president of Prince William Sound Aquaculture Corp. "I can see at least 4 million fish perishing – or more."

The aquaculture association is the nation's largest producer of hatchery fish. It normally sells a portion of the salmon returning to hatchery bays to help finance operations.

But this year the salmon run is the latest in history, 10 days behind schedule. And the pinks are darken-ing and taking on spawning hues as they mill around hatchery bays.

State fishery managers didn't want to allow a wide-open harvest for fear that fishermen would also sweep up many wild pinks, which have had extremely weak returns to the Sound.

Finally on Monday, biologists – under intense pressure from fisher-men – opened up several large areas of the Sound to the fleets. The fishermen caught 3.5 million salmon – a record catch for a single 12-hour period – and promptly flooded processors with fish. That brought the total pink catch to date to more than 15 million.

Prices paid fishermen remain stuck at 12 cents a pound, the lowest in more than a decade.

[*Anchorage Daily News*, 15.8.91]

8.49 Pink salmon market glut

By Jacques Picard

The only light at the end of the tunnel for a world market saturated with pink salmon appears to be new uses for the fish, according to Howard Johnson, marketing consultant from Seattle.

Among the bad news was the revelation that Europe considers PWS pinks among the lowest quality available. Pinks from Puget Sound and British Columbia are rated highest, he said.

Problems cited are soft flesh, bluish skin, and variable meat color.

The world inventory of frozen pink salmon rose 334 percent over the previous year, not including product held in supermarket warehouses. Johnson said that although the figures may not be accurate, they affect people's decisions.

Another problem on the market is the glut of frozen Norwegian salmon.

"There's 80 million pounds out there trying to be sold," Johnson said.

Johnson said Norway needs to get $2 a pound for the fish.

America and Europe have rejected the fish, fearing it would further depress prices this year.

And the Japanese are not interested in buying it because the meat has become pale while in storage.

[*Cordova Times*, 21.1.92]

8.50 Management response to the Exxon Valdez oil spill, 1989

April 24 Town meeting in Cordova to discuss the coming fishing season and the concern for seafood quality. Present are the fishing community including the union – the Cordova Fishermen United (CDFU), the Alaska Seafood Marketing Institute (ASMI), the ADFG and ADEC.

May 12 ADEC announce a set of emergency regulations, including rigorous inspection of boats and their catches for oil contamination.

May 14 ADFG hold a meeting in Cordova to discuss the management options for the season. Present are the cannery managers, ASMI, ADEC, ADFG, CDFU, PWSAC, Exxon Corporation, Native Alaskan organisations, National Atmospheric and Oceanic Administration (NOAA). A task force is set up: the PWS Salmon Harvest Task Force (SHTF). This meets twice weekly through May and June, reports on policy and makes adjustments.

May 28 SHTF announce a 'Zero Tolerance Policy' - a fishing District showing ANY shoreline or water contamination from oil will be closed for the season.

June 8 Memorandum of Understanding agreed between the two key State agencies, ADFG and ADEC, setting out their responsibilities and giving guidelines of how to prevent contaminated fish from entering the market.

June 14 ADFG announce a revised management forecast, and the closing of three Districts for the season.

---

chose to rent out to Exxon to assist the clean-up, much fishing continued. (Exxon paid up to $1200 a day to rent a boat.) The Copper River Delta District is popular with the Cordova boats. The area is sequentially fished for the two main local sub-species, sockeye and coho, as they 'run' for their spawning streams. Resource 8.52 follows the season and the management plan.

The counting of the number of fish that escape is done in the Copper River Delta District by a combination of aerial survey and a sonar gauge at Miles Lake. The main spawning areas lie upstream of this gauge and the ADFG measure the 'escapees' against estimates of how many are required to provide enough fry (young fish) to sustain the stock for future years. The graphs record the effect of the cut-back to one 'opener' per week from late June.

8.51 Copper River Delta District Management Plan, 1989

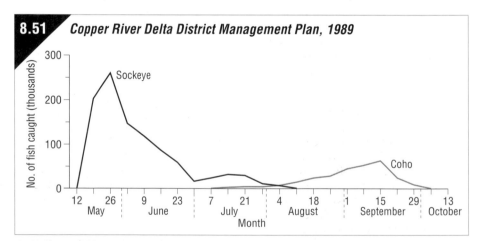

8–10 May ADFG and ADEC check the Copper River delta waters and early fish arrivals, and declare the District free from oil contamination

15 May Season opens as first major 'run' is located

15 May–29 June Two 24-hour 'openers' per week

18 May–1 August Net mesh size reduced for gill net boats to a maximum of six inches to allow larger chinook salmon to escape and so build up stocks

29 June–12 August One 24-hour 'opener' per week.

12 August Season declared closed.

The actual escape counts for July are above the anticipated levels. This ensures that the season's escapement quota is on target.

The August-early September harvest of the 'pink' runs in the central Districts of Prince William Sound, is the peak season for the Cordova fleet and the canneries. This harvest is the mainstay of the Cordova economy. Good catches and good prices mean good income. From the graphs, notice the importance of maintaining escapement levels. It was the disruption to these 'pink' runs which reduced Cordova's income from fish, from a normal $36 million to less than $20 million in 1989. In 1992, catches of 'pinks' were low, due largely to poor prices rather than scarcity of fish.

Threats to sustainability

The fundamental goal of management policy is to conserve the resource at such a level that fish harvests can be sustained to ensure thriving communities without depleting fish stocks over time. The hatchery programme is a vital element as it allows a closer control on stock and catch balances. If demand rises or fish stocks decline, then hatchery output can be altered accordingly. The 'wild' stocks are not threatened. This policy seemed to be effective, but remains vulnerable to three external forces:

1 External fishing practices

The ADFG management controls apply only within US territorial waters. Large, high-tech fishing vessels and factory ships from Seattle, Japan and Norway are fishing international waters more intensively. Using huge drift nets, they are capable of sweeping extensive areas clear of fish. They do not use the Alaska canneries and processing plants.

2 Extreme natural or technological events

The size of salmon runs is influenced by the climatic and water temperature fluctuations from year to year. Fish are susceptible to environmental conditions in both

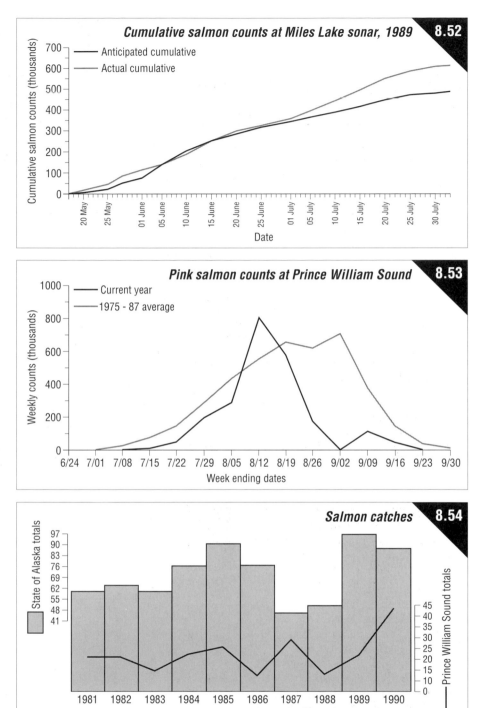

the spawning streams and the open North Pacific ocean. Equally, all marine life is vulnerable to disasters such as the Exxon Valdez oil spill.

3 World demand and price fluctuations

In the early 1990s the price for salmon dropped dramatically, partly as a result of increased supply. For example, in Britain, the supply of salmon from Scottish fish farms was increasing. As salmon is a 'quality' fish, the damage caused to the image of Alaskan salmon by the oil spill affected demand, price and income.

CASE STUDY 8.3 *Balancing economic, cultural and conservation values*

Community stresses in Cordova

One of the distinguishing features of NRCs is the combination of individual self-reliance and mutual inter-dependence. Cordova is relatively remote from the rest of the state. Fishing the North Pacific and living in the Alaskan climate demands considerable skill and fortitude.

Cordova fluctuates with the productivity of the fishing industry. A disaster such as the *Exxon Valdez* oil spill creates severe stresses upon the whole community. In 1989 and 1990 research into these human impacts was conducted. The researchers compared Cordova with a 'control' community, St Petersburg, a southern Alaska natural resources community not affected by the spill. The results summarised in Resource 8.56 show that although stress levels declined from 1989 to 1990, they remained significantly higher in Cordova than in St Petersburg.

Further research in 1991 and 1992 has revealed that frustrations and anger have increased as the legal processes have dragged on. Many people are still waiting for their full compensation payments despite Exxon's negating claims. In May 1994 the US Supreme Court finally ruled that Exxon were responsible for the disaster. This allowed claims to be processed, but it may be several years before all is settled. Furthermore, as fish prices collapsed and canneries closed, the community has remained divided between those who had refused to help Exxon in 1989, and those who had rented their boats and made considerable profits. These 'spillionaires' were able to upgrade their equipment and homes and are suffering less.

The oil spill crisis is being overlaid by fears for the economic future of salmon fishing in Cordova. This is intensifying the controversy over the proposed road into Cordova. One section of the community thinks this will improve the prosperity and the quality of life in Cordova, with tourism buffering the fluctuations of the fishing industry. The other section believes that the road will destroy the strength of the community and that tourists will increase the cost of living as businesses raise prices.

8.55

Cordova festival

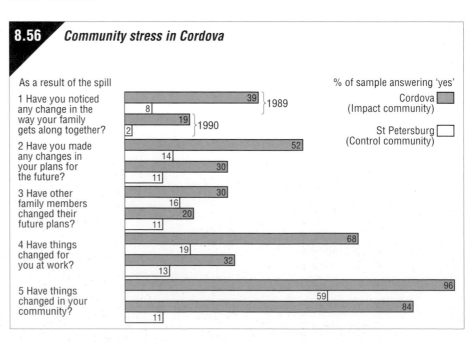

8.56 *Community stress in Cordova*

Exxon's viewpoint

8.57

The Exxon Claims Program

Within weeks after the Exxon Valdez spill, Exxon established claims offices in locations throughout the spill-impacted area so that any adverse economic impact on the fishing industry could be ameliorated. Claims adjusters gave advance payments to fishermen and others suffering hardship due to lack of income.

Through year-end 1990, Exxon reported that it had committed more than $302 million in damage compensation on 12,300 claims. This includes $169 million in payments to more than 7,300 commercial fishermen and individuals employed by fishing permit holders. An additional $133 million was committed to about 5,000 claims to seafood processors, cannery workers, tenderboat owners, and other individuals and businesses affected by the spill.

Role of Fishermen in the cleanup

Fishermen who work in Prince William Sound and the Gulf of Alaska proved to be a major resource of Exxon and government officials in their cleanup and wildlife-rescue operations. These fishermen had vessels and equipment that were needed for the operations, and they had expert knowledge of tides and geographical features in the affected areas. The vessel owners and their crews towed booms to contain oil, transported technicians and workers to remote beaches, served as pilots on research boats, helped clean beaches, and rescued sea otters and seabirds.

Exxon paid significant amounts for these services. For example, Exxon hired 1,440 individuals and firms in 1989, including about 1,160 commercial fishermen-claimants, and paid them cleanup wages and vessel-chartering fees in excess of $105 million in addition to the damage compensation they received.

Figures provides by Exxon Company, U.S.A.

[From: Royce W.F. et al., 'Alaskan Fisheries', Cook Inlet Fisheries Consultants, 1991]

Activities

1 Define what is meant by a *natural resource community*.

2 Describe the life rhythms of the Prince William Sound salmon, and how they influence the NRCs bordering the Sound.

3 Who are the key decision-makers in determining the utilisation of the fish resources of PWS? What are their priorities?

4 Use the PWS fish resource management strategy to discuss the concept of *sustainable development*.

5 What factors affect whether or not the owner of a fishing boat in Cordova decides to go out and fish?

6 What are the main limitations on the effectiveness of the PWS management strategy?

> ### Seward and its tourist attractions
> *Some Cordovans fear that a road will bring in tourists and change the character of the town as has happened to the former fishing port of Seward, Alaska, where tourism is now the dominant activity.*

8.58

CASE STUDY 8.4

The right to manage their own lives

Background

Countries throughout the world contain groups of people and communities whose geographical location and cultural identity in a region predate today's dominant society. They are known generally as 'indigenous peoples', for example, the Aborigines in Australia and the Yanomani in Amazonia. Like immigrants, they frequently face political, social and economic problems, geographical separation and isolation, and the dilemma of how to achieve economic success and social acceptance while retaining cultural identity.

These communities have a deep attachment to their territory, which provides the resources for their food, clothing and shelter. In turn, this environment and its resources provide the basis for beliefs, traditions and the whole cultural system. The inhabitants have a strong 'sense of place', and forced removal can have severe impacts on the communities. Today, the resources are also the basis for commercial activities and income.

Mutual interdependence encourages co-operation, sharing and group responsibilities. For instance, resources are usually communal property, not individually-owned, and are managed, allocated and utilised according to longstanding customs. In contrast, modern law emphasises individual ownership and government regulation, such as issuing hunting permits to individuals not communities, and setting 'open' and 'closed' seasons for resource use which may clash with local community traditions.

This case study examines these issues and management options from the perspective of the indigenous peoples of Alaska, known generally as 'Alaska Natives'. The 'conquering of the American Wilderness' by waves of largely European settlers over the past 300

8.59   *Some issues faced by the indigenous people*

- Rights to land and water – the space to live in.
- Rights to utilise natural resources.
- The concept of ownership of land and resources.
- The concept of subsistence and how it connects culture and environment.
- Rights of self-determination and self-government according to traditional customs and beliefs, while fitting within national governmental systems.
- The attainment of equal opportunities and social justice.

8.60   # *Native Canadians driven to suicide*

Clare Trevena in Toronto

Despair has driven 11 young people, trapped on the remote Pikangikum Indian reservation in north-western Ontario, to try to kill themselves in the past fortnight. Several succeeded.

The nearest city to Pikangikum is Winnipeg, nearly 200 miles to the south-east. The reserve, home to 1,600 people, is accessible only by air or water; in winter a road is built on the ice. Up to four families live in a single house. Unemployment stands at 80 per cent.

Pikangikum has been identified by the Royal Commission on Aboriginal Peoples as a "hot spot", a place where a large number of people have tried to kill themselves. Another is Davis Inlet, in Labrador. The Innu community was forcibly housed there by the government in the 1950s.

A year ago five children were discovered on the edge of death in an unheated shack; they had been sniffing petrol and were screaming that they wanted to die. They were sent to a native-run treatment centre in Alberta, which helped them break their addiction and value their heritage.

But the conditions on the reserve remain appalling. Poverty and unemployment in the 500-strong community are exacerbated by a shortage of piped water and no electricity.

The federal and provincial governments were accused of not reacting quickly enough, as the suicide attempts continued and some of the young people helped last year returned to petrol-sniffing. The Innu community is now being moved to Sango Bay, its old hunting ground on the mainland, and will get financial aid.

[*The Guardian* 9.3.94]

years is a mixture of fact and fantasy. North America was not an unpopulated 'wilderness'. It was a settled sub-continent which supported a human population of perhaps 10 million, with a wide range of cultures spread across all environments. The European settlers and pioneers were, to the indigenous people, invaders. Today, remnants of the traditional societies are fighting to re-establish or clarify their lands and rights, to nurture their traditional cultures and to attain greater management control over their own lives. Alaska provides an excellent focus to explore this process because Alaska Natives still make up 14% of the state population. Many communities have retained significant parts of their traditional ways and have title to a higher proportion of land than in any other American state.

Sustaining the way of life of Alaska Native communities

The context

There are approximately 82 000 Alaska Natives scattered across the state. At least 50 000 live in small natural resource communities, dependent upon subsistence practices. Apart from their Native Lands, they make extensive use of the federal wildlife refuges, national forests and national parks. In many of these designated areas, conservation values are given high priority and there are severe restrictions on hunting, fishing and collecting. There is clearly a tension between this conservation policy and the rights or desires of Alaska Native communities to continue their traditional practices, thereby retaining their way of life.

Key understandings

- Indigenous people may be marginalised socially, economically and politically by the dominant groups in a country.
- Native Alaskan communities are long-established natural resource communities with strong subsistence and cultural relationships to their resource base.
- NRCs have adapted their economic and cultural cycles to natural environmental rhythms, which may conflict with modern legal and commercial controls.
- As population grows and competition for resources intensifies, Native Alaskan communities struggle to retain control of the natural resources upon which they base their lives.
- Since 1970 laws have been passed and management schemes introduced, which accept Native Alaskan traditional rights and protect their management control over natural resources.

Tourists enjoying Alaska's resources

For all the natural resource communities of Alaska there is an intimate relationship between cultural and biological cycles and rhythms. This relationship can be expressed simply in terms of the *seasonal utilisation cycle*.

For the coastal Native Alaska communities this cycle is driven primarily by the rhythms of marine species, especially salmon and herring, although seal, walrus, whale and various crustaceans are also harvested. There is a significant use of land resources, for example, deer, bear, berries and wood. Because of the strong control on biological and cultural cycles by the Alaskan climate, the 'harvest' component of the utilisation cycle is essentially the summer (May–September). Each resource has its own 'harvest' times.

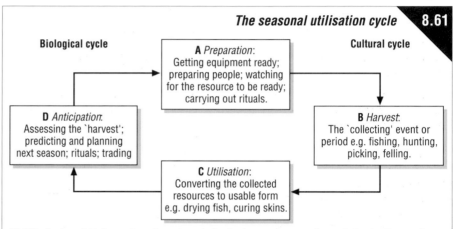

The seasonal utilisation cycle 8.61

Biological cycle | Cultural cycle

A *Preparation*: Getting equipment ready; preparing people; watching for the resource to be ready; carrying out rituals.

D *Anticipation*: Assessing the 'harvest'; predicting and planning next season; rituals; trading

B *Harvest*: The 'collecting' event or period e.g. fishing, hunting, picking, felling.

C *Utilisation*: Converting the collected resources to usable form e.g. drying fish, curing skins.

NB: This simple model is for one type of resource only. A natural resource community may be involved in more than one cycle, as each type of resource has its own biological cycle e.g. Eskimo hunt caribou in one season and seal in another. Such communities would be locked into two seasonal utilisation cycles.

8.62

CASE STUDY 8.4 *The right to manage their own lives*

Such an economy and culture has proved sustainable in environmental and social terms. However, it depends upon low population densities and abundant natural resources. Community order is based upon mutual respect and co-operation, not authority and external power. This system has come under increasing threat as Alaska's population has grown from 303 000 in 1970, to 534 000 in 1990. Economic development built upon the oil boom has accelerated. Many incomers are keen outdoor sportspersons and Alaska has become a popular tourist destination, hosting more than one million visitors a year. Businesses have been set up to organise and equip hunting and fishing trips. Trading has been part of Alaska Natives' economy, and tourists readily buy their skins and carvings.

Within an Alaska Native community, the median per capita 'harvest' of wild meat and fish for family and community use, exceeds 250 lb a year and may reach 1500 lb. It plays a vital role in their quality of life. Competition for natural resources has, however, increased. Between 1975 and 1985, the main caribou herd north-east of Anchorage fell from 70 000 to 8000 animals. Moose in the rich habitat south of Fairbanks dropped from 12 000 to 3000, due to increased hunting. By the mid-1970s, reductions in the fish and animal populations were threatening the Alaska Native way of life.

The management of subsistence rights

In 1971 the Alaska Native Claims Settlement Act (ANCSA) identified the 'Native Lands' entitlement as seen in Resource 8.36. The Alaska Natives gave up rights on 18 million hectares of traditional lands and received almost one billion dollars in compensation. However, because they continued to use the extensive federal (public) lands, subsistence users came under increasing pressure. In an effort to protect the interests of the Alaska Natives, the State passed further laws in 1978, to give Alaska residents in rural areas priority in the allocation of natural resources for subsistence use. To avoid dispute and because many non-Natives who live in rural areas adopt a partially-subsistence lifestyle, the 1978 laws included all rural residents. They defined 'subsistence' as *the customary and traditional uses by rural Alaskan residents of wild, renewable resources for direct personal or family consumption ... for the making and selling of handicraft articles ... for barter, or sharing for personal family consumption; and for customary trade* (ANILCA, 1980, quoted in Caulfield, 1992).

Disputes continued through the 1980s. Alaska Natives who had not been rural residents, claimed traditional rights. In 1986, the state defined 'rural' as *places where subsistence uses are a principal characteristic of the community or area.* Furthermore, the state resource managers were allowed to identify which fish and game

---

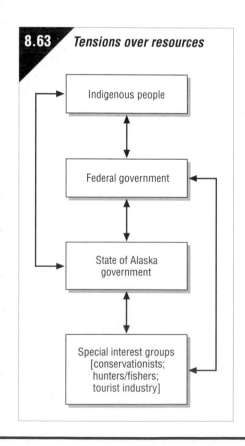

8.63 *Tensions over resources*

Indigenous people

Federal government

State of Alaska government

Special interest groups [conservationists; hunters/fishers; tourist industry]

8.64 ## Subsistence ruling cuts inlet fisheries
Judge says not everyone automatically qualifies

By David Hulen
Daily News reporter

In yet another abrupt twist in Alaska's long battle over who gets to fish and hunt where, a judge has ruled that subsistence fisheries for much of Cook Inlet are invalid, canceling about a dozen openings that had been scheduled between now and the end of September.

Superior Court Judge Charles Cranston of Kenai ruled Friday that all Alaskans are not automatically subsistence users – and therefore subsistence fisheries open to all Alaskans should be closed.

The ruling contradicts what state officials decided last fall when they opened up subsistence fishing and hunting to all Alaskans, not just residents of rural areas.

Rob Bosworth, acting subsistence director for Fish and Game, said the agency was trying to figure out a way to open fisheries in the upper Inlet would allow residents to take large, subsistence-like catches. It's possible, he said, that, with the new subsistence seasons thrown out, state policy in the region would simply revert to last year's personal use fisheries. That fishery was open the last three weekends in September, and closed when a total of 2,500 salmon were taken. The daily catch limit was the same as this year's subsistence fisheries: 25 fish for the head of a household, with 10 more fish for each additional household member.

[*Anchorage Daily News*, 13.8.91]

---

populations could be used for subsistence and when they could be used.

Sport fishing and hunting groups, and the tourist industry objected to the subsistence priority. Then, in 1989, the Alaska Supreme Court ruled that the policy of rural priority for subsistence use was illegal. The Alaska state constitution claims *that fish and wildlife resources must be reserved for common use by all Alaskans, that subsistence statutes could not create an exclusive right or special privilege of fishery*. Since the rural priority policy did not allow equal resource opportunities to *all* Alaskans, it was declared illegal. This illustrates how management policies aimed at the protection of indigenous societies can be quite difficult to operate. The fragmented system of resource management, thus leaves Alaska Native NRCs caught in the middle.

Example

The Nelchina caribou herd of approximately 40 000, migrates seasonally across the Copper River Basin and surrounding mountains in south-central Alaska. Before the 1989 court decision, state policy divided the hunting season into:

- 41 days in the autumn when both subsistence and general hunting were permitted, with a total 'harvest' of 2000 animals.
- 57 days during the winter for subsistence hunting only, when another 2000 animals could be taken.

As of 1990, however, there has been one season with a 'bag limit' (number of animals allowed to be taken) open to all on federal lands. On state lands, a modified subsistence priority policy continues. As the caribou migrate from one territory to another there is a much weaker control on the number of animals taken, or support for the subsistence users. The pressures are indicated by the statistic that some 17 000 people applied for general hunting permits for the 1990 season.

8.65

Caribou landscape

Natural resource disruption among the Eyak			**8.66**
In reference to how the Exxon Valdez oil spill has affected your natural resources ...	*Satisfied (%)*	*Not satisfied (%)*	*Neutral (%)*
How do you feel about the amount of local influence you have over the condition of the community?	35	58	7
How do you feel about the opportunities children have to continue their native traditions?	42	58	–
How do you feel about the opportunities children have to learn subsistence skills	29	61	10
	Agree (%)	*Disagree (%)*	*Neutral (%)*
Do you think subsistence activities such as fishing will ever be as successful as they were before the oil spill?	22	61	17
Do you think the oil spill will interfere with the teaching of subsistence skills to children?	61	29	10

CASE STUDY 8.4 *The right to manage their own lives*

Disruption to the natural resource base, puts Alaska Native communities at risk. Food supplies may be reduced, materials for equipment, clothing, building and household articles may be scarce, and there may be no surplus for trading. There are further impacts upon community life. For example, exchange and gifts within families and kinship groups are a central part of the social life, and have deep cultural meaning. If these patterns are disrupted, then stresses develop within the community. The Eyak of Prince William Sound, for example, fear that they are losing control of their resources and their way of life, particularly after the *Exxon Valdez* oil spill in 1989.

Gaining control of resource management

During the years since the oil spill, it has become clear that Native Alaskan communities need aid and support. Financial compensation to individuals is not enough. Native Alaskan leaders believe that compensation needs to be targetted at the community as a whole. This will then allow the traditional 'sharing' and communal property values to remain the focus of the benefits.

Alaska Natives frequently complain that management policies and controls have been imposed upon them, and that their cultural viewpoint has been ignored. Their perspective emphasises kinship and cultural identity, with lands and resources as the common heritage of the group. In the words of one Alaska Native: *Profit to non-Natives means money. Profit to Natives means a good life derived from the land and sea, that's what we are all about* (quoted in Berger, *Village Journey*, 1985). In consequence, there are now a number of schemes operating where the decisions concerning resource management have been given to the native communities.

Example: The Alaska Eskimo Whaling Commission (AEWC)

For centuries, hunting the bowhead whale has been the centre of the cultural and spiritual life of the Inupiat Eskimo. The hunt follows the seasonal migrations of the whales around the west and north coasts of Alaska. During the 1970s the annual 'harvest' averaged 32 whales, with at least as many hit by harpoons but not caught. As the total population of bowhead whales at this time was estimated at less than 1500, in 1977 the International Whaling Commission (IWC) imposed a ban on hunting this subspecies.

The Eskimo whalers immediately formed the Alaska Eskimo Whaling Commission (AEWC) to co-ordinate

their opposition to the ban which they believed to be an attack on their culture. The AEWC lobbied the American government, arguing that the IWC estimates of the bowhead population were too low. The US National Oceanic and Atmospheric Administration (NOAA) agreed to carry out a scientific research programme to determine the actual numbers. The promise of this research persuaded the IWC to agree to a temporary lifting of the ban and to allow an annual take of 12 whales. The Eskimo whalers felt that this figure was too low, and that they had not been sufficiently consulted by NOAA nor by the IWC.

The dispute rumbled on until 1981, when the AEWC and NOAA agreed that NOAA would delegate

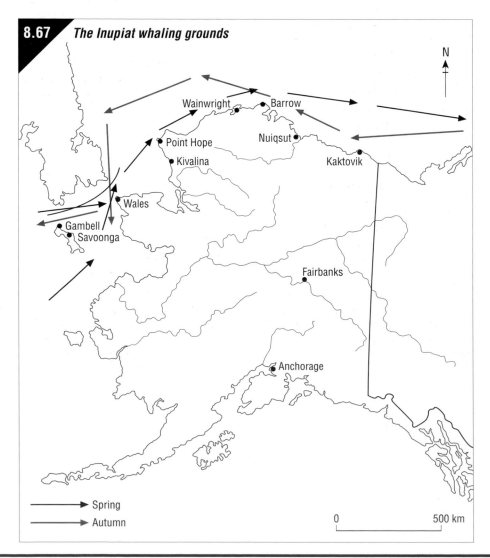

8.67 *The Inupiat whaling grounds*

N

Wainwright • Barrow
Point Hope • Nuiqsut
• Kivalina Kaktovik
Wales
Gambell •
Savoonga

Fairbanks •

Anchorage

→ Spring
→ Autumn

0   500 km

responsibility for managing Eskimo whaling to the AEWC. The IWC still sets the quota, but the management of the quota is in the hands of the AEWC. This responsibility includes 'policing' the hunt, and prosecuting any violators, that is, those whalers who exceed the permitted take. The AEWC report the number of whales landed and struck-but-lost to NOAA. In the mean time, the NOAA survey has shown the bowhead population to be approximately 7500, allowing IWC to raise the permitted hunt total. This quota stood at 41, landed or struck, for the 1989–92 seasons. The level was established on the basis of the balance between community need and sustainable yield. A further important advance has been the improvement of the hunting equipment and techniques during the 1980s. It has reduced the number of whales injured, and so improved the humaneness and efficiency of the hunt.

The effectiveness of the AEWC management relies on four things:

- The whalers themselves administer the management regime.
- The quota attempts to reflect the communities' needs.
- Whaling is a communal activity with a long tradition of cooperative effort.
- The goals of the AEWC have always been well-focused and supported by a unified community.

The principal remaining constraint on the Inupiat Eskimo control is that the IWC still set the quota, although the AEWC is involved in the negotiations.

Activities

1 One of the most disputed issues concerning the resource utilisation by Alaska Natives is what is precisely meant by 'customary and traditional use'. Conservationists and some state and federal government officials claim that the Natives try to bend the rules surrounding 'subsistence'. The following example illustrates just such an issue:

The Inupiat Eskimo hunt caribou, moose and whale. Hunters object to individual bag limits, inappropriate hunting seasons, and the need for individual harvest tickets for the take of animals such as caribou or moose. They also object to a ban on taking caribou from snowmachines, arguing that this is in violation of Inupiat customs and traditions. While many wildlife managers view herding and shooting of caribou from snowmachines as a violation of fair chase ethics, local hunters argue that the practice differs little from hunting patterns used with dog teams in the past.

a To what are the Inupiat objecting? Why?

b Who are opposing the Inupiat practices? What are their objectives?

c You are the judge in a court case on these issues. Giving reasons, make a decision.

2 Define the concept of 'subsistence use' and outline why it may clash with the policies of public sector (state and federal) resource managers.

3 As a member of an Alaska Native community, make a case for your right to have access to natural resources in order to sustain your traditional way of life.

CASE STUDY 8.5   *Conservation versus development*

Background

Making decisions about resource allocation is especially difficult when:

- demand for the resources exceeds existing supply.
- the sought-after resources are rare and highly-valued.
- there are several competitors for the resources.
- the ways in which the competitors want to use the resources are fundamentally different.

All of these conditions apply to the resources of North Slope Alaska, the extensive coastal plain which slopes gently northwards from the Brooks Range to the Arctic Ocean. The precious resources being fought over in this region, are oil and the tundra ecosystem. Two of the most powerful lobbies in American politics are in direct conflict - the oil industry and the environmentalists. This case study follows their long-running battle, focusing particularly on the Arctic National Wildlife Refuge. The balance of power seems to shift over time, dependent upon who is the United States President

and the politics of world oil supply. (The U.S consumes one third of all oil and oil products). The issue operates at the national, state and local scales, each with their own interest and priorities.

Key understandings

- ◆ The Arctic National Wildlife Reserve (ANWR) is a conservation area of the highest quality and value, but also contains significant oil reserves.

- ◆ In the ANWR there is a direct, and probably irreconcilable conflict between conservation values and development values.

- ◆ While the US demand for oil continues to grow and internal reserves continue to shrink, so pressure for oil development in the ANWR will recur.

- ◆ The future of the ANWR depends upon the shifts of political power within Alaska, within the USA, and internationally.

Protecting the caribou homeland in the Arctic National Wildlife Reserve

Round 1:
Gaining space for caribou

The Arctic National Wildlife Refuge (ANWR) was established in 1960 as the Arctic National Wildlife Range. It was extended from 3.6 to 8.0 million hectares, with the passing of ANILCA in 1980. It is the second largest of the 437 units in the US National Wildlife Refuge System. Its primary purpose is to protect wildlife by conserving wildlife habitats. The ANWR encompasses three main ecosystems: the mountainous spine of the Brooks Range, the South Slope with its extensive coniferous forests, and the tundra ecosystem of the North Slope. The Refuge, therefore, includes a unique transition zone between the northern boreal forest (taiga) and the arctic tundra, two major North American ecosystems.

Oil deposits lie beneath the coastal plain of the North Slope. The portion within the ANWR is about

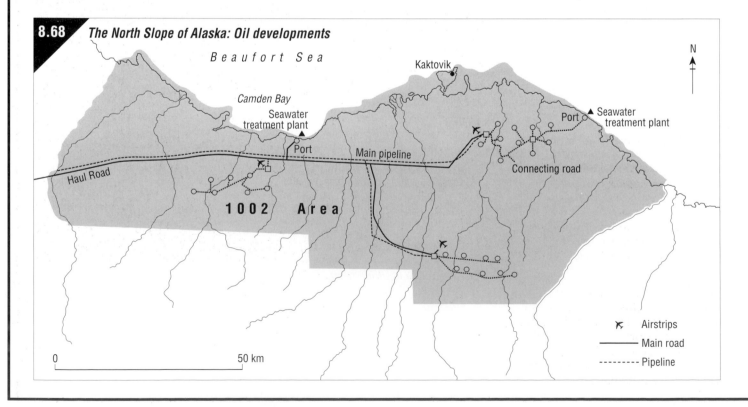

8.68   *The North Slope of Alaska: Oil developments*

Beaufort Sea

Kaktovik

Camden Bay

Seawater treatment plant

Port

Port   Seawater treatment plant

Main pipeline

Connecting road

Haul Road

1 0 0 2   A r e a

N

0   50 km

✗   Airstrips

—— Main road

-------- Pipeline

50 km wide and 180 km long, and is crossed by a series of braided snow-fed streams, which form important wildlife corridors.

The boundaries of the ANWR have been drawn to include substantial areas of forest, mountain and tundra, to conserve the distinctive bio-diversity of the region and to provide the range for the seasonal migrations of caribou. The largest herd is the Porcupine Caribou Herd, of up to 200 000 animals. The herd spends the winter in the mountain valleys and woods, but moves slowly northwards during spring and summer on to the tundra coastal plain. The females give birth to their young and feed on the nutrient-rich forage of tundra grasses, lichens and sedges. There are a number of 'insect-relief' zones. Access to them is important because many parts of the tundra generate enormous swarms of mosquitoes and other biting insects which torment the caribou. The animals move to the coastal waters or to sheltered inland sites to seek relief.

In 1964, the US federal government passed the Wilderness Act, which identified those areas within which conservation and wilderness values would be given highest priority. Environmentalists were keen to use this Act to have the ANWR designated as a Wilderness Area, to give it greater protection.

Round 2: Black gold

In 1968 ARCO and Humble Oil (later to become Exxon) announced that they had struck commercial reserves of oil at Prudhoe Bay, 80 km west of the ANWR. In 1969, the state of Alaska auctioned off 182 000 ha of the North Slope for over $900 million. The state negotiated with the oil companies to receive a percentage of every barrel of crude oil extracted.

The conservationists then battled with the oil industry over how to transport the oil from Prudhoe Bay. Ocean transport was impractical, highlighting the need for an overland route to an ice-free port. This route would have severe

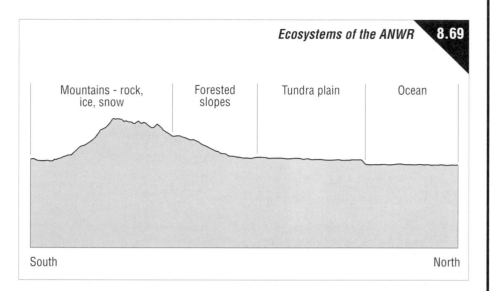

Ecosystems of the ANWR 8.69

Mountains - rock, ice, snow | Forested slopes | Tundra plain | Ocean

South   North

8.70

The forest and tundra region of Alaska

CASE STUDY 8.5 *Conservation versus development*

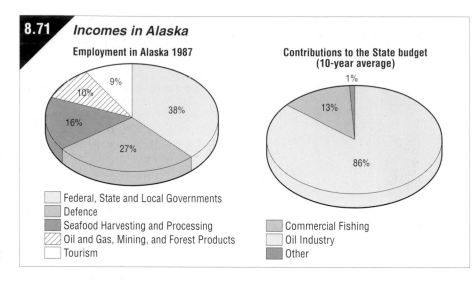

8.71 *Incomes in Alaska*

Employment in Alaska 1987

- 38%
- 27%
- 16%
- 10%
- 9%

☐ Federal, State and Local Governments
☐ Defence
☐ Seafood Harvesting and Processing
▨ Oil and Gas, Mining, and Forest Products
☐ Tourism

Contributions to the State budget (10-year average)

- 1%
- 13%
- 86%

☐ Commercial Fishing
☐ Oil Industry
☐ Other

environmental impact as it crossed permafrost, mountains and forest. The five-year battle ended in 1973 with the granting of a 1200 km 'utility corridor' to carry a pipeline from Prudhoe Bay South to the fishing settlement of Valdez on Prince William Sound. The first oil flowed through this Alyeska pipeline in 1977, establishing Alaska as an oil-rich state. By 1990, the 'Permanent Fund' for Alaska and its people stood at $10.6 billion. Each Alaskan resident receives an annual dividend of around $1000 and does not pay state income tax.

Round 3: Oil pressure

The oil development lay outside the ANWR, but the sheer scale of the wealth it involved gave the oil lobby considerable power inside Alaska. The political forces were further energised as the OPEC countries who trebled the price of crude oil during the 1970s. As US oil production outside Alaska had already peaked, the pressures to develop Alaska's reserves mounted steadily. The oil companies were convinced that the oil-bearing formations continued eastwards from Prudhoe, beneath the ANWR.

For these reasons, when ANILCA was passed in 1980, a holding operation covered 607 000 hectares of the North Slope coastal plain, including the ANWR. This temporary status was inserted to give the US Department of the Interior

(equivalent to the UK Department of the Environment) time to carry out an environmental assessment. The three alternatives in this Coastal Plain Resource Assessment were:

- inclusion within the National Wilderness Preservation System.
- to open up for oil and gas exploration and development.
- to leave the wilderness in its original state and manage it as such.

When the Resource Assessment report was published in 1987, the Secretary of the Interior firmly favoured development:

The Arctic Refuge coastal plain is rated by geologists as the most promising on-shore oil and gas exploration area in the U.S. It is estimated to contain more than 9 billion barrels of recoverable oil ... Based on the analyses conducted, and the national need ... I have selected as my preferred alternative ... making available for consideration the entire Arctic Refuge coastal plain for oil and gas leasing (quoted in Wilderness 54 (191), Winter 1991).

Round 4: The pendulum swings

Conservationists highlighted that scientists regarded 3.2 billion barrels as the likely average yield (less than three months supply at 1988 levels of consumption). The report admitted that animal, bird and fish populations would be

significantly affected. The debate over the details of the report and its implications continued until 24 March 1989, when the *Exxon Valdez* spilled 11 gallons of Prudhoe Bay crude oil into the waters of Prince William Sound soon after leaving the oil terminal at Valdez. This, the worst oil spill in U.S history, swung opinion in favour of the conservationists.

Round 5:
The pendulum swings back

Then, in August 1990, President Saddam Hussein of Iraq lurched into Kuwait ... Oil imports to the U.S. seemed suddenly threatened ... and the Coastal Plain of the Arctic Refuge once again was threatened. Oil companies immediately revived their claims that the only solution to America's dependence on oil from the uncertain Middle East was to exploit all available domestic resources (Watkins, Wilderness, 1990).

The political pendulum swung once more towards development, but no legislation was passed before Bill Clinton was elected US President in November 1992.

Round 6:
One more swing

Clinton campaigned on an environmentalist platform, and as the Middle East threat subsided and oil prices began to fall, the new president was able to pass legislation giving medium-term protection to the ANWR.

Round 7:
The dilemma for Alaska

The state of Alaska has become rich through oil, and its economy is dominated by oil revenues. In 1992, for example, oil supported 85% of the $3 billion state budget. However, Prudhoe Bay output is declining and new discoveries are not making up for this fall. Without the development of reserves beneath the ANWR, production and revenue from the North Slope will be halved by the year 2000. By 2015, the operation of the Aleyska pipeline

Oilmen ready for assault on great Alaska wasteland

Washington
Tim Cornwell

The frozen home of caribou and polar bear on the northern-most tip of the United States, one of the world's last untouched wildernesses, may be opened to oil exploration as a result of the Gulf war.

The 19-million-acre Arctic National Wildlife Refuge in Alaska could be the biggest oil reserve left in the US, and the White House, and most Alaskans, want it open to drilling.

Two years ago, the Senate was poised to approve oil exploration when the Exxon Valdez tanker began belching oil into the North Pacific in a slick that drowned Alaska's pristine coastline in black sludge.

The legislation was hurriedly withdrawn. Now, since the Gulf crisis has freshly underlined America's dependence on foreign oil, it is back, reintroduced by Alaskan Republican Senator Frank Murkowski.

The Valdez spill was called a 'defining moment' in the greening of America. Environmental groups gained new political clout and their memberships soared. But war and recession have renewed the economic costs of conservation ...

President George Bush's new National Energy Strategy, unveiled last month, give only a nod to saving energy and instead promotes new supply in the name of 'energy security'. It plans to ease licensing for nuclear power plants and emphasises pumping more gas and oil, calling for the opening up of the Arctic refuge.

Critics say America will be left to depend on cheap Middle East oil, and predict the strategy will be torn apart on Capitol Hill, whee a bewildering array of energy legislation has been thrown in the ring.

Saving the refuge, a habitat for grizzly and polar bear, musk ox, wild sheep, wolves and the peregrine falcon, is a vital issue for environmentalists. But Alaskans face declining oil production from Prudhoe Bay, their largest field. Without new oil, the 900-mile Alaskan oil pipeline will be under-utilised and the oil-based Alaskan economy could slump.

The other 48 states of the US have been extensively explored. The refuge is virgin frontier that may contain reserves of three billion barrels – small by Middle Eastern standards, but large for US oil companies.

Oil prices are now about $20 a barrel, but with the pipeline already in place, Alaskan oil will be relatively inexpensive to exploit, analysis say. Any new oil may not be pumped until the late 1990s, when prices are likely to be stronger.

Oil companies claim they can keep exploration clean. Lobbyists are armed with postcards of caribou grazing near oil installations; they even claim numbers have increased six-fold since development began ...

Washington Greenpeace spokeswoman Jeanne Whalen says oil production in Alaska dumps waste, toxic chemicals, and pollutes the air. She called the refuge 'one of very few places in this country where animals can be free, untouched by people and the problems people cause', a last 'tiny little area' of Alaska off-limits to oil.

But, she said, 'the President has done a good job of putting himself in a position where Arctic drilling is patriotic', to secure American energy. She said: 'I am pessimistic about the future of the Arctic.'

[*The Observer*, 24.3.91]

---

may no longer be viable. Pressures to develop the ANWR oil and gas reserves are rising once again. A 1992 report on Alaska's economic future emphasised the need to cut state spending on a range of public programmes, to phase out the annual 'citizen dividend' payments, and to diversify the economy through job growth in industries such as fisheries, timber, mining and tourism. The report concludes, however, that *oil still produces half the gross product of the state, and even in the best of all possible worlds (with other job growth), oil will still be the main game in town. The state needs to find ways to work more co-operatively with the industry* (Goldsmith, 1992, quoted in Bradner & Baker, 1993).

The dilemma for local communities

For several thousand Native Alaskans who identify themselves as Gwich-in, the continuation of the caribou migration to and from the ANWR is vital for their future:

This is a simple issue. We have the right to continue out Gwich-in way of life. We are caribou people. We still do caribou dance, sing caribou song, wear the hide, use bone for tools, and tell the story. Caribou is how we get from one year to another. Oil development in their calving and nursery grounds would hurt the caribou and could destroy our culture and way of life (Gwich-in Leader, quoted in Watkins, 1990).

Opinions differ among the communities, though, and because this impinges on deeply-held beliefs and cultural traditions, there is increasing social stress.

Activities

1 Construct a 'calendar' which summarises the chronology of the ANWR issue.

2 Why is the ANWR so important for conservation values?

3 Why is the oil industry so keen to exploit the oil potential of the ANWR?

4 What effects might the outcome of this issue have upon the economic future of Alaska and the quality of life of its people?

5 Write two letters to a national newspaper: one setting out your opposition to the development of oil reserves in the ANWR, and the other in support of oil development

8.73

"I don't want to see the country changed into an oil field."

By Debbie S. Miller

Fifteen years ago, I sat on the tundra next to Moses and Jenny Sam, two Athapascan Gwich'in elders, as they roasted a caribou head hanging from a tripod of spruce branches above a smoky fire. We were camped just south of Arctic Village on a long ridge known as Datchanlee, which means "timberline" in Gwich'in. The ridgeline of naked tundra rose above the spruce forests, gracing America's northernmost Indian settlement like a huge outstretched arm resting on the floor of the broad Chandalar River valley.

To the north, we gazed into the majestic Brooks Range and the heart of Arctic National Wildlife Refuge. Here, on Datchanlee, the Gwich'in and their ancestors had persevered in their hunting of caribou and other wild game for thousands of years. This long sweeping ridge, with an endless stretch of wilderness before us, was an ancient food store fotr the Gwich'in.

While the caribou head roasted, Moses and Jenny recalled stories of the past – accounts ofwinter hardship, starvation, and survival. They remembered years when the nomadic Gwich'in were unsuccessful in their search for caribou – harsh, lean years when caribou hooves were used to make soup because there was little else to eat. Henny still saves the hooves for survival, for "hard times."

For a people who have depended for centuries on caribou for food and clothing, it's not surprising that today's Gwich'in are strongly opposed to the proposed oil development on the summer calving grounds of the 180,000-member Porcupine Caribou Herd. The calving grounds are located about 150 miles north of Arctic Village, across the Brooks Range, along the Beaufort Sea coastal plain of the Arctic Refuge. To thw Gwich'in, the idea of tampering with the herd's birthplace is unthinkable.

But to the north of Arctic Village, along the Beaufort Sea, there are some Inupiat Eskimos in the village of Kaktovik, and other North Slope inupiat communities, who support oil development because of potential job opportunities and community revenues. Yet even in Kaktovik, support for development has waned in recent years, particularly after the Exxon Valdez oil-spill disaster. there is a growing fear that such development will adversely affect the Inupiat's access to subsistence resources in the Arctic Refuge and in offshore areas where villagers hunt for bowhead and beluga whales and fish for arctic char and other species.

Kaktovik would be the most directly affected community if oil development were to occur, since it is the only arctic coastal community located just beyond the 1.5 million-acre proposed development area.

Some of Kaktovik's 250 residents note that the village is split on the development issue and that there has been a gradual shift in the community's position. The current city Council has yet to reconsider the endorsement supporting onshore development that was adopted by the council several years ago. Perhaps, some point out, the village has compromised its ability to speak out against development because one exploratory oil well has already been drilled on some of Kaktovik's village lands. During the regime of Interior Secretary James Watt, many Kaktovik residents were unaware that their village had signed away sub-surface rights to a plot of land at the muth of the Jago River in a not-widely-publicized land trade deal orchestrated by the Department of the Interior. Chevron drilled a corporate test well on Kaktovik's land in 1983, leaving several hundred acres of scarred tundra. The results of that test are still the most highly guarded secret within the industry.

Some residents are becoming more vocal in their opposition to development. George Tagarook, the former mayor, personally opposes development of the Coastal Plain, and he believes that many residents are against development but won't speak out. But he, and others, feel that development may be inevitable and that the decision to open the refuge will be made thousands of miles away in Washington, D.C. Perhaps the greatest concern of villagers is the potential disruption of their centuries-old subsistence lifestyle, along with the far-reaching social problems that come with thousands of outside workers living in the vicinity, including the likelihood of an increase in alcohol and drug abuse.

[*Wilderness* 1991]

Index

Resource material is referred to in *italic*

Acknowledgements

The authors and publishers are grateful to the following for permission to reproduce copyright material. If any acknowledgements have inadvertently been omitted, this will be rectified at the earliest opportunity.

Penni Bickle: pp. 53, 90

Stuart Boreham: p. 187

J Allan Cash: pp. 81, 138, 185

James Davis Travel Photography: pp. 82, 100

Digital Wisdom: p. 62 (top)

Robert Harding Picture Library: pp. 15, 22 (left), 36, 44, 91

Hutchison: pp. 45 (top), 112, 113, 115, 140

Image Bank: p. 43

Images of Africa: p. 49 (top and bottom)

Mountain Camera: p. 62 (bottom)

Nottingham County Council: p. 118

Panos Pictures: p. 14

Robert Perron: p. 45 (bottom)

Robert Prosser: pp. 21, 22 (right), 28, 29, 31, 38, 59, 60, 65, 67, 70, 73 (left and right), 74, 75, 78, 98, 101, 105, 128, 129, 130, 132, 133, 135, 150, 152, 155, 163, 164, 208, 219, 221, 222, 228, 230, 231, 238, 239

Rex Features: p. 111 (top)

FPLA: p. 241

Salford County Council: p. 144

Science Photo Library: p. 30 (left and right)

Skyscan: pp. 87, 134, 142, 212

Still Pictures: p. 15

Tony Stone: pp. 92, 111 (bottom), 119, 137, 145, 168, 195, 199, 243, 247, 249

Trip: pp. 48 (bottom), 58, 143, 190, 205 (top)

Tropix: pp. 16, 117, 184

WWF UK pp: 48 (top), 50

Countryside, Resources 3.36, 3.40; Daily Mail, Resource 8.43; Farmers Weekly, Resources 3.42, 3.43; Financial Times, Resources 6.9, 6.10, 6.11, 6.12; Guardian News Service, Resources 1.2, 2.33, 3.50, 7.9, 7.22, 7.33, 8.3, 8.60, 8.72; Hereford Times, Resources 1.6, 7.33; HMSO, Resource 7.38; Newspaper Publishing plc, Resource 6.27; Stornoway Gazette, Resources 8.12, 8.17; Times Newspapers, Resources 3.38, 5.28, 5.37, 5.43, 5.44, 6.31, 7.23